ENGINES
AND
INNOVATION

...IT SHALL BE THE DUTY OF THE ADVISORY COMMITTEE FOR AERONAUTICS TO SUPERVISE AND DIRECT THE SCIENTIFIC STUDY OF THE PROBLEMS OF FLIGHT WITH A VIEW TO THEIR PRACTICAL SOLUTION...

ACT OF CONGRESS, APPROVED MARCH 3, 1915

NASA SP-4306

ENGINES AND INNOVATION

Lewis Laboratory and American Propulsion Technology

Virginia P. Dawson

The NASA History Series

National Aeronautics and Space Administration
Office of Management
Scientific and Technical Information Division
Washington, DC   1991

Library of Congress Cataloging-in-Publication Data

Dawson, Virginia P. (Virginia Parker)
    Engines and innovation : Lewis laboratory and American propulsion
technology / Virginia P. Dawson.
        p.   cm. -- (NASA SP ; 4306)   (The NASA history series)
    Includes index.
    Supt. of Docs. no.: NAS 1.21:4306
    1. Propulsion Laboratory (U.S.)--History. I. Title. II. Series.
III. Series: The NASA history series.
TL568.P76D38 1991 20.01
629.4'06'079493--dc20
                                          90-20747
                                              CIP

For sale by the Superintendent of Documents, U.S. Government Printing Office,
Washington, D.C. 20402

CONTENTS

		Page
Preface		vii
Chapter 1.	Aircraft Engines for War	1
Chapter 2.	Trouble-Shooting: The Wartime Mission	19
Chapter 3.	Jet Propulsion: Too Little, Too Late	41
Chapter 4.	Testing Their Mettle	65
Chapter 5.	New Educational Demands	89
Chapter 6.	Operations Research	109
Chapter 7.	Pushing Innovation and Industry Resistance	127
Chapter 8.	Seizing the Space Initiative	149
Chapter 9.	The Apollo Era: Opportunities and Dashed Hopes	177
Chapter 10.	Down-to-Earth Problems	201
Essay on Sources		219

Appendices

A.	Land Acquisitions and Name Changes	225
B.	Facilities (1942–1987)	227
C.	Management Structure	241
D.	Budget (1942–1977)	257
E.	Lewis Research Center Personnel (1941–1983)	261

Index	263
About the Author	273

PREFACE

When Francis Bacon wrote the *New Atlantis* in the early 17th century, he envisioned a state-supported research institution in which knowledge could be applied to "enlarge the bounds of Human Empire, to the effecting of all things possible."[1] Among the research facilities to increase the protection and material comforts of the inhabitants of his imaginary island, Bacon imagined an Engine House to study all types of motion, including flight. National aeronautical research laboratories in Europe and the United States in the early 20th century reflected Bacon's vision of science applied to the practical problems of flight. Commitment to innovation accompanied Bacon's belief in progress. His utopia honored inventors, not politicians or academics.

In 1941 the same commitment to innovation and industrial progress won federal funding for a laboratory in Cleveland, Ohio. Local and national leaders expected the new laboratory to promote innovations in aircraft engine technology to help win the war against Germany. Contributions to the development of superior engines for military and passenger aircraft after World War II justified the large federal investment in research facilities and personnel. Today this laboratory is the NASA Lewis Research Center. In contrast to the isolation of the ideal research institution of Bacon's vision, Lewis took shape in a flesh-and-blood world of personalities, national security concerns, and postwar capitalism.

Two transitions, both precipitated by advances in propulsion technology, provide the structure for my history: the revolution in jet propulsion during World War II, and the launch of Sputnik in October 1957. Each had significant national political, military, and economic repercussions. Each forced the laboratory to restructure its research program and to redefine its relationships with its three constituencies—the military, industry, and academia. Within this framework I have distinguished one theme that recurs throughout the laboratory's history—the tension between fundamental or basic research and development. In the process of writing my history I found that these terms could not be defined in any absolute sense. Their meaning is enmeshed in the history of Lewis, and the definitions of research and development changed as Lewis evolved. As an institution, Lewis engaged in a continuing reevaluation of its role within the American propulsion community and, after the formation of NASA in 1958, within a vastly expanded federal bureaucracy.

My book is neither an administrative history of Lewis nor a chronicle of its technical achievements. This type of history would have been impossible to write, had I wished, because of the serious lack of raw material out of which to craft a history. Lewis does not have a laboratory archives. Few administrative records survived the periodic review and disposal by conscientious records managers. Of necessity, much of the documentation for the early chapters of my book came from the National Archives and Records Service in Suitland, Md., where the records of the NACA Main Committee and Power Plants Committee are stored. John Sloop's *Liquid Hydrogen as a Propulsion Fuel, 1945–1959* and Alex Roland's *Model Research: The National Advisory Committee for Aeronautics 1915–1958* provided me with useful background for the NACA period.[2] I also used technical papers produced by Lewis staff. For the period 1958 to 1977, I found brief references to Lewis in books about the space program.

Inevitably, I have passed over much interesting and significant work at Lewis. Nevertheless, the paucity of documents may also have liberated me to ask broad questions and to dig for historical context. Thus, the chapter entitled Jet Propulsion: Too Little, Too Late focuses on the national strategy to develop a gas turbine engine in the United States. By understanding decisions reached at a national level, I was better able to tackle the subsequent transition of the laboratory from research on piston engines to jet propulsion. James R. Hansen's original research in *Engineer in Charge* contributed to my understanding of the NACA's early efforts in jet propulsion. Edward W. Constant's *The Origins of the Turbojet Revolution* was important in framing some of the questions I asked in this chapter. Moreover, his essay and others in *The Nature of Technological Knowledge* stimulated me to think about shifts in technological knowledge shared by a community of practitioners both within and outside Lewis.[3] The chapter entitled Seizing the Space Initiative focuses on the crisis precipitated by Sputnik. I found the role of Abe Silverstein and his team from Lewis significant in shaping the early years of NASA. Moreover, I traced the roots of some of Lewis's future problems to the organizational structure conceived during T. Keith Glennan's years as NASA's first administrator.

I hope that my book is a contribution to the current effort among historians of technology to understand technological innovation as a social activity or process.[4] I was interested in the strategies developed by the engineering community at Lewis in response to the new theoretical demands of the gas turbine engine and how the laboratory acquired new engineering knowledge. When I looked at the relationship of Lewis with Case Institute of Technology, I was surprised to find that in the early postwar era, Case was on the receiving end of Lewis's expertise in gas turbine and rocket technology. Later, as Case Institute of Technology developed graduate programs, this scenario was reversed.

Bruno Latour's article, "Give Me a Laboratory and I will Raise the World," stimulated me to consider the question of the laboratory's leverage or destabilizing influence on constituencies outside its gates.[5] Latour's analysis seemed particularly cogent with respect to the laboratory's relationship with the intensely competitive engine companies. Instead of focusing on specific innovations, I considered innovation in the context of the laboratory's role within the American propulsion community. What were the mechanisms of technology transfer from the government to the private sector in the NACA era? How did this relationship change under NASA?

Some former Lewis staff may wonder why I included an entire chapter on Lewis's operations research. No doubt this work occupied one of the lower rungs in the research hierarchy, but I thought general readers might find icing and crash fires of greater interest than more recondite areas of engineering. I used the chapter to demonstrate why the government undertakes certain types of research, the leverage of federal safety regulations, and the response of industry. I am indebted to the late William Olsen for some of the documents and insights in this chapter.

I wrote two thirds of the book between 1984 and 1987 under a contract funded through the NASA History Office. It took me two more years to complete and revise the manuscript. My contract stipulated that my work was to be guided and judged by the standards of a professional historian. I was free to interpret Lewis history as long as my statements were supported by evidence and my speculations clearly indicated. Beyond the requirement to submit forty reports, I was left alone. In general, there was no restriction on my access to documents. However, I did not see a portion of the NACA collection on nuclear propulsion in the National Archives because it has not been declassified. Two professional historians, Clayton Koppes and James Hansen, and two former NACA-NASA Lewis staff, John Sloop and Seymour Himmel, reviewed the manuscript. Their critical reading helped to improve the technical details of the book and to sharpen my arguments. At no time did I feel pressure to change my interpretations. Despite their careful review, I am sure that my work is both imperfect and incomplete, for which I bear full responsibility.

Many people at Lewis and elsewhere willingly submitted to taped as well as less formal interviews. I would like to thank them most heartily for their cooperation. They are too numerous to name individually, although a list of formal interviews can be found in my essay on sources. In addition, Clinton Brown, Robert English, John Evvard, Bruce Lundin, Hans von Ohain, Stan Moore, Ben Pinkel, and Abe Silverstein commented on some of my early drafts. I cannot refrain from mentioning the support and enthusiasm of Louis Chelko, Melvin Hartmann, the late George Mandel, Walter Olson, Irving Pinkel, Warren Rayle, Roger Luidens, John Stanitz, Ernest Walker, Isidore Warshawsky, and Alan Willoughby. Lynn Bondurant and the staff of the Educational Services Division were my official link with Lewis and provided me with office space and graciously assisted me in myriad ways. I also received extensive and timely support from the staff of the NASA Lewis Technical Library, especially Evelyn Carnahan, who cheerfully provided access to Lewis records stored at Plum Brook and elsewhere.

I am indebted to Richard Wood and his successor, John Butler, at the National Archives and Records Service, Suitland, Md.; Lee Saegesser of the NASA History Office, Washington, D.C.; Richard Leyes of the National Air and Space Museum, Washington, D.C.; Richard Layman at Langley Research Center, Hampton, Va.; and Donald Hess and Janet Kovacevich, Johnson Space Center, Houston, Tex. I would like to thank Richard Hallion, Albert Misenko, Marvin Stibich, and Lois Walker for their assistance at various archives at Wright-Patterson Air Force Base, Dayton, Ohio; also, Helen Near, FBI Headquarters, Washington, D.C.; Ann Sindelar, Western Reserve Historical Society, Cleveland, Ohio; Dennis Harrison, Case Western Reserve University Archives, Cleveland, Ohio; Anne Millbrooke and Harvey Lippencott, United Technologies Archives, East Hartford, Conn.

I am especially grateful to Sylvia Fries and the staff of the NASA History Office for their professionalism, confidence, and forbearance. Fellow historians Michal McMahon, Edwin Layton, Walter Vincenti, and John Mauer generously agreed to comment on individual chapters. Colleagues in NASA history Elizabeth Muenger, James Capshew, and Craig Waff supplied documents and encouragement. I received many insights, practical advice, and strong support from James Hansen of Auburn University, Auburn, Ala. I do not know how to express my gratitude to Clayton Koppes of Oberlin College, Oberlin, Ohio, who shared the adventure and guided and inspired me. LaVaughn Craig improved my style with grace, wit, and efficiency. Finally, my thanks to Dave, Jeff, and Emily, who supported the enterprise from beginning to end, and to my father, Alfred Parker, for stimulating my interest in engineers and engineering.

NOTES

[1] Francis Bacon, *The New Atlantis and The Great Instauration*. Jerry Weinberger, ed. (Arlington Heights, Ill: Harlan Davidson, 1989), p. 71.

[2] John L. Sloop, *Liquid Hydrogen as a Propulsion Fuel, 1945–1959* NASA SP-4404 (Washington, D.C.: U.S. Government Printing Office, 1978); Alex Roland, *Model Research: The National Advisory Committee for Aeronautics 1915–1958*, NASA SP-4103 (Washington, D.C.: U.S. Government Printing Office, 1985).

[3] James R. Hansen, *Engineer in Charge: A History of the Langley Aeronautical Laboratory, 1917–1958*, NASA SP-4305 (Washington, D.C.: U.S. Government Printing Office, 1987); Edward W. Constant II, *The Origins of the Turbojet Revolution* (Baltimore: The Johns Hopkins University Press, 1980); *The Nature of Technological Knowledge: Are Models of Scientific Change Relevant?* Rachael Lauden, ed. (Boston: D. Reidel, 1984).

[4] See, for example, Andrew Jamison, "Technology's Theorists: Conceptions of Innovation in Relation to Science and Technology Policy," *Technology and Culture* 30:505–533.

[5] Bruno Latour, "Give Me a Laboratory and I will Raise the World," in *Science Observed*, Karin D. Knorr-Cetina and Michael Mulkay, eds. (London: Sage, 1983), p. 141–170.

CHAPTER ONE

AIRCRAFT ENGINES FOR WAR

On January 23, 1941 George Lewis, the Director of Aeronautical Research for the National Advisory Committee for Aeronautics (NACA), drove a special nickel-plated pick into the frozen Ohio earth. Standing huddled in a semi-circle around him, representatives of the military, the aeronautical community, and Cleveland city officials watched Lewis break ground for the new NACA Aircraft Engine Research Laboratory. This laboratory would one day bear his name. Lewis paid tribute to Cleveland as a "beautiful site, ideally located, adjacent to one of the finest airports in the world, with all the desirable facilities that the city of Cleveland offers." He remarked that it was appropriate that the laboratory was only an hour's flight from Dayton, where Wilber and Orville Wright had constructed their first airplane—including the engine. The Wright brothers had not tackled the job of constructing their 12-horsepower engine by choice. It was an "honor that was forced upon them" because no engine company was willing to accept the unusual job of adapting an automobile engine to power an aircraft.[1]

The predicament of the Wright brothers in 1903 foreshadowed the attitudes of the aircraft engine industry on the eve of America's involvement in World War II. Conservative management and the drive for profits of the two major aircraft engine companies—Wright Aeronautical and Pratt & Whitney—made them reluctant to accept radical changes in existing engine designs. In a piece of machinery as complex and precisely put together as an aircraft engine, innovations could compromise an engine's reliability. Commercial airlines adopted the rugged radial engines produced by the two American companies because they were dependable and conserved fuel. However, the Europeans, particularly the Germans, had begun to develop engines capable of greater speeds and higher altitudes. Indeed, a British technical mission to the United States in 1940 informed military leaders of a radical new form of aircraft engine based on jet propulsion.[2] Regardless of whether jet propulsion proved feasible, no one doubted that for the first time in history air power would be among the technical factors to determine victory or defeat. To match the accelerated development of European aircraft technology, the U.S. government would have to invest in aeronautical research during World War II on an unprecedented scale.

Cleveland's new NACA Aircraft Engine Research Laboratory had a role to play in the nation's preparedness. Government engine research represented an investment in innovation. By assuming the costs of research and testing, the government could pursue promising new technology, regardless of blind alleys and false starts. NACA engineers could determine the technical feasibility of an engine design or component before handing it over to the engine

The frozen ground required both pick and shovel at the ground-breaking ceremony for the new Aircraft Engine Research Laboratory next to the Cleveland Municipal Airport. Left to right in the foreground are William R. Hopkins, former city manager who developed the airport; John Berry, Airport Commissioner; Frederick C. Crawford, President of the Cleveland Chamber of Commerce; General George Brett, Edward Warner, and Captain Sidney Kraus of the NACA Main Committee; Edward Blythin, Mayor of Cleveland; and George W. Lewis, NACA Director of Aeronautical Research.

companies for development. In theory, government research took the risk out of innovation. Future practice, however, would determine whether the laboratory fulfilled this ideal. It was clear that building rapport with the intensely competitive aircraft engine companies would not be easy. Only the war could force them to suspend their historic distrust of government interference.

NACA: Anomaly Among Government Institutions

Clevelanders who read the newspapers the day after the 1941 ground-breaking ceremony had probably never heard of the National Advisory Committee for Aeronautics, usually referred to as the NACA. It was a small, civilian research organization, highly regarded within the world aviation community, but unknown to the general public. The 1915 Naval Appropriations Bill that had created the NACA during World War I mandated its close relationship with the aircraft industry. It was charged with the supervision and direction of "the scientific study of the problems of flight, with a view to their practical solution."[3] The Advisory Committee, which directed the NACA's research program, consisted of 12 prominent members of the American aeronautical community: two each from the Army and Navy; one representative from the National Bureau of Standards, the U.S. Weather Bureau, and the Smithsonian Institution; and five additional at-large members, selected because of recognized expertise in aeronautical science or engineering. Members received no financial compensation. Although the at-large members might be from industry or affiliated with a university, they were expected to rise above politics and narrow commercial or professional interests to serve the aeronautical needs of the country as a whole. It was a mark of professional achievement to serve the NACA in this advisory capacity.

Because government funding of scientific or engineering research in the pre-World War II period was unusual, constant vigilance was necessary to prevent the NACA from being swallowed up by larger institutions within the federal bureaucracy. According to one author, the NACA was "a political freak, riding on the glamour of aviation to escape the prewar pattern of government relations with research."[4] Although at times its very existence seemed precarious, in the years between the two world wars, the NACA established itself as an enduring institution. It was not the glamour of aviation alone that allowed government-sponsored research in aeronautics to flourish while federal funding in other scientific and technical areas languished. The NACA's technical achievements and careful stewardship of its finances earned the NACA respect within the Washington bureaucracy. Always an anomaly because of its unique committee structure, which was more like the board of directors of a company than a government agency, the NACA's significant role in the development of aeronautics in the 1920s and 1930s ensured its survival.

More than any other individual, credit belongs to George William Lewis (1882–1948) for building the fledgling agency into a respected and enduring federal institution. Lewis served as Director of Aeronautical Research from 1923 to 1947. A 1908 graduate of Cornell University with a master's degree in mechanical engineering, Lewis taught mechanical engineering at Swarthmore College from 1910 to 1917. He then became head of research for Clarke Thomson, a private foundation established in Philadelphia, Penn., to promote aviation, especially advances in aircraft propulsion. One of the problems Lewis investigated during his tenure at Clarke Thomson was the potential of gas turbines to power aircraft. This early experience with gas turbines may have left Lewis pessimistic about the future of jet propulsion, a factor of considerable significance in planning the Cleveland laboratory in 1940.[5]

Lewis's work at Clarke Thomson during World War I brought him to the attention of the NACA, and he served on the NACA Power Plants Committee. Originally the NACA had intended to appoint a scientist to organize and direct its aeronautical research, but the first three candidates rebuffed the NACA. As the new Langley Memorial Aeronautical Laboratory in Hampton, Va. neared completion in 1919, the NACA recruited Lewis to become its first Executive Officer. Although Lewis lacked scientific credentials, he proved to be an excellent administrator and an inspiring technical leader. The rest of his life would be devoted to the NACA. He aggressively recruited scientific and engineering talent to staff the Langley Laboratory. He obtained funding for the expensive tools of research. By the late 1920s the NACA's research facilities, such as the Variable Density Tunnel and the Propeller Research Tunnel, were as advanced as any in the world.

Lewis kept a close watch over NACA research programs during those early years, visiting Langley as often as once a week. He did not believe in rigid chains of command expressed in elaborate organization charts. He set a tone of congenial informality and flexibility to encourage engineering creativity and, above all, teamwork. He paid scrupulous attention to every detail of the research program to the point of personally reviewing every procurement order. Under Lewis's direction in the 1920s and 1930s, the NACA made solid contributions to aeronautics. The NACA cowling (which partially covered the engines to reduce drag and allow engines to cool more efficiently), retractable landing gear, and studies of the effects of streamlining all contributed to the NACA's solid reputation in the aeronautical community.

The NACA's family of airfoil shapes for wings, tails, and propellers expressed what was meant by the NACA's duty to use scientific knowledge in the design of aircraft. To develop an air-foil shape, for example, required a theoretical understanding of the science of fluid dynamics, but to make this knowledge of practical use to industry, designers needed engineering research. Each shape had to be tested in the wind tunnel to determine its actual lift and drag. With the characteristics of each shape defined through testing, it was a simple matter for industry designers to select a particular airfoil to satisfy specific design requirements.[6]

George W. Lewis, NACA Director of Aeronautical Research from 1924 to 1947.

George Lewis served as the liaison between the Advisory Committee and the Langley Laboratory. He testified at Con-gressional hearings at which NACA ap-propriations were considered. His associates on Capitol Hill trusted his technical judgment, for he had the ability to translate complex scientific and engineering language into plain English. Lewis was also skilled in his dealings with the military, which funded a substantial portion of the NACA's research. This was an important aspect of his job, for without the con-fidence of the Army and Navy, the NACA, in his own words, would have been a "dead duck."[7] Innovations suggested in NACA research reports often became specifications in the design of military aircraft.

John Victory, the NACA's first salaried employee, served as George Lewis's right-hand man in the NACA's small Washington office. With political savvy he attended to the administrative detail required of federal institutions—even one as unencumbered with bureaucratic structure as the early NACA. To keep the NACA within the bounds of its enabling legislation, Victory kept a copy of the 1915 bill in his breast pocket, ceremoniously drawing it out to arbitrate questions of policy. On the eve of World War II, the personalities of Lewis and Victory reflected the image of the NACA. It was a responsible, competent, if somewhat conservative organization that had earn-ed the respect of its two constituencies, the military and the aircraft industry. Yet by the late 1930s, the NACA seemed to be resting on its laurels. The development of aeronautical research in Germany began to shake it out of its complacency.[8]

FROM INERTIA TO ACTION

At first the NACA watched European developments in engine technology without full awareness of their implications for American national security. In September 1936, George Lewis visited Germany to evaluate reports of recent expansion and decentralization of German aeronautical facilities. He found that research under Adolf Baeumker was being funded and staffed on a grand scale hardly dreamed of in the United States. Baeumker reported directly to Hermann Goering, Hitler's Air Minister, and there seemed to be no limit to the funds available to finance Baeumker's grandiose scheme of aeronautical laboratories. The Germans, he wrote, were contemplating a long-range research program. Its major emphasis was to increase the speeds of airplanes, regardless of the expense.

Lewis pointed out that, prior to Chancellor Adolf Hitler's rise to power, funding for the Deutsche Versuchsanstalt für Luftfahrt (DVL) at Adlershof near Berlin, the German counterpart of Langley Laboratory, had been limited. Hitler apparently made unlimited funds available to Baeumker. For military reasons, the Germans had decided not to concentrate all their aeronautical research and development at one location; therefore, Adlershof was to be supplemented by two additional stations, one entirely devoted to engine research at Stuttgart, the other for more fundamental aerodynamic research at Braunschweig. A large and elaborate pressure-type wind tunnel had been completed at the University of Goettingen under the direction of the famous aerodynamicist Ludwig Prandtl. Lewis noted the extensive facilities for aircraft engine research and testing at the DVL, in particular, altitude test facilities for both air-cooled and liquid-cooled engines. Research in fuels and lubricants, stimulated by the impending acute shortages of fuel in Germany, took place in a special room containing an array of single-cylinder test engines. He pointed out, slightly disparagingly, that the electric dynamometers and other gadgets made him wonder whether he was. "in an engine-testing laboratory or a small edition of the Licke observatory."[9] Although Lewis considered NACA facilities superior to those in Germany, the number of personnel and the advanced level of their training worried him. He estimated that in the near future there would be about 1000 employees engaged in aeronautical research at four separate sites compared to a mere 350 at Langley Laboratory. Even more serious was the superior technical training of German scientists and engineers. Graduate engineering education in the United States would become increasingly important as the theoretical demands of aeronautical engineering increased.

Lewis's report on his 1936 trip to Germany was the first intimation that the NACA's Langley Laboratory might be inadequate for the nation's future research needs. In response to Lewis's report, the NACA set up a special committee under General Oscar Westover, then Chief of the Army Air Corps. It took three years for the committee to address the question of the relation of the NACA to defense of the United States in the event of war.[10]

Meanwhile, military aeronautical technology in Germany was rapidly overtaking that of the United States. As early as 1937 John Jay Ide, the NACA's technical assistant in Europe, warned of the results of German advances. He reported that Germany was producing extraordinary airplanes and engines that had enabled them, with their ally Italy, to set a "holocaust of records." Ide noted that in the development of aircraft engines there had been no spectacular breakthroughs. Steady incremental improvements were nevertheless pushing European engine development to new heights. Both England and Germany had developed liquid-cooled engines with two-speed superchargers to power fighter aircraft. By 1939 Ide had concluded that, so great was the German emphasis on the development of new technology, the next war would be a "war of workshops." The country able to develop the most advanced aircraft would have a strategic advantage. Ide emphasized that for the Europeans it was *speed* above all that was important. The

Germans had airplanes that could reach speeds of over 400 miles per hour. The fastest planes, he noted, all had liquid-cooled engines.[11]

In letters to the NACA from England, Charles Lindbergh also described European advances in aircraft propulsion. In his letter of August 1937 he expressed mild concern: "As Dr. Ames said in one of his letters, American aviation is, generally speaking, still well ahead of European aviation. However, I believe we must work very much harder in the future in order to maintain our leadership."[12] Lindbergh was especially impressed by the new facilities at the Junkers and Heinkel aircraft companies in Germany, built at government expense. The British also seemed to be pushing ahead of the United States with new engine types. He noted that Europeans were developing rockets and urged the NACA to begin work in rocket development. He recommended that the NACA contact America's lone rocket pioneer, Robert Goddard, about future cooperation. Unlike Wernher von Braun, the architect of the Nazi's fearsome V-2 rocket who closely scrutinized Goddard's papers, the NACA considered Goddard too visionary.[13]

As Europe moved closer to war, Lindbergh's increased sense of urgency drove him home from Europe in 1939. He went straight from his steamship to a meeting with the future chief of the Army Air Corps, Henry Harley Arnold. Arnold recalled, "Nobody gave us much useful information about Hitler's air force until Lindbergh came home in 1939."[14] After the slow-moving Westover committee recommended a second laboratory for research in aerodynamics and aircraft structures (the future Ames Aeronautical Laboratory in Sunnyvale, Calif.) Lindbergh agreed to chair a Special Committee on Aeronautical Research Facilities. Lindbergh was convinced that the United States needed better aircraft engines.[15] As Hitler's September *Blitzkreig* swept through Poland, Lindbergh's committee urgently recommended the construction of an engine research laboratory in a location accessible to the engine companies. Lindbergh was convinced that the development of liquid-cooled engines was not receiving sufficient attention in the United States. Other high-level aviation experts shared his view. The periodical *Science* warned that the nation needed research facilities above all because of "the superiority of foreign liquid-cooled engines."[16]

The recognition of the gravity of the engine situation coincided with the strengthening of the leadership of the NACA. The same day that Lindbergh made his recommendations, the NACA elected Vannevar Bush to take charge of forging a wartime research program. A former Dean of Engineering and Vice President of the Massachusetts Institute of Technology, Bush appreciated the value of research. He greatly admired the NACA and looked upon its organization as a model for the mobilization of science. Known as both a scientist and a hard-headed practical engineer, he considered the best engineering to be applied science. For him, the NACA exemplified this ideal.[17]

The NACA elected George Mead, former Vice President of United Aircraft and one of the country's most respected engine designers, Vice Chairman. Shortly afterwards he replaced Bush as head of the Power Plants Committee. He would oversee the design of the new NACA Aircraft Engine Research Laboratory in Cleveland, Ohio. Mead's experience with engine development was long and impressive. From engineer-in-charge of the Army's Power Plants Laboratory in Dayton, Ohio, Mead had become chief engineer for the Wright Aeronautical Corporation. In 1925 he left Wright with Frederick B. Rentschler to found the Pratt & Whitney Company in East Hartford, Conn. Mead's engineering genius was responsible for the successful design of the Wasp and Hornet engines, which turned the fledgling company into a formidable competitor of Wright Aeronautical.[18]

The defection of some of Wright Aeronautical's most able staff and the subsequent success of Pratt & Whitney had created a bitter rivalry between the two companies in the commercial development of air-cooled engines. Neither company, however, had taken great interest in the development of engines with liquid cooling. Profits for both companies clearly lay in the continued development of the air-cooled, or radial, engine. In a country with vast distances to cover, the air-cooled engine was more rugged, lighter, and consumed less fuel than its liquid-cooled counterpart. It could be maintained easily, and it did not require a radiator, which might be punctured by enemy fire. To increase the power of the radial engine during World War II, up to four additional banks of cylinders were added behind the initial nine, making the engine more difficult to cool.

By the early 1930s the military concluded that for strategic reasons the United States should not depend exclusively on air-cooled engines, despite their dominance of both the military and commercial markets. For military applications, where speed and high altitude were important, the liquid-cooled engine had great advantages. The sleek in-line arrangement of its cylinders meant that the engine could be placed in the wings, rather than up front in the fuselage behind the propeller, where the bulky engine could obstruct the vision of the pilot. The Army supported the development of liquid-cooled engines by several companies. However, by 1940 only the Allison V-1710, made by the Allison Division of General Motors, was ready to be mass-produced for fighter aircraft. Before 1943 the Allison was inferior to comparable European liquid-cooled engines like the British Merlin, but to power fighter aircraft it was superior to the best air-cooled engines produced by Wright Aeronautical and Pratt & Whitney.[19]

Among the executives of the two established engine companies, only George Mead had taken a strong interest in the development of a liquid-cooled engine. In 1937 he returned from a trip to England impressed with a British liquid-cooled engine with an H-type sleeve valve. He urged Pratt & Whitney to make the investment in the new engine type.[20] The corporate leadership of the company, however, was cool to the idea, although design studies were initiated. In June 1939 the company decided to concentrate its efforts on the development of superior air-cooled engines. This seems to have precipitated Mead's resignation, making him available to serve the NACA on the eve of America's entry into World War II. One of his first accomplishments was to reform and strengthen the Power Plants Committee. He insisted that all three engine companies, Wright Aeronautical, Pratt & Whitney, and Allison, as well as the petroleum industry have representation.[21]

The job of the Power Plants Committee was to figure out how to encourage innovations in engine design. The first step toward this goal was to implement as quickly as possible Lindbergh's recommendation for the new federally funded engine research laboratory. Mead formed a Special Committee on New Engine Research Facilities to hammer out the design of the proposed laboratory. Gaylord W. Newton represented the Civil Aeronautics Administration, Commander Rico Botta, the Navy, and Major E. R. Page, the Army Air Corps. Carlton Kemper, head of the Engine Research Division at the Langley Laboratory, and George Lewis were the NACA members. Although membership was balanced among the engine companies the military, and the NACA, the engine companies, wielded considerable power. In addition to Mead, Ronald Hazen, President of the Allison Company, and Arthur Nutt, Vice President of Engineering for Wright Aeronautical, were key members.

Sam D. Heron, an executive of the Ethyl Corporation in Detroit, Mich., served as a valuable link between the NACA and the petroleum industry. After work on the design of air-cooled cylinders at the Royal Aircraft Factory in England, Heron had pioneered the development of sodium-cooled engine valves for the Army Air Corps at Wright Field in Dayton, Ohio. Mead called on Heron to persuade the engine laboratory planners to include a fuels and lubricants facility. Heron emphasized that, despite the large amount of research being carried on by the petroleum industry, "it was impossible to do too much work toward improving fuels." Heron presented a detailed proposal for an elaborate facility that was adopted without opposition.[22] This commitment to fuels research would some day bear fruit in the future laboratory's role in the development of liquid hydrogen as a high-energy rocket fuel.

It was decided immediately that research on both liquid- and air-cooled engines would be conducted at the new NACA Aircraft Engine Research Laboratory. Testing would be carried out on models and full-scale engines, as well as on the various components, such as superchargers, carburetors, instruments, and both fuel injection and fuel ignition systems. To implement the basic plan of the engine laboratory, the NACA formed a design group at Langley that consisted of a nucleus of 15 seasoned men and 11 enthusiastic recent engineering graduates. The group worked feverishly at Langley under Smith DeFrance, who was responsible for the early designs for both the new aircraft structures laboratory at Sunnyvale, Calif., and the new engine laboratory. When DeFrance was sent to Sunnyvale, Ernest G. Whitney took over. While DeFrance took with him the problem of the aerodynamic design of the engine laboratory's wind tunnels, Whitney faced the formidable task of coordinating all the elements in the complex design, as well as supervising the early construction of the new laboratory.[23]

An item that raised considerable debate among the laboratory planners was the decision to include a wind tunnel. Only three facilities existed in the United States for altitude testing of aircraft engines: the Bureau of Standards, the Naval Aircraft Factory in Philadelphia, Penn., and the Army's Power Plants Laboratory at Wright Field. None of the three could test engines at sufficiently high altitudes. George Mead argued strongly in favor of a wind tunnel. He was critical of the limited facilities for engine testing at Langley.[24]

The inclusion of a wind tunnel in the plan became a bone of contention because wind tunnel tests could be construed as development. The NACA did not approve of "mingling research and development work in the same organization," but how this principle applied to engine research was not clear.[25] The established engine companies, Pratt & Whitney and Wright Aeronautical, argued that an altitude wind tunnel would allow the NACA to compete with industry in engine development, but the Allison Division of General Motors supported the wind tunnel because it needed help in developing its liquid-cooled engine. The two established companies feared that more vigorous competition from a wider field of engine companies would affect their ability to continue to reap large profits on commercial engines. The issue of the relationship of the new laboratory to industry remained one of the thorny problems left to be tackled once peace was restored. The nation, however, could no longer afford to leave engine development exclusively in the hands of industry.

At the January 1940 meeting of his planning committee, Mead called for the opinion of Frank W. Caldwell, a man he respected for his expertise in developing the variable pitch propeller for Hamilton-Standard Propellors Company. Caldwell argued strongly in favor of an altitude wind tunnel to study the influence of engine vibration on the propeller. After his presentation, Mead's committee reached the long-sought consensus that an altitude wind tunnel, capable of testing engines up to 3000 horsepower, be included in the plan. Caldwell also suggested that the engine laboratory include a propeller research laboratory, a proposal that was also adopted. George Mead submitted the final report of his committee to Vannevar Bush on January 23, 1940. It stated that "the proposed facilities are urgently needed and are vital to both the national defense and to the future success of our commercial aviation."[26]

The role of the new government engine research laboratory was carefully described by Vannevar Bush when he testified before the Subcommittee of the Committee on Appropriations in the U.S. House of Representatives. Bush asked for an appropriation of $8,400,000. He stressed that the engine research facilities at Langley were extremely limited, that private industry did not conduct the necessary research, and that government would not compete with industry. Both General Arnold, Chief of the Army Air Corps, and Admiral Towers, Chief of the Bureau of Aeronautics of the Navy Department, strongly supported the proposed legislation.[27] Called on to describe the nature of the proposed laboratory in detail, George Lewis estimated that it would have a staff of 220 and an annual operating cost of $650,000. The single most expensive item, the altitude wind tunnel, Lewis called "very, very desirable." Such a facility did not exist anywhere in the world. He estimated that, at a simulated altitude of 30,000 feet, the speed of the wind tunnel would be 490 miles per hour. In the proposed tunnel the engine, supercharger, and propeller could be studied at full scale both separately and as a unit, so that months of flight testing could be eliminated.

A congressman's question gave Lewis the opportunity to emphasize the importance of government research and the void that it was intended to fill: "There is no governmental research of engines being done in the United States now? It is all done by the private establishments, is it?"

Lewis's response was terse: "There is very little scientific research being done on engines in this country. Private establishments are concerned chiefly with development problems relating to their own engines. The aircraft engine research work that is being done at Langley Field represents the major portion of all fundamental research on aircraft engines in this country."

Lewis continued to be pressed by the congressman: "And that is very limited?"

Lewis replied that, although the Army and Navy had research facilities for engine testing, this was only development work. The Army's Power Plants Laboratory at Wright Field in Dayton, Ohio, and the Navy's Aircraft Factory in Philadelphia, Penn., were used to evaluate engines produced by a particular company to determine whether they met military specifications. This was not fundamental research—the purpose of the new laboratory.[28]

Although Lewis was not asked to define fundamental research, it would have been an appropriate question. Did congressmen understand the difference between fundamental research and development? What could the government do that industry would not, or could not, do? It was clear that the engine companies were not happy that such vast sums would go to a new government laboratory. In early June, in a final attempt to prevent the authorization of government engine research, they proposed that, instead of spending $8,400,000 for the new laboratory, the government give each company $3 million to do its own research. The NACA responded by memo that the essence of a government research laboratory was to tackle problems common to the entire industry and to see that the information was equally accessible to all companies in a given field. This is what the NACA called fundamental research. Competition prevented the exchange of information, so that each company had to work independently "to solve problems common to them all," an unnecessary duplication of research effort. Moreover, if the engine companies were given money directly, they would focus their research on immediate problems "of perhaps low fundamental significance but of high specific interest to that individual company." Thus, research would be too closely tied to development. Moreover, the NACA memo pointed out, research on components would be neglected, because the engine companies bought these parts from other manufacturers. In the NACA's view, the entire aircraft engine deserved equal and impartial scrutiny.[29]

With the forced evacuation of the Allied Forces at Dunkirk and the fall of France in early June 1940, could Great Britain resist invasion? Alarmed by the implications for the national security of the United States and already committed to supplying aircraft to Great Britain, Congress approved the funding for a new NACA aircraft engine research laboratory in June 1940 as part of the First National Defense Appropriations Act.[30] A site for the new laboratory remained to be chosen.

CLEVELAND WINS THE BID

At this point the efforts of the Cleveland Chamber of Commerce moved into high gear. Cleveland's location, industrial base, and particularly the connections and active involvement of Frederick C. Crawford, President of Thompson Products, won the new laboratory for Cleveland. Crawford worked with energy, determination, and tact to make sure that the NACA chose Cleveland. His motivation was simple. The new laboratory would be good for his company. Thompson Products made automotive and aircraft engine parts and was just beginning its wartime expansion. [Thompson Products became Thompson-Ramo-Wooldridge Corporation (TRW) in 1958.]

Crawford's behind-the-scenes action began in 1939, as soon as he heard that the NACA was considering a second laboratory to supplement or possibly replace the one at Langley. He asked Clifford Gildersleeve, the Industrial Commissioner on the staff of the Chamber of Commerce, to prepare an invitation to the NACA in August.

Selling Cleveland was not new to Gildersleeve. His job was to attract new industries to the city, and he was well aware of the opportunities for industrial expansion created by the war in Europe. With the infusion of federal funds for new plants and the modernization of old ones already under way, a large government research facility would make the city all the more attractive to industry.[31]

The invitation that Gildersleeve prepared for the NACA described Cleveland in alluring terms typical of Chamber of Commerce brochures. Located in the nation's industrial heart, the city stood as the industrial nexus between the Pennsylvania coal fields and the iron of the Mesabi Range in Minnesota. The great coal-fired open hearth furnaces of the mills in the Flats along the Cuyahoga River processed the iron ore into steel. Gildersleeve's invitation pointed out that half of the population of the United States and more than half of the country's manufacturing were located within 500 miles of the city. Cleveland was also a hub of transportation. The airport handled a daily average of 100 planes, making it among the busiest airports in the country. In addition to highway connections, six major railroads served Cleveland, and the Great Lakes were used by industries like Republic Steel to transport iron ore cheaply. Electric power in Cleveland, supplied by the Cleveland Electric Illuminating Company, was "plentiful and dependable." In addition, Cleveland owned and maintained its own water system.[32] What the invitation did not state was that the city, still recovering from the Depression, desperately needed jobs for its workers. The city's reputation for tightly organized unions made new industries reluctant to locate in Cleveland. To cope with 87,000 poor relief cases, the city received federal assistance, but it still faced a large poor relief deficit of over $1 million.[33]

Clevelanders, however, loved aviation. The city's sponsorship of the enormously successful National Air Races had first brought Crawford into contact with the NACA through his association with John Victory. Victory had visited Cleveland frequently as one of the officials of the National Air Race Association Committee. Crawford's company awarded the coveted Thompson Trophy each year, and his enthusiasm for aviation was well known. Although the manufacture of parts for automobile engines was the major business of Thompson Products, the company also sold sodium-cooled valves to the two giants in the aircraft engine field, Wright Aeronautical and Pratt & Whitney, a business that flourished during World War I with the production of valves for the Liberty engine.

Other Cleveland companies were in the parts business. In 1940 Cleveland boasted no less than 80 to 90 companies "catering directly to aviation."[34] Eaton Industries also produced sodium-cooled valves, and Cleveland Pneumatic had pioneered the development of pneumatic landing gears. With a new plant for Wright Aeronautical's engines under construction outside Cincinnati, Crawford saw that Cleveland aircraft parts industries could anticipate substantial expansion as a result of the war in Europe. What could be more appropriate for the city than a major research laboratory for aircraft engines?

The city's identification with both the romance and commercial potential of aviation had begun during World War I, when a group of Cleveland investors persuaded a gifted, if somewhat eccentric, aircraft designer, Glen L. Martin, to locate his aircraft company in Cleveland. During its years in Cleveland, Martin's company produced the important Martin GMB-1 bomber and attracted some of the most talented airplane designers in the country: Dutch Kindelberger, Lawrence Bell, and Donald Douglas. When Martin moved his company to Baltimore in 1929, he left as his legacy to the city his role in spearheading the development of Cleveland's municipal airport.[35]

The large size and careful design of Cleveland's airport made it a natural site for the National Air Races. The Air Races brought Crawford and the NACA together. Held in Cleveland 8 of 11 years between 1929 and World War II, the races provided the opportunity to push beyond the existing speeds of aircraft. Prominent Cleveland industrialists like Crawford and Lewis W. Greve, President of Cleveland Pneumatic, supported them enthusiastically. Many of the engine improvements first demonstrated on racing aircraft were later adopted by the aircraft engine companies.[36] What could be more natural than a new federal laboratory to continue to encourage engine innovation?

Cleveland lost out to Sunnyvale, Calif., as the location for the Ames Aeronautical Research Laboratory because Sunnyvale was close to the California aircraft industry, which exercised its political clout on Capitol Hill. Nevertheless, when Congress authorized funds for an aircraft engine laboratory, Cleveland was ready to push for its selection. Gildersleeve and Walter I. Beam, the Executive Secretary of the Chamber of Commerce, had already convinced Cleveland's local officials of the desirability of the city as a site for a government research laboratory. As an incentive, the city had agreed to make nearly 200 acres of land next to the Cleveland Airport available for $1 an acre, as well as raise $550,000 locally for power facilities.[37]

The NACA was determined that the competition for the site for the new engine laboratory be properly and impartially administered. After the engine laboratory was funded, the NACA selected a blue ribbon committee, chaired by Vannevar Bush, to recommend a site.[38] The committee sent letters to all interested congressmen, Chambers of Commerce, and other interested individuals stating the requirements to enter the competition. Because the new laboratory would require facilities for flight testing, the city had to be able to make available title to 100 acres either on or adjoining an airport owned by a municipality or already owned by the federal government.

George Lewis explains the plan for the new engine research laboratory to top NACA staff.

With a large wind tunnel planned, the site also needed adequate power as well as ample water for cooling. The city should be an industrial center, accessible to the engine companies located either on the East Coast or in the Midwest. The site also had to be near "centers of scientific and technical activity." Another factor to be considered was "strategic vulnerability." Since there was a perceived danger that the United States might be attacked on either coast, where the NACA's other two laboratories were located, there was a general feeling that the Midwest offered the safest location. The NACA used an elaborate point system, originally devised for the Sunnyvale site selection, to judge the contenders for the new engine laboratory.[39]

In July the Cleveland Chamber of Commerce issued a formal bid to the NACA for the new laboratory, responding directly to the list of criteria. The Chamber of Commerce enlisted the support of the local Society of Automotive Engineers to impress the NACA with the city's engineering community. In addition, the presidents of the Case School of Applied Science and Western Reserve University wrote letters that described in glowing terms the excellence of the educational resources of the city.

Cleveland faced stiff competition. Of the 72 sites in 62 cities that submitted bids, 14 cities, offering a total of 20 sites, met the stipulated criteria. A Special Committee on Site Inspection visited the top-ranking cities. The major contenders, as presented at the September meeting of the Bush Committee on Site Selection, were Cleveland, Ohio; Dayton, Ohio; Detroit, Mich.;

Cincinnati, Ohio; and Aurora, Ill. However, by October, Glenview, near Chicago, took the number one position in the ratings, with Cleveland running second. Officials in Chicago had convinced the NACA that the Chicago area, with its many university and industrial research laboratories, could provide a superior research environment. The drawbacks of the Cleveland site were the unusually high rates for electric power charged by the Cleveland Electric Illuminating Company and the spectator stands for the National Air Races on the proposed site. Would the continued operation of the races interfere with the plans for the new engine laboratory? Because the Material Division of the Army Air Corps was already located at Wright Field near Dayton, where the Army had its own power plants laboratory for testing engines, the Army urged the NACA to consider the Dayton site. Not surprisingly, Orville Wright, a prominent member of the NACA, put his weight behind his home town.[40]

Nevertheless, John Victory and Rudolf Gagg, a Wright Aeronautical consultant retained by the NACA, favored Cleveland over the other cities under consideration and were willing, while keeping a public stance of impartiality, to go out of their way to help Cleveland win the bid. This was no doubt due to the "personal relationships of long standing" between Frederick Crawford and the NACA.[41] Not only had Crawford "gone to Washington for a number of conferences, had conferred with people in New York, and had given up much time to Cleveland's effort to obtain the laboratory," but he had also taken a personal hand in the negotiations between the NACA and the Cleveland Electric Illuminating Company. In order for the Illuminating Company to avoid the capital investment involved in building new generating plants to supply the proposed engine laboratory, Crawford came up with the idea that the company could offer reduced rates if the NACA were willing to run its large testing facilities at night.[42] This was a shrewd move on the part of Crawford, although at first the conservative Illuminating Company resisted the proposed arrangement.

To discuss the problem of the power rates and the city's intentions as far as the National Air Races were concerned, Victory, Gagg, and Russell Robinson visited Cleveland on October 14. Their trip had an extremely favorable outcome. As Victory recalled, "one fly in the ointment" was the skepticism of Evan Crawford, the President of the Illuminating Company. Evan Crawford doubted that the wind tunnel could be run on an off-peak basis. Victory remembered:

> The electrical rates he offered were considered prohibitive. Into this breach stepped Fred Crawford, just in time to prevent the collapse of negotiations. I shall never forget the final scene in Evan Crawford's office when he yielded and then promised that, if Cleveland were selected, his company would "ooze cooperation from every pore."[43]

The Illuminating Company agreed to a substantial reduction in the monthly electric rates. From a minimum annual charge of $120,000 in the original proposal, the power company agreed to a minimum charge of $50,000. This clinched the choice for Cleveland. In addition to the concessions of the electric company, Major John Berry, superintendent of the airport, reported that the park commissioners had agreed to offer part of the park adjoining the airport to the NACA. This would create a buffer around the new laboratory of a mile on every side. Crawford indicated the likelihood that the operation of Cleveland's National Air Races would be suspended and the willingness of the National Air Race Association Committee to have the stands removed.[44]

The selection of Cleveland as the site was formally announced to the press on November 25, 1940 by Vannevar Bush. After political maneuvers to avoid objections over whether the municipal government could turn over the land at less than the fair price, the Mayor of the City of Cleveland, Harold H. Burton, sold 200 acres of land for $500 to the federal government. The

A squadron of U.S. Marine planes flies over the site of the future Aircraft Engine Research Laboratory during the National Air Races, 1935. The Brookpark Road Bridge is at the right.

NACA was granted the right to use the airport free of charge, and it was agreed that neither the airport nor the NACA would erect buildings that would interfere with the operations of the other. If the laboratory's activities ceased, the land would revert to the City of Cleveland.

Soon the stands for the spectators would be pulled down to make way for the new buildings of the NACA Aircraft Engine Research Laboratory. Roscoe Turner carried off the Thompson Trophy for the last time in 1939. The air races had kept interest in aviation alive through the Depression. They had contributed to increasing the speeds of aircraft through the tinkering of talented mechanics. With the most advanced engine research facilities the country could muster about to be built at the edge of the airport, engine innovation would become more rational and systematic. People with professional training in engineering and science would take over from the racing buffs the job of increasing the speed of aircraft. Nevertheless, the role the laboratory would play in engine innovation was not entirely clear. Over the objections of the engine companies, which feared that government research might interfere with healthy competition, Congress had funded the NACA's new engine laboratory. Vannevar Bush and George Lewis had used their considerable prestige to assure the Congress that fundamental research would foster innovation. They argued that the NACA would tackle engine problems common to the entire industry. The development of new engine prototypes would remain the province of the engine companies. Yet the construction of a wind tunnel belied these assurances. Testing full-scale engines in a wind tunnel strained the definition of fundamental research. However, with the impending war, there was no time to debate the fine points of the respective boundaries of fundamental research and development.

As he stood in the frigid wind on that January for the ground-breaking ceremony, Crawford may have reflected that the heyday of the National Air Races was about to end. Military airplanes had reached speeds beyond those of any plane ever entered in the air races. These new machines of war had "out-raced the races."[45]

NOTES

[1] "Lewis's talk at ground-breaking ceremonies," 23 January 1941, NASA Lewis Records, 298/110-411.

[2] A British technical mission, headed by Sir Henry Tizard, visited the United States in September 1940. For a general discussion of the mission, see Daniel J. Kevles, *The Physicists* (New York: Vantage Books, 1979), p. 302-303. Specific reference to the disclosure of British advances in jet propulsion made by Tizard are found in Bush to Arnold, 2 July 1941, 47/208, and Papers of H. H. Arnold manuscript Division, Library of Congress. Arnold to Tizard, 4 June 1941, 47/208.

[3] Jerome Hunsaker, "Forty Years of Aeronautical Research," *Smithsonian Report for 1955,* p. 246. For the administrative history of the NACA, see Alex Roland, *Model Research: The National Advisory Committee for Aeronautics,* NASA SP-4103 (Washington, D.C.: U.S. Government Printing Office, 1985), vol. 1.

[4] Daniel S. Greenberg, *The Politics of Pure Science* (New York: The New American Library, 1967), p. 108.

[5] James R. Hansen, "George W. Lewis and the Management of Aeronautical Research," in *Aviations's Golden Age: Portraits from the 1920s and 1930s,* William M. Leary, ed. (Iowa City: University of Iowa Press, 1989), p. 93-112. See also Jerome C. Hunsaker, "George William Lewis (1882-1948)," in *Year Book of the American Philosophical Society* (Philadelphia: American Philosophical Society, 1948.)

[6] For the history of Langley Laboratory and the NACA's pre-World War II technical contributions, see James Hansen, *Engineer in Charge: A History of the Langley Aeronautical Laboratory, 1917-1958,* NASA SP-4305 (Washington, D.C.: U.S. Government Printing Office, 1987). For the NACA methodology of testing airfoil shapes, see Walter Vincenti, "The Air-Propeller Tests of W. F. Durand and E. P. Lesley: A Case Study in Technological Methodology," *Technology and Culture* 20:712-751.

[7] Hansen, *Engineer in Charge,* p. 160.

[8] Roland, *Model Research,* vol. 1, p. 147.

[9] Lewis's report on his 1936 trip, George Lewis biographical file, NASA History Office, Washington, D.C.

[10] The Special Committee on the Relation of the NACA to National Defense in Time of War, chaired by General Oscar Westover, Chief of the Army Air Corps, made its recommendations in August 1939. The Special Committee on Future Research Facilities, chaired by Rear Adm. Arthur B. Cook, recommended the Sunnyvale, Calif. site in December. For the full story, see Roland, *Model Research,* vol. 1, 154 ff.

[11] John J. Ide Report appended to Minutes of 7 January 1937 Meeting of the Executive Committee and "Notes on European Aeronautical Developments in 1938," 10 January 1939, Minutes of the Executive Committee, National Archives, Record Group 255, Box 7.

[12] Lindbergh to Lewis, 26 August 1937, Lindbergh biographical file, NASA History Office, Washington, D.C.

[13] Lindbergh to Lewis, 23 September 1937, Lindbergh biographical file, NASA History Office, Washington, D.C. The Navy assigned Robert Truax to evaluate Robert Goddard's work. Truax reported that Goddard was "visionary and without any definite purpose or proposal to submit to the Bureau." Memo from C. C. Helms to Lewis, 19 June 1941, Records of NACA Committees and Subcommittees, National Archives, Record Group 255, 117.15.

[14] Henry H. Arnold, *Global Mission* (New York: Harper & Row, 1949), p. 169. Charles Lindbergh, *The Wartime Journals of Charles A. Lindbergh* (New York: Harcourt Brace Janovich, 1970), p. 254.

[15] Minutes of the Executive Committee, 19 October 1939, National Archives, Record Group 255, Box 7.

[16] *Science,* 12 January 1940.

[17] Daniel Kevles, *The Physicists* (New York: Vintage Books, 1979), p. 296. Bush's idea of technology as applied science has been mentioned by several authors. See, for example, Edwin T. Layton, "Technology as Knowledge," *Technology and Culture* 15:34; see also articles on the science-technology relationship in *Technology and Culture,* vol. 17.

[18] See Robert Schlaifer, *The Development of Aircraft Engines* (Boston: Harvard University Press, 1950), p. 192.

[19] Schlaifer, *The Development of Aircraft Engines,* p. 50.

[20] Schlaifer, *The Development of Aircraft Engines,* p. 285.

[21] Alex Roland (*Model Research,* p. 163 ff.) views the chairmanship of Mead as indicative of the increasing industry influence over the NACA. He is correct that during World War II the NACA was "dependent on industry expertise to launch its engine-research program," but dependency did not continue in the postwar period.

[22] Schalifer, *The Development of Aircraft Engines*, p. 125. Minutes of the Special Committee on New Engine Research Facilities, 21 November 1939, National Archives, Record Group 255, Box 1, file 19–2. Report of the Special Committee on New Engine Research Facilities can be found in National Archives Record Group 255, Lewis Research Authorizations 123.22.

[23] Rudolf F. Gagg, "State of the Work on the Aircraft Engine Research Laboratory of the National Advisory Committee for Aeronautics," 11 February 1941, NASA Lewis Records, 34/110. See also Elizabeth Muenger, *Searching the Horizon*, NASA SP-4304 (Washington, D.C.: U.S. Government Printing Office, 1985), p. 9.

[24] Mead to Lewis, 13 November 1939, National Archives, Record Group 255, Power Plants Committee files.

[25] Minutes of the Executive Committee, 19 October 1939, National Archives, Record Group 255, Box 7.

[26] Minutes of Special Committee on New Engine Research Facilities, January 1940, National Archives, Record Group 255, Lewis Research Authorizations 123.23.

[27] Appendix to the Congressional Record, 11 June 1940, vol. 86, pt. 16, p. 3778.

[28] Ibid.

[29] Memorandum, 11 June 1940, National Archives, Record Group 255, Lewis Research Authorizations 123.22.

[30] Appendix to the Congressional Record, 11 June 1940, vol. 86, pt. 16, p. 3779a.

[31] John Holmfeld, "The Site Selection for the NACA Engine Research Laboratory: A Meeting of Science and Politics," Master's Essay, Case Institute of Technology, 1967, p. 27. Holmfeld's essay is an excellent example of primary research. However, he overestimates Gildersleeve's role and fails to recognize the behind-the-scenes work of Crawford described in the records of the Chamber of Commerce, Ms 3471, container 55, vol. 108, Minutes 1940–1941, Greater Cleveland Growth Association Records, Western Reserve Historical Society.

[32] Cleveland Chamber of Commerce Invitation to the NACA, 29 August 1939, NASA Lewis Records, 298/116.1.

[33] Chamber of Commerce, Greater Cleveland Growth Asso. Records, Ms 3471, vol. 105, 11 October 1939, Minutes 1939–40, Western Reserve Historical Society.

[34] Cleveland Chamber of Commerce Invitation to the NACA, 29 August 1939, 298/116.1, NASA Lewis Records.

[35] "Wings over Cleveland, A summary of the development of aviation in Cleveland," pamphlet published by Cleveland Chamber of Commerce, 1948, 1, NASA Lewis Records 298/116/1 and Western Reserve Historical Society. On Glen L. Martin Co., see also Lois E. Walker and Shelby E. Wickam, *From Huffman Prairie to the Moon: The History of Wright-Patterson Air Force Base* (Washington, D.C.: U.S. Government Printing Office, 1987), p. 186.

[36] Bob Hull, *A Season of Eagles* (Cleveland: Bob Hull Books, 1984), p. 13.

[37] Holmfeld, "Site Selection," p. 42.

[38] Other members of the Site Selection Committee, chaired by Vannevar Bush, included Dr. Lyman J. Briggs, Director of the National Bureau of Standards, Captain Sidney M. Kraus of the Navy Bureau of Aeronautics, and Major General George H. Brett, Acting Chief of the Air Corps. See John Holmfeld, "Site Selection," p. 21.

[39] Holmfeld, "Site Selection," p. 27.

[40] Ibid., p. 80.

[41] Chamber of Commerce, Greater Cleveland Growth Association Records, M. 3471, container 55, vol. 108, 24 October 1941, Minutes, 1940–41, Western Reserve Historical Society.

[42] Interview with Frederick C. Crawford, 2 October 1985.

[43] Speech by Victory to Chamber of Commerce, 23 January 1951, NASA Lewis Records 298, 116.1.

[44] Holmfeld, "Site Selection," p. 85.

[45] "Statement by Frederick C. Crawford, President of the Cleveland Chamber of Commerce," 13 December 1940, National Archives, Records Group 255, Engine Research Lab., Box 1, 23-1.

CHAPTER TWO

TROUBLE-SHOOTING: THE WARTIME MISSION

As the country's aircraft engine needs intensified during World War II, fundamental engine research took a back seat to trouble-shooting to solve the problems of engines in production. The wartime mission of the new engine laboratory was simple. It had to assist the engine companies to make their engines more powerful and reliable. General Arnold wanted engines that were comparable to the best European models. He ordered Pratt & Whitney and Wright Aeronautical to develop fuel injection systems within 12 months to make their engines comparable to the German BMW-801, at that point the world's best aircraft engine.[1]

Arnold blamed the engine companies for the country's dismal aircraft engine situation, but he expected the NACA to correct it. On October 14, 1942 he issued an official directive that the NACA must "do everything practicable to improve the performance of existing engines." The engine companies had failed to provide the nation with "small, light, high performance, highly supercharged engines" suitable for fighter airplanes. Their exclusive focus on large, heavy, air-cooled radial engines reflected their drive for profits at the cost of preparedness. "Our engines were nearly all built as all-purpose engines, with an eye on the world market, and not specifically for fighter aircraft."[2] The United States could not enjoy the luxury of fundamental research until the problems of reciprocating engines then in production—the Wright 2600 and 3350, the Pratt & Whitney 1830 and 4360, and the Allison V-1710 had been resolved.

Arnold's directive that the NACA concentrate on improving existing engines was made in the context of his knowledge of a radically new propulsion technology: the development of the turbojet engine. Days before his letter to the NACA, Lawrence Bell's Airacomet (P-59A), powered by a turbojet developed by General Electric, had flown successfully for the first time over Muroc Dry Lake in California. Seasoned Langley veterans in charge of overseeing the design and construction of the new Cleveland laboratory had no inkling of the impending revolution in jet propulsion. They assumed that the improvement of the aircraft piston engine would continue to follow the evolutionary pattern of the past. They worked with energy and determination to build a laboratory to assist in winning the war.

FROM BLUEPRINT TO LABORATORY

The miles of 36-inch blueprint paper produced by Langley's design group began to take real form in the winter of 1941. In February Charles Herrmann, Chief Inspector, was transferred to Cleveland from Hampton, Va. He was accompanied by Helen G. Ford, a secretary from the NACA

Washington office. They immediately set about hiring inspectors to oversee local contractors. Braving their first Cleveland winter, they took up temporary quarters in the Radio House, a small building owned by the Cleveland airport. The Airport Commissioner allowed the NACA to store new equipment temporarily in the air races grandstands awaiting demolition. Ford attended to a myriad of pressing administrative details and threw coal into the furnace, while Herrmann supervised the building of the hangar and engine propeller research building by the laboratory's first contractor, the R. P. Carbone Construction Company.

The intense grind of daily routine was broken by occasional visits from officials from the Washington office and Langley staff who "spurred us on when we felt isolated and primitive and forgotten." Ford and Herrmann processed applications from the Cleveland community, and by July the staff had outgrown the two rooms of the Radio House. They moved to the Farm House, a white clapboard structure overlooking the Rocky River. "As the Langley Field people began to arrive they were squeezed in wherever we could find room," wrote the intrepid Ford to a friend at City Hall.[3]

From the time of the ground-breaking ceremony in January 1941 to the following winter, construction work proceeded at an agonizingly slow pace. It was difficult to obtain an adequate supply of labor because the fixed-price contract negotiated by the NACA with its original contractors did not allow overtime pay. Buildings could not be completed on schedule or within budget because of the extremely high labor costs in Cleveland and the rising costs of materials and construction.[4] To take firm control of construction, in August 1940 Lewis called Edward Raymond Sharp back to Langley from Ames to serve as Construction Administrator for the new engine laboratory.

After Pearl Harbor, the pace quickened. In mid-December Ray Sharp moved with Ernest Whitney and his design group from Langley to Cleveland. They occupied temporary offices in the Farm House and the recently completed hangar. Charles Stanley Moore took responsibility for the thousands of drawings for the Engine Research Building. In the hectic days when one decision after another had to be made, a Kipling verse posted in Moore's office seemed to express their sense of teamwork as they struggled to plan each building and to supervise contractors. No individual or army, but the "everlasting team work of every blooming soul" would allow them to accomplish the impossible.[5]

Ray Sharp charted the course of the laboratory's construction. He reviewed contracts, established rapport with city officials, smoothed relations with the engine companies, and kept Wright Field and the NACA Washington office informed of progress. Named Manager of the laboratory in 1942 and Director in 1947, he remained at the helm of the Cleveland laboratory until his retirement in 1960.

Sharp had an amiable and gracious style of management that earned him the affection and loyalty of those who worked under him, but he was not an engineer. At Langley and Ames the laboratory head was the "engineer-in-charge." The Cleveland laboratory functioned differently. Sharp created an atmosphere that encouraged cooperation among the staff, but he wisely left the technical questions to the engineers. As one engineer explained, "Since he did not have any background in engineering, he left us alone. His idea was to provide us with the equipment, money, and the space and made it easier for us to work."[6]

Born on a farm in Elizabeth City, Va., in 1894, Sharp had enlisted in the Navy in World War I. His connection with the NACA began when he was employed by the Army to assemble the Italian airship *Roma*, accepted as partial payment of the Italian war debt. In 1922, upon completion of this work, which was carried out at Langley, Sharp seized the opportunity to join the fledgling NACA laboratory as Langley's 54th employee. In three years he rose from hangar boss to construction administrator. After earning a law degree from the College of William and Mary through a correspondence course, he became a member of the Virginia bar in 1924.

Sharp's first duty upon arrival in Cleveland was to use his legal skills to negotiate a contract with a different construction company, the Sam W. Emerson Company. This was the first cost-plus-fixed-fee contract for the NACA, authorized by an act of Congress on December 17, 1941. This type of contract, used extensively by the Army and Navy, made it easier to get contractors to agree to undertake risky new ventures for the federal government. The government agreed to pay a fixed fee, or guaranteed profit, to the contractor and assumed all the costs of the project.

With the country at war, the federal government moved unusually quickly. The cost of the remaining buildings was estimated on December 24; after Christmas, Sharp took on Emerson's lawyer, an experience that Sharp described as "fight all the way."[7] He had a 47-page contract typed, and by the evening of December 31 the contract was signed. One week later the Emerson Company began construction on the Engine Research Building, planned to house a variety of laboratories to cover the gamut of authorized research projects: multicylinder and single-cylinder test facilities, supercharger rigs, and laboratories for research on exhaust turbines, heat transfer, carburetion, fuel injection, ignition, automatic controls, and materials. The building covered more than four acres of floor space, designed so that the areas were flexible enough to be converted to other uses as research needs changed. The Emerson Company also rapidly constructed the Administration Building, the Gatehouse, and the service and office buildings for the wind tunnel.

With a solid reputation in Cleveland, Sam W. Emerson was active in the Cleveland Chamber of Commerce. The Emerson Company specialized in industrial construction, but had also won bids for buildings at the Case School of Applied Science, where Emerson had studied engineering and served on the Board of Trustees. As the *Cleveland Plain Dealer* described Emerson, "Many of the substantial buildings he has erected in Cleveland seem to reflect his personality—unadorned, capacious, usable, plain and adequate."[8] These were the very qualities reflected in the buildings Emerson constructed for the laboratory. Carefully set at intervals along the roads of the former air races parking area, their low-slung tan brick exteriors gave the laboratory a college campus atmosphere.

While construction proceeded, in May 1942, when the staff numbered 399, research was officially initiated in the recently completed Engine Propeller Research Building. The fruits of the cooperation between the NACA and the

The intrepid Helen G. Ford braves her first Cleveland winter.

While the Administration Building was under construction, staff squeezed into the old Farm House.

city of Cleveland could be seen in the group of dignitaries who attended the formal ceremonies: George Lewis and John Victory from the NACA; Walter I. Beam, Executive Vice President of the Chamber of Commerce; Mayor Frank J. Lausche; Major John Berry, Commissioner of the Airport; and William A. Stinchcomb, Director of Civilian Defense for Cuyahoga County. Huddled in the control room, they waited in suspense until, with the push of a button, George Lewis set in motion the huge propeller of a 14-cylinder R-2600 Wright Cyclone engine mounted in a test cell. While it roared, a battery of instruments produced a graphic record of various research parameters needed to evaluate lubricating oils. This was an appropriate engine on which to direct the laboratory's most concerted effort, because it was plagued with undefined problems. Beneath the hearty congratulations offered on the occasion must have been the nagging question, could the laboratory find the flaws that eluded the manufacturer? Could they be fixed in time? The laboratory's first technical report on lubricants tests of the Wright R-2600 by members of the Fuels and Lubricants Division, Arnold Biermann, Walter Olson, and John Tousignant, showed the promise of the youthful staff. How government research could be transformed into concrete engine improvements remained to be demonstrated.[9]

In January 1943, when Carlton Kemper arrived to take up the duties of Executive Engineer, it was not clear what his role in the new laboratory would be. Ten years as head of the Power Plants Division at Langley had not earned him the expected position of engineer-in-charge of the new laboratory. Why Sharp was chosen to take the helm of the Cleveland laboratory, rather than Kemper, is not clear. As the construction of the Cleveland laboratory went forward, Kemper stayed behind at Langley to contribute to the NACA's secret jet propulsion project—a project that failed to provide the country with a practical and timely jet propulsion system. Kemper, a 1923 graduate of the University of Pennsylvania in mechanical engineering, had joined a handful of power plants engineers at the NACA after two years with the Packard Motor Car Company. Four years later, when he took charge of the division, his staff numbered 20. After 1934, when a new power plants laboratory was built at Langley, his staff worked in cramped offices above the roar of engines being tested on the floor below.[10] Kemper would never regain his role as a leader of power plants research. In 1945 the NACA sent him Europe to join the Alsos mission as its expert on aircraft

Edward Raymond Sharp (1894-1961), Director of Lewis Laboratory through 1960.

engines. Addison Rothrock became Chief of Research, and it was he who would oversee the laboratory's difficult transition from the piston engine to jet propulsion.

LANGLEY'S POWER PLANTS DIVISION MOVES TO CLEVELAND

In the research hierarchy at Langley, engine research occupied one of the lower rungs. Aerodynamics, experimentally studied in wind tunnels, expressed the research heart of the 1930s NACA. Even the famous NACA cowling that allowed airplanes to go faster and cool more efficiently had more to do with aerodynamics than power plants. The two major engine companies, Wright Aeronautical and Pratt & Whitney, were fiercely competitive and jealous of their proprietary rights. They did not welcome government interference. Through an agreement reached in 1916, the government left engine development to the engine manufacturers, although a limited amount of engine research was carried on by the National Bureau of Standards.

Technical judgment as well as the attitudes of the engine companies may have influenced the NACA Power Plants Division to focus on the diesel, or compression-ignition engine. Most power plants experts of the 1930s thought that aircraft engine advance would occur in the diesel engine, which did not have the problems that held back the development of the air-cooled engine: ignition, knock, and the metering of fuel into the carburetor. After the first flight of a Packard aircraft engine in 1928, the diesel seemed to be the aircraft engine to overcome the limitations of the

Carlton Kemper, Executive Engineer.

air-cooled piston engine. However, development of the diesel engine, because of its weight, proved to be a dead end.

Because of its decision to focus on the diesel engine, the NACA was left out of the dramatic development of the air-cooled spark-ignition engine in the 1930s. Its improvement came unexpectedly from fuels research by the petroleum industry on the branched paraffin, octane. This increase in performance spurred supercharger development to keep engines from starving for air at high altitudes. However, the problems of knock and pre-ignition (faulty combustion within the engine's cylinders) remained. With increased supercharging, effective engine cooling was also a problem.

Gradually, in the late 1930s, research on the diesel engine declined, and the NACA began to be pulled into the mainstream of engine development. With the formation of a Subcommittee on Aircraft Fuels and Lubricants in 1935, research at Langley was initiated on the knocking characteristics of various fuels, although this research played only a peripheral role in the rapidly evolving understanding of hydrocarbons.

To advance the NACA's research on combustion, Cearcy D. Miller invented a high-speed camera that could take pictures of the combustion process within the cylinder of an engine at the rate of 40,000 frames per second. With this new high-speed photography, the exact point at which the engine began to knock could be determined for the first time. It was an exciting breakthrough.[11]

Miller's work is an example of what the NACA meant by fundamental research. He took a problem common to all air-cooled radial engines and invented a method to analyze it. Publication of Miller's reports put this new knowledge in the hands of industry designers—the point of all NACA research. The Army's fuels agenda for the Cleveland laboratory included study of the fuel additives xylidine and triptane to increase the performance of combat aircraft. The laboratory tackled the problem of replacement cylinders worn down by sand from unimproved airstrips in Africa. Oil foaming, which drained the engine's oil during flight, also received attention.[12]

In 1940 the NACA was pushed back into supercharger development, a field in which it had pioneered in the late 1920s. A supercharger section, with Oscar Schey as its head, launched a new program with strong backing from the Army and direction by the Power Plants Committee. Well known for his early work on the Roots supercharger, Schey had made outstanding contributions to power plants engineering throughout his career, beginning at Langley in 1923 after graduation with a degree in mechanical engineering from the University of Minnesota. His advocacy of valve overlap and fuel injection in the piston engine resulted in lower supercharger requirements, and his study of the finning of engine cylinders contributed to better cooling.[13] While American manufacturers were slow to take up Schey's suggestions, the Germans successfully used the large valve overlap idea, and especially fuel injection. Shortly before the war, when George Lewis visited Germany, he was surprised to see Schey's reports on the desks of his German counterparts at the Deutsche Versuchsanstalt für Luftfahrt (DVL).[14] During the war Schey advocated abandoning the NACA Roots-type supercharger, which he believed would not be as effective at high altitudes as the turbosupercharger designed by Sanford A. Moss at General Electric.[15] He was correct.

Oscar Schey, Chief of the Supercharger Division.

Schey's group was the last of the four sections of the Langley Power Plants Division to transfer to Cleveland, in July 1943. Interviewed at that time by the laboratory's newspaper, *Wing Tips*, Schey declared unequivocally that the supercharger was so essential that his division was "looking forward to a not distant future when they will be asking you not 'What kind of supercharger have you got on your engine?' but 'What kind of engine have you got on your supercharger?' "[16]

Ben Pinkel, one of the NACA's leading propulsion experts, directed the NACA's research on the exhaust gas turbine, another name for the turbosupercharger. Pinkel had come to the NACA in 1931 from the University of Pennsylvania with a degree in electrical engineering. In 1938, when Pinkel was appointed head of the Engine Analysis Section, it had a staff of three. By 1942, Pinkel's division had expanded to over 150 people. Although facilities were lacking at Langley, as soon as the Cleveland Laboratory was ready, Pinkel's Thermodynamics Division launched a strong program to improve exhaust gas turbines. In a talk to the staff, all of whom, he humorously remarked, demonstrated the principle of "heat in motion," Pinkel illuminated the importance of their work to the war effort. Adding a turbosupercharger to the engine of the B-17 "Flying Fortress," once thought obsolete, had made it a high-speed, high-altitude airplane. "This caused considerable excitement at the time because there wasn't a pursuit ship in the airforce that could keep up with it."[17] Testing in 1939 by Ben Pinkel, Richard L. Turner, and Fred Voss confirmed the predictions of a German, Hermann Oestrich, who suggested that the horsepower of an engine could be increased by the redesign of the nozzles of the airplane's tailpipes. The Power Plants Division became an advocate of "exhaust stacks" added to the tailpipes of aircraft. Once they were adopted by the aircraft manufacturers, they led to dramatic increases in performance fighter planes, including the North American P-51 and the British Spitfire.[18]

Laboratory staff was less enthusiastic about its work on the Allison liquid-cooled engine. Although many of their research programs were simply a carryover of work begun at Langley,

Army Research Authorization E-1 to improve the power output of the Allison-1710 engine was different. Issued in October 1942, it was the laboratory's first new research project.[19] Hap Arnold, Chief of the Army Air Forces, counted on the Cleveland laboratory to assist in the redesign of the Allison supercharger and intercooler.[20] Three engines were sent to the laboratory. Schey's division investigated the supercharger to give it better performance. Rothrock's division explored its limitations in terms of knock; Pinkel's division took on the problem of cooling. Moore's Engine Components Division improved the distribution of fuel and air in the carburetor.

The Allison engine, however, never met the expectations of the Army Air Forces. The Cleveland Laboratory's work on the Allison engine increased its horsepower through the use of water injection and supercharging. However, from Ben Pinkel's point of view, this work

A technician readies the Allison V-1710 for test on one of the dynamometer test stands in the Engine Research Building.

was a "tremendous waste of effort" because of the basic flaws in the engine's design.[21] Only after the Army substituted the British Merlin engine, in the P-51 Mustang did the United States finally have a fighter for high-altitude flight.[22]

THE ALTITUDE WIND TUNNEL

As the Altitude Wind Tunnel neared completion in October 1943, Abe Silverstein transferred to take over as the head of the new Engine Installation Division. Of those who made the trek from Langley during World War II, it was Silverstein, the aerodynamicist, not a member of the original Power Plants Division, who would leave an indelible mark on the technical history of the laboratory. A native of Terre Haute, Ind., Silverstein had graduated from Rose Polytechnic Institute in 1929 with a degree in mechanical engineering. When the NACA hired him, he was assigned to work on the design for the full-scale tunnel. Silverstein quickly immersed himself in the project that launched his career. With the tunnel completed, Silverstein landed the job as head of the tunnel's research program, largely devoted to measuring the drag and performance characteristics of specific airplanes. His first paper, published in 1935, tackled the problem of wind tunnel interference with reference to wing placement and downwash at the tail.[23]

Hap Arnold wanted the new Altitude Wind Tunnel pressed into service at the earliest possible moment.[24] Had better German facilities for altitude research contributed to their engine superiority during the early years of the war? Wright Aeronautical and Pratt & Whitney were developing increasingly powerful engines, but the achievement of adequate engine cooling eluded the efforts of the overburdened engine companies. Only through full-scale testing in the new wind tunnel could these problems be analyzed and solved. With the amount of electricity required to operate the tunnel for a single test equivalent to the daily needs of a small city, no single engine company could have afforded to build and operate it. Yet full-scale engine testing thrust the NACA squarely into development, heretofore the bailywick of industry. With such a large and expensive facility, would the NACA be able to return to fundamental research at the end of World War II?

While the aerodynamics of the tunnel were worked out at Ames, A. W. Young and L. L. Monroe took charge of overall design and construction, an undertaking that presented unusual engineering challenges.[25] Steel shortages delayed the fabrication of the nickle-steel shell of the tunnel. Even after a review of the original plans by Beverly G. Gulick reduced the structural steel requirements by 250 tons, it was difficult to pry steel loose from the federal procurement system until the tunnel's rating was changed to priority. One of the fruits of the cordial relations that Ray Sharp had established with the Chamber of Commerce was the temporary assignment to the NACA of Clifford Gildersleeve. When procurement reached a crisis in April 1942, Gildersleeve was able to expedite delivery, and construction was begun in July 1942 by the Pittsburgh-Des Moines Steel Company.

Part of the expense and complexity of the tunnel resulted from its requirement for an extensive refrigeration system to serve both the Altitude Wind Tunnel and a smaller Icing Research Tunnel, added to the plan during construction. Although the NACA excelled in wind tunnel design, the refrigerating equipment and heat exchanger for the tunnel were beyond its technical expertise. More comfortable approaching the problem from the point of view of aerodynamics rather than heat transfer, NACA engineers originally proposed a scheme of cooling coils consisting of streamlined tubes. When progress on the design faltered, the NACA turned to the Carrier Corporation and its founder Willis H. Carrier. Carrier, the "father of air conditioning," was at first

Top: The Altitude Wind Tunnel urgently needed for full-scale engine testing. Bottom: Innovative Carrier compressors chill the tunnel's airstream.

reluctant to let his already overburdened company undertake yet another war-related task, but he finally agreed. When the job was finished, he had no regrets. He viewed the NACA project as his life's greatest engineering achievement. Not only did it break new ground in terms of a large-scale engineering feat, but it enabled Carrier to put his skills to work for his country. He proudly wrote that "because of its success, high officials in the Air Force told me that World War II was shortened by many months."[26]

Carrier urged the NACA to abandon streamlined tubes and to accept his proposal to use "jackknifed" sections of coils, "folding them down like a collapsed accordion until the coils fitted into the tunnel."[27] Turning vanes were added on the downstream surface to straighten the flow. To get the NACA to accept his design for the heat exchanger, Carrier went straight to Vannevar Bush, who was then Director of the Office of Scientific Research and Development (OSRD), a special agency created by President Roosevelt to tap the scientific talent of the country. Bush called a luncheon with Jerome Hunsaker, the new NACA Chairman, and Lewis. Carrier revealed a low opinion of the NACA's initial design:

> Dr. Lewis asked me if I thought the tests on the streamline coils at Langley Field had value. My answer was not polite, and I'm afraid I scared our representative by my outburst. I told Dr. Lewis that the boys conducting the tests did not know what it was all about, and that too much money and, of more importance, too much time had been wasted already. "Heat transfer experts should be called in," I told him and suggested, among others, Professor William H. McAdams of Massachusetts Institute of Technology.[28]

So unusual was the NACA project that the Carrier Corporation had to use many entirely original components, which they built and tested themselves. Although Carrier gave little credit to the NACA, the sometimes heated give-and-take that occurred between the NACA staff and the representatives of the Carrier Corporation contributed to the design of the remarkable heat exchanger and compressor. Carrier decided to use freon-12 as a refrigerant and redesigned the famous Carrier centrifugal compressor to be used with it. Carrier realized that, although the wind tunnel was a one-of-a-kind installation, the new compressor might have commercial applications after the war. In fact, it later became one of the company's standard products. Moreover, Carrier recognized that gains in terms of prestige in the engineering community more than made up for the headaches. Postwar Carrier publicity featured the tunnel.[29]

While construction slowly proceeded, problems with the Wright R-3350 Duplex Cyclone became critical. Development of the R-3350 had been troublesome from the start. Its powerful supercharger, an indication of Wright Aeronautical's advanced work in this area, caused the carburetor to malfunction. The attempt to switch to fuel injection in 1941 did nothing to solve the carburetor problems. The engine's ignition was faulty; oil leaked excessively; cylinder heads blew almost as soon as the engine turned over. Worst of all, the engine overheated and caught fire in flight.

Arnold was counting on the B-29 Superfortress, powered by the Wright R-3350, for the strategic bombing of Japan from the China mainland. When the engine caused the crash of a prototype in February 1943, it placed Arnold's plans in jeopardy. In October, with the problems not yet solved, Arnold informed President Roosevelt that the bomber would not be ready to be sent to China until March or April of the next year because of a "holdup in production of engines."[30] Roosevelt was furious. He wrote to General George Marshall that this was the "last straw."[31] The engine situation was now at the point of crisis. Still the Altitude Wind Tunnel was not ready for full-scale testing of the Wright R-3350.

Engineers at the Cleveland laboratory knew only that the perplexing problems of this complex engine had to be untangled. The group under Stan Moore discovered that, with a new spray bar, fuel and air mixed more efficiently in the carburetor, and cooling improved. However, there was no time to redesign components for engines in production. The Engine Research Division, supervised by John Collins, studied the valves of the engine and discovered that an extension of

A representative from Wright Aeronautical instructs staff on the principles of the radial engine.

the cylinder head by the addition of a small amount of metal avoided the excessive heat that sometimes caused the valve to collapse. This was a "fix" that parts manufacturers like Thompson Products, which supplied Wright Aeronautical, could implement immediately.[32]

As tunnel construction slowly inched forward, engine technology was about to be transformed by a new propulsion system. Ironically, when the elaborate Altitude Wind Tunnel was at last ready for its first test run in February 1944, the I-16, a turbojet secretly developed by the General Electric Company, took priority over the Wright R-3350. The entire fuselage of the Bell Aircraft P-59A, with its wings sawed off into stubbs, was squeezed into the tunnel's cavernous space.[33] This secret test of the I-16 foreshadowed the laboratory's radical transition to jet propulsion after World War II.

Technicians prepared the Wright R-3350 for the tunnel's first official tests in May. Testing solved many of the engine's problems. Abe Silverstein's group, in charge of engine installation and testing, found that when they adjusted the cowling of the engine and extended the baffles that directed the air around each cylinder, they detected a dramatic increase in the engine's ability to cool effectively. One enthusiastic Carrier employee claimed that the tunnel was so effective that in ten days of testing "the entire cost of the tunnel was recaptured during this brief period of its operation."[34]

By spring 1943, it was apparent that the program laid out by the Army for the Cleveland laboratory was "calculated to solve detailed difficulties rather than furnish foundations for new progress." At least one member of the Power Plants Committee bemoaned this exclusive concentration on "trouble shooting." He urged the NACA to develop "a program promising new progress rather than mopping up ground already covered."[35] The laboratory did find the "quick fixes" needed to keep engine production moving, but it is one of history's ironies that jet propulsion would render obsolete most of the facilities so carefully planned by George Mead's special committee. It is symbolic that America's first turbojet, rather than a piston engine, had the honor of the first test in the Altitude Wind Tunnel. In 1944, with victory in sight, the limited focus of NACA wartime engine work was clear. George Mead, with perhaps a twinge of remorse, wrote to Sam Heron: "This war has certainly been a vindication of the two-row, air-cooled radial engine and of the two-speed, two-stage supercharger, so that I feel the work done here was not in vain."[36] Yet, the facilities they designed were obsolete by the end of the war.

BUILDING AN *ESPRIT DE CORPS*

Almost without exception, the staff of the new laboratory came from outside Cleveland. Addison Rothrock and Ben Pinkel took advantage of their long and lonely evenings in a new city to expose new personnel to the nature of engineering research—not only the specific urgent problems that they would be required to solve during the war, but also the nature of fundamental engineering research in the NACA tradition. Just as the NACA had created an aeronautical research community at Langley in the years between World Wars I and II, they hoped to see a new propulsion community put down roots in this midwestern industrial city.

On Wednesdays at 5:00 sharp, the research staff met to hear lectures on various aspects of engine research. New staff members were expected to take an active part in the discussions that followed each formal presentation. One of Rothrock's first lectures illuminated the purpose of the laboratory. He defined the common values shared by members of the government research community and what distinguished the NACA engineer, who identified with the engine community as a whole, from the more narrow loyalty to his company of an engineer employed in industry.

He pointed out that, in terms of equipment for engine research, the laboratory was probably superior to any found in the world; but, he warned, no matter how good the facilities, it was the quality of the staff that counted. No amount of investment in facilities could make up for mediocrity. He advised the "fresh outs," who far outnumbered experienced engineers, that the way to get ahead was to become an authority on one aspect of an aeronautical problem "so that when anyone thinks of this particular phase of the field of aeronautics, he thinks of your name." Teamwork was more important than the genius of one particular individual—"no one of us, or any group of us, has any corner on the brains of this organization." Honest technical disagreements were inevitable and usually demonstrated a lack of data, not a lack of expertise.

Rothrock advised the young engineers to respect the technicians who worked for them. "Let them know that you want your job accomplished, but don't try and bulldoze them into doing it."

People in engineering support services had the uncanny ability to bring an engineer's rough sketch on the back of an envelope to life.

Rothrock stressed that what he looked for in an engineer was the ability to think logically and to plan step-by-step tests to yield accurate and concise data. Joined to the ability to conceive a test was the need to analyze the data. Anyone could report data, but few could take the new information and draw broad conclusions to show the way "this small group of pieces fits into the main picture." Finally, the new knowledge had to be published in a report that could be understood and used by industry.[37]

Because knowledge is the end product of a research laboratory, the preparation of the research report received special emphasis in the orientation of new engineers. Pearl Young described the role of the Editorial Office in assisting engineering authors to present their data "tactfully, strategically, and with telling force."[38] These were the words of an editor who knew that the readership for the NACA report was the aircraft industry. Unless the report was accurate and well organized, innovations carefully proposed by the government researcher after laborious testing would go no farther than the bookshelf. Young had high editorial standards. She brought the traditions of the Langley Editorial Office to Cleveland and trained its new staff—among them Margaret Appleby, a woman of grace and efficiency, who later headed the office from 1951 until her retirement in 1987.

The preparation of a NACA report was a long process—so long that some industry representatives complained that they did not always receive them in time to be useful. First, a report was reviewed carefully by a committee composed of the writer's engineering peers. After revision, authors were assigned to an editorial clerk, responsible for reading rough drafts and checking accuracy. Young described the painstaking labor of preparing a report, which was "checked and rechecked for consistency, logical analysis, and absolute accuracy."[39] The point of publishing reports was to communicate new knowledge to industry to be used to improve engine designs. However, the shop tricks, instruments, or techniques developed to analyze a problem were not to be shared with industry. "Antonio Stradivari," George Lewis warned, "made a success by making the world's finest violins and not by writing articles on how others could construct such instruments."[40] The NACA made its music by honing and keeping the unique knowledge of instrument specialists like Robert Tozier and Isidore Warshawsky within its walls. Later, when the NACA became part of NASA, this in-house philosophy would change.

Although the shaping of the professional staff had the highest priority, careful attention was also given to the training of the support personnel by Ray Sharp himself. To recruit alert and able young men from Cleveland area technical high schools, he created an "Apprenticeship School" modeled on the one he had started at Langley. Apprenticeship offered an avenue to learn a trade, such as carpentry, forging, casting, and other skills necessary in a laboratory. The apprentices developed their own *esprit de corps*. In addition to on-the-job training, some 80 youths were given formal courses in physics and mathematics, and careful records of each apprentice's progress were kept. Apprenticeship was "the process of passing manual skills and necessary related knowledge from one person to another." This continuity guaranteed that this proud NACA shop tradition transmitted from Langley through James Hawkins, and later carried on by people like William Harrison, would continue. However, the apprenticeship program could not prevent a serious wartime shortage of skilled machinists and tool makers because NACA employees could not be protected from the draft until 1944, when new legislation changed the selective service policy. NACA employees were then inducted into the Air Corps Enlisted Reserve and placed on inactive status.

As Cleveland's industrial plants expanded, the NACA had to compete for personnel with companies such as Thompson Products, Eaton Industries, and Cleveland Pneumatic. A new plant to be operated by the Fisher Body Division of General Motors near the airport created an additional need for no fewer than 25,000 skilled workers. As the draft claimed 80 of 85 original apprentices in the program, the head of Technical Services summed up the laboratory's problem when he wrote plaintively in the laboratory newspaper that "idle equipment pleads for men."[41]

So acute was the shortage of skilled machine operators, electricians, metal workers, and instrument technicians that the laboratory made a strong effort to hire women for jobs normally taken by men. However, women generally worked in a support capacity, not one of direct engineering responsibility. A few women with college degrees in physics and chemistry managed to enter the professional ranks, but at a time when technical schools were producing few women graduates, women with degrees in mechanical engineering were extremely rare. With a shortage of engineers to solve pressing technical problems in aircraft propulsion, women were viewed as useful for relieving the engineer of his more repetitive tasks. "Behind the research engineers who are working on these problems must be ready hands—women's hands," a press release stated.

The laboratory offered a one-year training program for women with "mechanical aptitude" with starting salaries of $1752 per year. This was the same salary paid to "junior aviators"—boys under 18 who built model airplanes for the NACA. Although the machine shop was staffed largely by men, about 25 women were employed to work the lathes and drills.

The staff had strong reservations about the long-term benefits of employing female workers, who were expected to return to homemaking after the war. One employee commented in the laboratory's newspaper that the trouble with the female worker was that she lacked "aptitude, ambition and perseverance" and changed jobs "with no consideration of the valuable time skilled journeymen spent in training her." Men, he argued, chose nonrepetitive work because it "feeds the ambition," while women preferred "repetitive piecework" to spare themselves mental effort.[42]

The utilization of women in their supporting role was carefully documented. In 1943 there were 232 women employees at the Engine Laboratory; in 1944 their number had increased to 412, "indicative of the desire of the management to replace men with women where they can be used at their highest skill." The laboratory made an effort to recruit women chemists, engineers, and mathematicians, but few professional women were attracted to the laboratory during the war years. However, there was a place for women without special training to relieve engineers of "routine, detailed work." The engineer did the brainwork: he planned his tests and made the preliminary designs for his test equipment. Once he had broken down the job into a logical series of small steps, women could take over. This was particularly true in the Computing Section, which employed about 100 women. Women were used during wind tunnel testing as "data takers." Probes affixed to the object under test to measure pressures provided data recorded in mercury-filled glass manometer tubes mounted on a wall near the tunnel. During the test a tube-pinching technique trapped the mercury in the manometer tubes when the desired operating point was reached. Another method to garner test data was to photograph the manometer board. Female "computers" then plotted the data on graphs for analysis by the engineer. The NACA preferred single women because they had fewer family demands, and they were less likely to object to working at night, when many of the tests were run.[43] The gender-based division of labor during World War II set the pattern for the future. With few exceptions, women remained "computers" or secretaries until the 1960s, when the demand for skills in computer science made salaries more competitive, and men were hired in this area for the first time. It is no coincidence that Margaret Yohner, the first female division chief, came not from the traditional male divisions but from the ranks of the "computers."

The newspaper *Wing Tips* bound the laboratory community together. Engineer and apprentice, women and men, new arrivals and old hands from Langley, all eagerly awaited this lively amateur production. The first issue, distributed in October 1942, was turned out on a mimeograph machine by employees with a sense of mission as well as humor. It was used to acquaint new employees with the rich tradition inherited from Langley. Pearl Young wrote a series of articles devoted to "The Place of NACA in American Aviation." She pointed out that in five years the staff had grown from 400 to 4000. She explained that, while the NACA was well known in aeronautical circles, it was nearly unknown to the general public. This was by choice. "A research organization not in business to make money, gains nothing by blowing its own horn, and the results of a slow accumulation of fundamental knowledge does not often produce spectacular results." Nevertheless, the NACA cowling and the family of low-drag air foils developed by Eastman N. Jacobs were impressive contributions to aeronautics. Young spurred the new recruits to identify with this tradition as they were assimilated into the organization. "There are just as many aeronautical research problems for you to solve by the application of brains and hard work as there were on the day Orville Wright piloted the first airplane at Kitty Hawk in 1903."[44] This remark was

Staff in the machine shop.

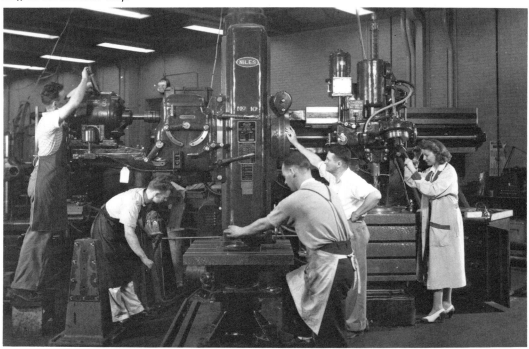

Wartime social life centered around the laboratory.

prophetic of the engineering challenges of jet propulsion that awaited these young engineers after the war.

Wing Tips combined employee education with interesting quasi-gossip in the form of "Lobby Lines," by Mary Lou Gosney. Her central post as receptionist in the lobby of the Administration Building made her an information crossroad. In addition to devoting space to articles on administrative changes, specific research projects, and social and sporting events, the newspaper portrayed the colorful Langley personalities as they assumed leadership after the "trek" from Langley. The pages of *Wing Tips* reflected a "do-it-yourself" attitude when materials were scarce and the hours long. Enthusiasm for hard work and cooperation overcame the problems of a critical housing shortage, rationing, and forced car-pooling.

Because of the youth of the staff, most of whom came to the laboratory unmarried, after hours socials and sports clubs were important in creating an *esprit de corps*. There were enough displaced New Yorkers from the City College of New York to support an alumni group. Not surprisingly, the laboratory celebrated a large number of marriages among employees in its early years. NicNACA, a volunteer group elected by the staff, put on dances and parties. The staff marked the completion of each new building with a social event. When the Machine Shop was ready, it was transformed for one evening into a roller rink. The laboratory provided plots for Victory Gardens and organized enormously successful War Bond and Red Cross fund drives.

Although the Langley contingent shaped the engineering culture of the new engine laboratory, their NACA traditions took root in urban soil. Unlike the contempt of native Hamptonians for Langley's "NACA nuts," Clevelanders regarded the new federal facility as a feather in the city's cap. The staff participated in community activities from leadership of Boy Scout troops to variety show benefits. The cordiality of the city-laboratory relationship was due in no small measure to the efforts of Ray Sharp, who promoted the involvement of local, state, and federal officials in the well-being of the laboratory—a vital link sorely missed in the 1970s, when the laboratory could no longer take Congressional support for granted.

Many of these officials formed their first impression of the new Aircraft Engine Research Laboratory on May 20, 1943. Despite threatening weather and a "mud soup" surrounding the new buildings, the whole laboratory turned out for the outdoor dedication. They were regaled by speeches by NACA and military representatives on the laboratory's future role in advancing aviation. Mayor Frank J. Lausche hoped that the laboratory would be a boon to Cleveland's industries. "We were the cradle of the auto industry, but we lost it," he lamented. "We don't intend to have the same thing happen again." At the climax of the ceremony William T. Holliday, head of Standard Oil, solemnly presented the American flag to John Victory on behalf of the Cleveland Chamber of Commerce. Victory laid it in the hands of Ray Sharp. As a recording of the Star Spangled Banner was played, the flag was solemnly raised. Orville Wright, who attended the ceremony with other members of the Main Committee, wryly commented to the *Cleveland Press* that some 40 years ago he and his brother had worked in a "mite smaller lab."[45]

The enduring legacy of the war years was the creation of a new propulsion research community that cut its teeth on the piston engine, and through its participation in solving wartime engine problems, absorbed NACA traditions that would continue their hold on the laboratory well into the space age. The piston engine provided a solid apprenticeship. Combustion, heat transfer, and the perplexing aerodynamic problems of the supercharger offered a strong foundation on which to tackle future problems of jet propulsion. A young and eager staff, led by a few seasoned Langley hands, stood poised on the edge of a new era.

When the laboratory was dedicated on May 20, 1943, the NACA Main Committee met in Cleveland. Left to right: Charles G. Abbott, Major General Oliver P. Echols, William F. Durand, Orville Wright, Jerome C. Hunsaker, Theodore P. Wright, Rear Admiral Ernest M. Pace, Francis W. Reichelderfer, and Lyman J. Briggs.

NOTES

[1] H. H. Arnold to Mr. Lovett, "Fuel Injector Directive," 3 November 1941, H. H. Arnold Papers, 42/80, Manuscript Division, Library of Congress. For a guide to the H. H. Arnold Papers, see Marvin W. McFarland, "The H. H. Arnold Collection," *LC Quarterly Journal of Current Acquisitions*, IX (4):171–181. At the time of the Lindbergh interview, Arnold was Assistant Chief of the Army Air Corps. He succeeded Westover as Chief of the Army Corps in September 1939. He was named Chief of the Army Air Forces in 1941, Commanding General in 1942, and Full General in 1943.

By the end of the war, the performance of Pratt & Whitney's R-2800 was equal to that of the BMW-801, but not before six complete engine failures and 26 partial failures had caused P-47 fighters to crash. Arnold urged that "drastic measures be taken to remedy such a terrible situation." General Arnold to General Echols, "Engine Failures of P-47's," 17 April 1943, H. H. Arnold Papers, 42/76, Manuscript Division, Library of Congress. See also Robert Schlaifer, *The Development of Aircraft Engines* (Boston: Graduate School of Business Administration, Harvard University, 1950), p. 230; note 21, p. 523.

[2] Arnold to Hunsaker, 14 October 1942, National Archives, Record Group 255, 62–A–411. Copy in NASA History Office Archives. Debate over the engine situation in the Power Plants Committee resulted in a stinging response to Arnold's charges by Arthur Nutt of Wright Aeronautical and Leonard S. Hobbs of Pratt & Whitney. Hobbs went so far as to insist that a long rebuttal be inserted in the revised minutes of the meeting. The Army Air Forces, he argued, had demanded speed "to the exclusion of other qualities, and as far as he knew, they had obtained it." He felt that there was a basic fallacy in Arnold's assessment of the nation's engine needs. Small engines would never be superior to large ones, and he believed that reliance on "small engines to eventually get the initiative and step above the Germans was simply the continuation of a basic error which could not be corrected by any kind or amount of concentrated laboratory work." Minutes of the Power Plants Committee, 11 December 1942, National Archives, Record Group 255, Power Plants Committee Files. For an example of prewar NACA fundamental engine research, see Oscar W. Schey, Benjamin Pinkel, and Herman H. Ellerbrock, Jr., "Correction of Temperatures of Air-Cooled Engine Cylinders for Variation in Engine and Cooling Conditions," *NACA Technical Report* 645, 1939.

[3] Helen Ford, "From Historical Viewpoint." Letter to Miss Scott, 23 December 1942, in History looseleaf, NASA Lewis Records.

[4] Rudolf F. Gagg, "State of the Work on the Aircraft Engine Research Laboratory of the National Advisory Committee for Aeronautics," 11 February 1941, NASA Lewis Records, 34/110.

[5] Interview with the author and notes courtesy of Charles Stanley Moore, 9 August 1984.

[6] Transcript of interview with Ben Pinkel, 4 August 1985, p. 4.

[7] Letter from Ray Sharp to Vera Sharp, 28 December 1941, Private Papers of Mrs. Edward R. Sharp. Biographical information on Sharp from Roland, *Model Research*, p. 175; *Cleveland Press*, 23 September 1942; miscellaneous clippings and press releases from Sharp biography file, NASA History Office; Robert Graham, "Four Giants of the Lewis Research Center," NASA TM-83642. On the cost-plus-a-fixed-fee, see Richard Polenberg, *War and Society* (Philadelphia: J. B. Lippincott, 1972), p. 12–13.

[8] *Boys Grown Tall, A Story of American Initiative*, a book privately published by the *Cleveland Plain Dealer*, 1944, p. 41–42. Case Western Reserve University Archives.

[9] The Wright R-2600 engine was produced at the company's new Lockland plant near Cincinnati, Ohio. Problems may have been caused by supercharger development begun in 1937 after the engine was in production. In addition, Wright had to switch to the Holley carburetor around 1941 because of cooling problems. See Schlaifer, *The Development of Aircraft Engines*, p. 525, note 23. However, its problems appear ultimately to be traceable to production, not design. An investigation, carried out 5 April 1943 by R. A. Lovett, Assistant Secretary of War, concluded that management was not competent, especially in the lower echelons; defective materials caused corrosion and rust of cylinders; and inspections were faulty. A second investigation carried out by Senator Harry Truman resulted in a shift in production at the Lockland plant from the R-2600 to the R-3350 on 26 February 1944. Documents can be found in the ASC History Office, Wright Patterson Air Force Base, Dayton, Ohio.

[10] Biographical information on Carlton Kemper from *Wing Tips*, 8 January 1942, NASA Lewis Technical Library.

[11] Gray, *Frontiers of Flight* (New York: Alfred A. Knopf, 1948), p. 241. The Miller camera was also used in the study of the aerodynamics of the centrifugal compressor. See also A. M. Rothrock, R. C. Spencer, and Cearcy D. Miller, "A High-Speed Motion Picture Study of Normal Combustion, Knock and Preignition in a Spark-Ignition Engine," NACA Report 704, 1941; and Cearcy D. Miller, "A Study by High-Speed Photography of Combustion and Knock in a Spark-Ignition Engine," NACA Report 727, 1942. (Miller changed his name to Carl David Miller in the late 1940s.)

The best discussion of the NACA's focus on the diesel is Ira H. Abbott, "A Review and Commentary of a Thesis by Arthur L. Levine Entitled 'United States Aeronautical Research Policy, 1915–1958: A Study of the Major Policy Decisions of the National Advisory Committee for Aeronautics,' dated 1963," NASA History Office HHN-35, 1964, p. 129–133. A review of introductions to *Annual Reports of the NACA*, (Washington, D.C.: U.S. Government Printing Office) from 1936 to 1940 revealed that by 1935 the NACA was no longer concentrating exclusively on the diesel but did not give it up entirely until 1940. It was noted by C. S. Moore that NACA research on fuel sprays and combustion chambers has been incorporated into diesel engines built today. 1930s NACA fuel-spray technology can be found in the combustors of current turbojet engines. See also Hartley A. Soulé, "Synopsis of the History of the Langley Research Center (1915–1939)," typescript, Langley Research Center Archives, p. 74; S. D. Heron, *Development of Aviation Fuels* (Boston: Graduate School of Business Administration, Harvard University, 1950), p. 555–558, 618. In 1937 the NACA, the Army Air Corps, and the Navy Bureau of Aeronautics supported the creation of a petroleum laboratory at the National Bureau of Standards at which paraffin hydrocarbons were studied intensively.

[12] George Gray, *Frontiers of Flight*, p. 244–252; interview by author with Edmund Bisson, 22 March 1985. Interview with Irving Pinkel by Walter Bonney, 22 September 1973, p. 4, NASA History Office Archives, Washington, D.C.

[13] *Wing Tips*, 16 July 1943, NASA Lewis Technical Library.

[14] Interview by author with John C. Sanders, 7 April 1986. Sanders may have mistakenly recalled that Schey had gone to Germany. Other conversations have led me to conclude that it was on Lewis's 1936 trip that he saw the Schey reports.

[15] *Wing Tips*, 16 July 1943, NASA Lewis Technical Library. Why the NACA neglected to focus on supercharger development, a field in which it had pioneered, in the 1930s is a question to which no one has given a definitive answer. However, it is possible that the NACA thought that the supercharger served merely to give better fuel distribution, rather than to squeeze greater performance out of the engine at high altitudes. By default, it appears that the geared centrifugal supercharger, originally developed in Great Britain at the Royal Aircraft Establishment and manufactured in the United States by General Electric, had become standard on most aircraft engines. However, the NACA was not alone in its neglect of research on the supercharger. Robert Schlaifer, *The Development of Aircraft Engines*, p. 501–502, attributes the relatively late development of the supercharger to a general failure on the part of the engine community to "realize what was to be gained by it, and this in turn was due to a rather astonishing lack of detailed information about what existing superchargers were actually doing." He credits Wright Aeronautical with recognizing that improvement of the supercharger depended on a more thorough understanding of fluid mechanics.

[16] *Wing Tips*, 9 July 1943. NASA Lewis Technical Library.

[17] Ben Pinkel, "Smoker Talk," Thermodynamics Division, 24 May 1944, History looseleaf, NASA Lewis Records.

[18] Ibid. Also Gray, *Frontiers of Flight*, p. 268.

[19] A complete list of Research Authorizations through 2 April 1945 can be found in 34/376, NASA Lewis Records.

[20] On the checkered history of the Allison V-1710 see Major J. H. Doolittle to H. H. Arnold, "Allison Engines," 19 January 1941, H. H. Arnold Papers, 42/76, Manuscript Division, Library of Congress. See also "Case History of the V-1650," W-61348, History Office, Aeronautical Systems Division, Wright-Patterson Air Force Base, Dayton, Ohio; and Alexander De Seversky, *Victory through Air Power* (New York: Simon and Schuster, 1942), p. 235.

[21] Interview with Ben Pinkel by the author, 2 August 1985.

[22] See discussion by Robert Schlaifer, *The Development of Aircraft Engines*, comparing the Allison V-1710 and the Merlin, p. 309–313.

[23] For biographical background on Abe Silverstein, see transcript of interview by Eugene Emme, 14 May 1974, and transcript of interview by Walter Bonney, 21 October 1973. Biography file, NASA History Office, Washington, D.C. See also his Wright Brothers lecture, "Research on Aircraft Propulsion Systems." *Journal of the Aeronautical Sciences* 16:197-226. Silverstein also gave the 49th Wilbur Wright Memorial Lecture, "Researches in space flight technology," *Journal of the Royal Aeronautical Society* 65:779-795.

[24] H. H. Arnold to J. C. Hunsaker, 2 December 1941, H. H. Arnold Papers, 44/123, Manuscript Division, Library of Congress.

[25] Ernest Whitney speech in History looseleaf, NASA Lewis Records. See also: A. W. Young and L. L. Monroe, "Design and Performance Specifications for Altitude Wind Tunnel," revised ed., 15 June 1943.

[26] Margaret Ingels, *Father of Air Conditioning: Willis Haviland Carrier* (New York: Arno Press, 1972, reprint of Doubleday, 1952 ed.), p. 97. For further information on Willis Carrier, see Robert Friedman, "The Air-Conditioned Century," *American Heritage*, August–September 1984, p. 20-33; Cloud Wampler, *Dr. Willis H. Carrier, Father of Air Conditioning* (New York: The Newcomen Society of England American Branch, 1949). I am also indebted to Mr. E. P. Palmatier, former employee of the Carrier Corporation, for his letter of 29 May 1987, which describes Carrier's achievement in detail.

[27] Ingels, *Father of Air Conditioning*, p. 99. See also memo by L. L. Lewis, 26 September 1956, "Carrier in World War II Wind Tunnel Air Conditioning," United Technologies Archives, East Hartford, Conn.

[28] Ibid, p. 98.

[29] Memo by L. L. Lewis, "Carrier in World War II Wind Tunnel Air Conditioning," United Technologies Archives.

[30] Thomas M. Coffey, *Hap* (New York: The Viking Press, 1982), p. 334. See also Steve Birdsall, *Saga of the Superfortress* (Garden City: Doubleday, 1980).

[31] Michael S. Sherry, *The Rise of American Air Power: The Creation of Armageddon* (New Haven: Yale University Press, 1987), p. 160.

[32] Gray, *Frontiers of Flight*, p. 251-253. Also interviews with John C. Sanders, 6 April 1986, and Charles Stanley Moore, telephone interview, March 1985. On Wright R-3350 engine problems, see Schlaifer, *Development of Aircraft Engines*, p. 503-504, 525–526, and 539.

[33] The fact that the Bell P-59A (G.E.I-16) and not the Wright R-3350 for the B-29 was the first engine tested in the Altitude Wind Tunnel appears to have been kept secret even from the Carrier employees who worked on the tunnel project. It has been documented by consulting the first volume of the original AWT log and confirmed by Ronald J. Blaha, "Completed Schedules of NASA Lewis Wind Tunnels, Facilities and Aircraft; 1944-1986" (February 1987). See also G. Merritt Preston, Fred O. Black, Jr., and James M. Jagger, "Altitude-Wind-Tunnel Tests of Power-Plant Installation in Jet Propelled Fighter," *NACA Wartime Report*, MR ESL 17, February 1946. NASA Lewis Technical Library.

[34] Memo by L. L. Lewis, "Carrier in World War II Wind Tunnel Air Conditioning," United Technologies Archives.

[35] H. C. Dickinson, National Bureau of Standards, to George Lewis, 12 March 1943, 34/376, NASA Lewis Records.

[36] Mead to Heron, 21 December 1944, quoted in Cary Hoge Mead, *Wings Over the World* (Wauwatosa, Wisc.: Swannet Press, 1971), p. 275.

[37] Addison M. Rothrock, "Address Made to Research Staff at AERL," 30 December 1942. History looseleaf, NASA Lewis Records.

[38] *Wing Tips*, 3 September 1943, NASA Lewis Technical Library.

[39] Ibid.

[40] George Lewis to Cleveland, "Reports on Instruments and Subjects for Bulletins," 4 October 1944, 34/317.7, NASA Lewis Records.

[41] *Wing Tips*, 2 April 1943; 24 December 1942; 22 January 1943, NASA Lewis Technical Library. See also "NACA Apprenticeship Manual," 1 October 1954, NASA Lewis Photo Lab Collection.

[42] *Wing Tips*, 12 February 1943, NASA Lewis Technical Library.

[43] "The Utilization of Women at the Aircraft Engine Research Laboratory," June 1944, History looseleaf, NASA Lewis Records.

[44] *Wing Tips*, 14 May 1943 and 28 May 1943, NASA Lewis Technical Library. Also, memos from Langley Archives, courtesy of James Hansen. See also Hansen's discussion of women at Langley, particularly Pearl Young, in *Engineer in Charge* NASA SP-4305 (Washington, D.C.: U.S. Government Printing Office, 1987), p. 206–207.

[45] *Cleveland Press*, 20 May 1943 and 21 May 1943; *Wing Tips*, 21 May 1943, NASA Lewis Technical Library.

CHAPTER THREE

JET PROPULSION: TOO LITTLE, TOO LATE

Late in 1943, when the first turbojet engine was brought to the Cleveland laboratory, the entire subject of aircraft jet propulsion was so secret that only eight members of the laboratory staff were aware that the British and the Germans had actually flown aircraft powered by this radically new type of engine. Ben Pinkel, Chief of the Thermodynamics Division, recalled that he and seven other members of his division were summoned to the Administration Building to a special meeting with Ray Sharp and Colonel Donald Keirn of Wright Field. They were sworn to secrecy and told the remarkable story of how the United States had obtained a valuable piece of technology from the British—the plans for the Whittle turbojet engine.[1]

Keirn reported that in April 1941 General Arnold had learned during a visit to England of the development of a turbojet engine by Air Commodore Frank Whittle. At a meeting at Lord Beaverbrook's estate outside London, Arnold was surprised when his host, Churchill's minister of aircraft production and one of his most intimate advisors, turned to him and said, "What would you do if Churchill were hung and the rest of us in hiding in Scotland or being run over by the Germans, what would the people in American do? We are against the mightiest army the world has ever seen." Those present at the meeting agreed that Germany could invade England "anytime she was willing to make the sacrifice."[2] This was the context in which Great Britain agreed to turn over the plans for the Whittle turbojet engine, provided utmost secrecy were maintained and a strictly limited number of persons were involved in its development. Arnold personally inspected the Whittle engine several weeks before its first flight and arranged to have General Electric's Supercharger Division at West Lynn, Mass., take on the American development of Whittle's prototype. Arnold selected Bell Aircraft of Buffalo, N.Y., to work concurrently on an airframe for a fighter, or pursuit-type aircraft.[3]

Arnold dispatched Keirn to England in August. He returned two months later with the plans for the Whittle W2B (an improvement of the original model), and an actual engine, the W1X. In addition to the plans and the engine itself, Keirn arranged to bring to the United States one of Whittle's engineers and several technicians. Frank Whittle himself, the new engine's designer, visited the project during the time of intense development at General Electric's Supercharger Division at West Lynn, Mass. So new was the concept of a compressor-turbine combination propelling an airplane that, even with the plans and the reassembled engine, the supercharger experts remained skeptical. The British engineer recalled that "until we pushed the button and showed this thing running, the Americans wouldn't believe it would work."[4] The General Electric group succeeded in translating the British specifications and produced, not without difficulty, an American copy of the Whittle engine.

Arnold's selection of the General Electric Supercharger Division was no coincidence. In 1917, at a time when there was a general lack of interest in superchargers, Sanford Moss pioneered the development of a turbosupercharger, a turbine that utilized the waste gases in the engine exhaust, a concept first advanced by the Frenchman Auguste Rateau. At General Electric's West Lynn Plant this work continued under Army sponsorship until Moss retired in 1937. Part of the success of the General Electric turbosupercharger must be attributed to the development of materials for the turbine. Special alloys, such as Hastelloy B for the turbine blades, Timkin alloy, and later Vitallium for the turbine disks, enabled the turbine to withstand the extreme temperatures of the gases that passed through it.[5]

Colonel Edwin R. Page, Chief of the Power Plant Branch at Wright Field from 1926 to 1932, played an important role in encouraging Moss's work. Page calmly kept faith, despite what appeared to be an enormous waste of goverment funds, while turbines at General Electric exploded to the right and left of him.[6] Because of his association with the development of General Electric's supercharger, the Army called on Colonel Page to nurture the relationship between General Electric and the fledgling NACA laboratory in Cleveland. He was appointed the laboratory's first Army liaison officer in May 1943.

So secret was the development of the Whittle engine that only after the classification of the project was downgraded from "super-secret" to "secret" early in the summer of 1943 was Keirn allowed to inform the NACA of this important project—over two years after Arnold's visit to England. Keirn furnished the select group at the meeting in Sharp's office with a set of plans by General Electric for a Jet Propulsion Static Test Laboratory, which was begun in July. Pinkel picked Kervork K. Nahigyan to head the new Jet Propulsion Section.

In September contractors had hastily completed an inconspicuous one-story building at the Cleveland laboratory. It was surrounded by a barbed wire fence at the edge of the airport's runway. A heavily guarded truck delivered the General Electric I-A for testing.[7] The Static Test Laboratory consisted of spin pits lined with wood to protect workers from the dangers of blades flying off in all directions when engine compressors reached their limits during endurance testing. The secret work carried on in this modest structure, set apart from the carefully designed permanent laboratory buildings for the investigation of the piston engine-would, after the war, become the major effort of the entire laboratory.

If the success of the Whittle engine was news to the group in Sharp's office, the jet propulsion concept was not. Pinkel and Nahigyan had assisted work at Langley on a jet propulsion device, inspired and directed by one of the NACA's outstanding aerodynamicists, Eastman Jacobs. The Army had unceremoniously canceled this project the previous February.

Before World War II, many experts throughout the world shared the assumption that better aircraft engines would result from small improvements of the components of the piston or reciprocating engine. Because the aircraft engine was an adaptation of the automobile engine, radical innovations were expected to appear first in the automobile engine. Roy Fedden, then an engineer for the Bristol Aeroplane Company, wrote in an article ironically titled, "Next Decade's Aero Engines Will Be Advanced But Not Radical," published in the *Transactions of the Society of Automotive Engineers* in 1933: "I do not anticipate any radical changes in the type of four-cycle internal-combustion engine as used today... When the present form of gasoline engine is superceded by a radically different power unit, it seems logical that this development will most probably be accepted first in the automotive field before it is introduced into aircraft."[8] Fedden's prediction was wide of the mark, for it was precisely Whittle's independence from the automotive background of traditional power plant experts that enabled him to seek a new engine uniquely suited for flight.

In 1940 the sections within Langley's Power Plants Division reflected the conventional, incremental approach to the reciprocating engine. Unconventional power plants, radically new means of aircraft propulsion, had no place in the research of the division. Typical of the evolutionary rather than revolutionary, approach to engine development during the 1930s was the study of the fin geometry necessary to cool individual cylinders. NACA research suggested methods to improve the baffles and cylinder shrouds to direct air around the

Arnold appointed Colonel Edwin R. Page to be the Army's liaison with the laboratory in 1943 because of his expertise in turbosupercharger development.

cylinder for better cooling. One of the important reports issued by the NACA in 1939 concerned a method for predicting how much engine temperatures would fluctuate as the ambient air temperature changed. Cylinders from seven engine types were compared to establish this prediction method.[9]

The architects of the turbojet revolution, however, did not inherit the evolutionary approach of automotive engineers. Whittle and Hans von Ohain (who developed a turbojet independently in Germany) were able to look at aircraft propulsion with a freshness lacking among the engine experts in Europe and the United States. The positive qualities of *flying* the gas turbine made up for the deficiencies observed in stationary industrial turbines. Whittle wrote: "There seemed to be a curious tendency to take it for granted that the low efficiencies of turbines and compressors commonly cited were inevitable. I did not share the prevalent pessimism because I was convinced that big improvements in these efficiencies were possible, and, in the application of jet propulsion to aircraft, I realized that there were certain favourable factors not present in other applications."[10] The first positive factor that he singled out was that low temperatures at high altitudes actually made the engine more efficient. More energy was available to power the airplane. Second, Whittle thought the forward speed of the aircraft created a ram effect, which increased the efficiency of the compressor; third, only a portion of the energy released into the turbine had to be used to drive the compressor—the rest could be used for propulsive thrust. These were the criteria of an engineer-test pilot. Although Whittle also had a strong background in aerodynamics, it did not play a significant role in his early thinking.

Jet propulsion was not a new idea when Frank Whittle and Hans von Ohain took up the gas turbine problem.[11] Every airplane, in fact, is propelled by a stream of air. The forward motion of any body through the air depends on Newton's third law: for every action there is an equal and opposite reaction. In airplanes powered by a reciprocating engine, the propeller creates a jet of air that rushes backward to drive the aircraft forward. In a jet engine, however, the air is funneled into the engine, compressed, and heated. The air stream has reached a high velocity by the time it is ducted out the back end. Jet propulsion devices were conceived as early as c. 150 B.C. when Hero of Alexandria designed an aeolipile that produced jets of hot steam to rotate a spherical ball. In the late 18th century a British inventor patented the first gas turbine design, and by the early 20th century, through the innovations of Charles Parsons and others, industrial steam turbines were in general use for power generation. However, until the early 1930s few dreamed that the heavy turbines then in industrial use could be made light enough to be flown. Between the concept of a gas turbine and a successful aircraft engine lies the pitted terrain of development.

Successful development involves a combination of technical ingenuity and determination on the part of the inventor. A less tangible factor, the role of scientific theory in invention, is more difficult to determine.[12] In the case of the turbojet, the theoretical understanding of the science of fluid mechanics was far ahead of the ability to design practical machines. Although American and German theorists had directed attention to an understanding of the aerodynamics of both axial and centrifugal superchargers for aircraft, there is little evidence that this understanding played a direct role in the development of the turbojet.

When Whittle began to consider the idea of using a gas turbine to propel an airplane about 1928 to 1929, many engineering experts had already concluded that jet propulsion had no future. The report prepared at the National Bureau of Standards by Edgar Buckingham at the request of the engineering division of the U.S. Air Service in 1923 was typical of generally accepted opinion. Buckingham's report concluded that at the highest speeds (which at the time were not more than 250 miles per hour) a jet engine would consume five times the amount of fuel of a conventional engine-propeller combination. He thought that its weight and complexity would make flying impossible. Buckingham recommended against any further research on jet propulsion, conceding only that if thrust augmenters could be made workable, there might be some future for a jet propulsion device as a prime mover.[13]

This suggestion may have encouraged Eastman Jacobs to take up the problem of thrust augmenters in 1926. Although this work had no practical application at the time, "this study stirred in Jacobs the beginnings of a strong interest in high-speed aerodynamics."[14] As early as 1935, at the Fifth Volta Congress in Rome, Italy, the world's leading aerodynamicists gave serious consideration for the first time to the theoretical feasibility of flight at speeds at or faster than the speed of sound. A German aerodynamicist, Adolf Busemann, suggested in his Volta paper that a sweptback wing could solve some of the compressibility problems that aircraft would encounter at extremely high speeds.[15] However, in the 1930s aerodynamicists and propulsion experts did not see how their fields complemented each other. Although theoretically it seemed possible to fly faster than the speed of sound, a propeller-driven aircraft could never reach the necessary speeds. The engine manufacturers were oblivious to the implications of the high-speed conference. According to von Ohain, "it should have scared the hell out of them... because that showed that the airplane, sooner or later, could *easily* break the supersonic barrier."[16] That would render the piston engine obsolete.

However, contrary to Edward W. Constant's thesis in *The Origins of the Turbojet Revolution*, Whittle and von Ohain revolutionized aircraft propulsion, not because of a knowledge of aerodynamics superior to that of American engineers, but through their insight that the combination of compressor and turbine was *uniquely suited as a power plant for flight*.[17] Although the potential problem of compressibility as propeller tip speeds neared the speed of sound should have influenced Whittle and von Ohain, there is little evidence that this relatively unstudied phenomenon in the 1930s was a factor in their decision to look for a radically new type of power plant for aircraft. Rather, it appears that both were drawn to the turbojet because of its simplicity and potential as a power plant specially adapted to aircraft. It was their independence from the automotive-aircraft engineering tradition that enabled them to think outside the paths of accepted practice. When they began their work, the aircraft reciprocating engine had become a mind-boggling example of mechanical complexity. To attain higher speeds, designers added cylinders to increase power. To compensate for the decreased density of the air at higher altitudes that reduced power, they added superchargers. With added cylinders and superchargers, cooling became a problem solved by the addition of yet another component, the intercooler. In contrast to the difficult to maintain array of components and subcomponents, the turbojet offered the possibility of a light-weight engine of extraordinary simplicity. The engine, as conceived by Whittle and von Ohain, potentially could perform better at the higher altitudes that caused problems for the reciprocating engine, and its efficiency was likely to increase with speed.

Like Whittle, von Ohain started with the idea that *flight* required a power plant specially adapted to motion through the air. His enthusiasm stemmed from the insight that an engine that burned continuously was "inherently more powerful, smoother, lighter and more compatible with the aero-vehicle" than the clumsy four-stroke cycle of a piston engine. His first idea was to "accomplish this process without employing moving machinery by bringing the inflowing fresh air in direct contact with the expanding combustion gas," a kind of ram jet.[18] However, he soon realized that in order to get an efficient engine he needed to separate the two phases of compression and expansion. He finally arrived at a turbojet configuration similar to that of Whittle, whose 1930 patent he did not discover until after the development of his own design.[19] Von Ohain's engine powered the first flight of a turbojet plane in August 1939 from the Marienehe Airfield in Germany.

Although the turbojet created a revolution in aircraft propulsion, it was not as radical a break with the technology of the reciprocating engine as the word revolution might imply. The technology of the supercharger, a component *added to* the reciprocating engine, provided the continuity between the old technology and the new. The supercharger was, in fact, a compressor. However, in the turbojet, the compressor took its place as an *intrinsic* part of the engine system. For the inventors, the choice of the compressor was significant, and it was not by chance that both Whittle and von Ohain chose a centrifugal compressor; the centrifugal supercharger was in common use in conventional engines. In contrast, axial superchargers were extremely demanding experimental devices. Both von Ohain and Whittle knew that the centrifugal compressor was a "brute force device" and that eventually they would "go axial," but they started with the centrifugal compressor because it was simpler to build.[20] In the same year that von Ohain demonstrated the feasibility of the turbojet concept, Anselm Franz, Germany's expert on superchargers, designed the first turbojet with an axial-flow compressor.

INDEPENDENT AMERICAN EFFORTS TO DEVELOP A TURBOJET

Sir Henry Tizard, science advisor to the British Ministry of Aircraft Production, visited the United States in September 1940. Although it is well known that Tizard informed his American allies of British technical advances in radar and opened discussions concerning British cooperation in the development of atomic energy, Tizard also brought with him the first news of the British developments in the new field of jet propulsion. Tizard met with both Vannevar Bush and George Lewis, but he revealed very little except the seriousness of British efforts in jet propulsion. Bush later recalled: "The interesting parts of the subject, namely the explicit way in which the investigation was being carried out, were apparently not known to Tizard, and at least he did not give me any indication that he knew such details."[21]

In February General Arnold became aware of new and unforeseen developments in aircraft propulsion from German intelligence sources. At first Arnold appears to have identified jet propulsion with rocket-assisted take-off, and he encouraged the setting up within the NACA of a subcommittee on auxiliary jet propulsion. However, on February 25, 1941, after hearing reports of European developments of jet-assisted take-off and, more ominous, as a primary source of power, engine research took on new urgency. He asked Vannevar Bush, then Chairman of both the National Defense Research Committee (NDRC) and the NACA, to form a jet propulsion committee with a much wider mandate. He was concerned that the Germans' experimental use of rockets to assist take-off would make existing fighter planes obsolete. Arnold considered the Army-supported work at the California Institute of Technology inadequate. He did not expect this group, led by the irrepressible Frank Malina and advised by aerodynamicist Theodore von Kármán, to yield "practical results" in the near future. Arnold stressed the urgency of giving the problem to a "large group of able scientists."[22]

In his response to General Arnold, Bush firmly disabused him of any wishful thinking that jet propulsion research should be undertaken by the NDRC rather than the NACA. He pointed out that, while rockets as weaponry could legitimately come under the purview of the NDRC, aircraft propulsion was the province of the NACA, an organization he greatly admired and may have used as his model when the country called upon him to mobilize science.[23] He acknowledged that the well-known physicist from the California Institute of Technology, Richard C. Tolman, was investigating "certain aspects of rocket propulsion," but he anticipated that the research in jet propulsion would be long and expensive. He did not think that it was "proper for NDRC to devote its funds to aircraft propulsion problems." Bush therefore recommended the formation of a special committee that would act independently but under the general umbrella of the NACA Power Plants Committee.[24]

Before deciding on the composition of the committee and a suitable chair, Bush consulted with Rear Admiral John H. Towers, Chief of the Bureau of Aeronautics. Towers agreed with Bush that the committee should be composed of "personnel other than those who deal with conventional power plants" and focused on high-level scientists. He looked on Hugh L. Dryden of the Bureau of Standards as "particularly suitable for such a committee, where practicability should be combined with theoretical considerations."[25]

After canvasing several prominent members of the aeronautical community, Bush selected Stanford University's emeritus professor, William Frederick Durand, still vigorous at the age of 82, to head the new committee. Durand was a man of intellect and professional integrity, "calm tolerance and the driving power of a will to work."[26] Durand had served as Chairman of the NACA from 1917 to 1918. He had made his reputation in the field of aeronautics through a systematic presentation of propeller performance data (with Everett Parker Lesley), a standard reference work relied on by early aircraft designers. Durand's reputation as a scientist was enhanced through his role as editor of a definitive multivolume work on aerodynamics in the 1930s. In urging Durand to assume leadership of the committee, Bush wrote: "The matter is of such importance, however, and so definitely requires mature and independent judgment of a high order, that I believe it is worthy of your attention as chairman, no matter how much you might be relieved on the details of the work." The scope and the authority of this new committee was to be extremely wide. Bush wrote that after consultation with Arnold, they agreed that if the committee concluded that "full-scale experimentation was in order," they would find "several million dollars" to fund it.[27]

The new Special Committee had a broad responsibility to investigate all aspects of jet propulsion. Even members of the NACA would be asked to serve only in an ex officio capacity: "The backbone of the committee should be men of independent background and with them should be joined men of special capabilities in the process of evalua-

William F. Durand, chairman of the NACA's Special Committee on Jet Propulsion.

tion."[28] Pratt & Whitney, Wright Aeronautical, and Allison, the major manufacturers of piston engines, were deliberately excluded from participation on the committee, despite the interest that each company had shown in early jet propulsion schemes. For example, Pratt & Whitney had supported the development of a design by Andrew Kalitinsky of the Massachusetts Institute of Technology and by December 1941 had learned of the successful flight of Whittle's engine from a friend of the pilot "who flew the British straight propulsion machine."[29] Wright Aeronautical may have learned of the Whittle engine during Tizard's visit and attempted in 1941 to negotiate for the American license from Whittle's Company, Power Jets, Ltd.

Representation by industry was limited to three manufacturers, all with prior experience not with aircraft engines, but in industrial steam turbine design: Allis-Chalmers, Westinghouse, and the General Electric Steam Turbine Division at Schenectady, N.Y. The rationale for excluding the engine companies from membership on the committee was not that they were too overburdened with war-related work, because the steam turbine manufacturers were in the same situation. What Bush seems to have meant by the euphemism, "special capabilities in the process of evaluation," was that the engine companies, with a vested interest in maintaining the status quo, should not be included. Bush knew that engineers who worked with steam turbines had experience with the aerodynamics of compressors and turbines. In addition to these manufacturers and representatives of the military, Bush recommended three scientists: Professor C. Richard Soderberg of the Massachusetts Institute of Technology, an authority on turbines who shouldered the duties of vice-chairman; A.G. Christie of The Johns Hopkins University, and Hugh Dryden. The deliberate omission of the aircraft engine manufacturers may have led the committee to underestimate what a demanding undertaking it would be to develop a new aircraft engine. More important, the selection of steam turbine manufacturers influenced the choice of the axial-flow compressor with multiple stages, a compressor used in industrial steam turbines. If the engine companies had been included, they would have been more likely to favor a design with a centrifugal compressor because of their experience with superchargers. In hindsight, it would have been wise to include at least one design based on the centrifugal compressor.

By April 1941 the Special Committee was ready to get to work, but the minutes show how far they were from the turbojet concept. Still sharing Arnold's impression that jet propulsion involved rockets, the committee considered and dismissed Goddard's rocket experiments. By consensus, the committee decided that the problem of jet-assisted take-off was of greatest importance and "the most immediately practical." Obviously, Arnold had made information on the striking results of the California Institute of Technology's JATO (jet-assisted take-off) rockets available to the group.[30]

Eastman Jacobs was invited to give a full report on the progress of the jet propulsion project that the NACA had begun at its laboratory at Langley. No doubt Jacobs's invitation to make this presentation to the committee was due in part to the enthusiasm that Vannevar Bush had already developed for the NACA scheme. In the letter he wrote to Durand asking him to chair the committee, he revealed that, of the many jet propulsion proposals already submitted to the Army, the Navy, and the NACA, the Jacobs project seemed to hold the most promise. "The group at Langley Field and Jacobs, in particular, have been very active in developing one jet propulsion scheme in which I have acquired a large amount of interest and perhaps even enthusiasm, for it seems to have great possibilities and I cannot find any flaw in their arguments."[31]

Jacobs's scheme for a ducted fan, nicknamed "Jake's Jeep" by his NACA colleagues, was among several embryonic efforts to develop a gas turbine power plant for aircraft in the United States prior to the importation of the Whittle engine.[32] Jacobs received the high-level support of Bush and Durand. As a result of his prestige, the designs that the industry representatives on the Durand Committee later developed owed a great deal to preliminary studies made at Langley. Jacobs was riding a crest of prestige for the development of NACA laminar-flow airfoils. His reputation as an aerodynamicist made the NACA effort more credible than other proposals.

About 1931 the Italian Secondo Campini had first conceived a ducted-fan engine design, and Jacobs may have learned of this scheme when he attended the Volta Congress in Rome in 1935. The ducted fan, a hybrid scheme consisting of a conventional piston engine and compressor, lacked the simplicity of the turbojet. Air entered a long cylindrical nacelle through a duct, where it was compressed. The section of the nacelle in back of the compressor served as a combustion chamber. Fuel was injected into the chamber and ignited. The heated gases, directed out the back through a high-speed nozzle, produced thrust to drive the engine forward. The Campini engine had a two-stage centrifugal compressor; Jacobs modified Campini's design. He chose an axial compressor with two stages. Jacobs had problems not only with the compressor, but also with the combustor, which failed to function properly.[33] Nevertheless, in the view of Clinton E. Brown, who worked on the project, the Jeep was a sound idea. Jacobs proved the feasibility of his ducted-fan concept.[34] However, compared to Whittle's far simpler design for a turbojet, its development in 1941 was embryonic.

In April 1941, prior to Arnold's return from England, the Jacobs engine looked promising enough to win the backing of the country's gas turbine experts. In its early stages, the project had consisted of a "simple program of burning experiments." It was only after Durand placed the full weight of the Special Committee on Jet Propulsion behind the project that Jacobs expanded the scope of the work from a simple burner test rig to "more nearly a mock-up of a proposed airplane for ground testing."[35]

At the April 22 meeting, members of the Special Committee also heard summaries of British reports on the development of axial-flow compressors, probably those of A. A. Griffith and Hayne Constant of the Royal Aircraft Establishment, who had been working for many years, with limited success, on axial compressors. Their goal was a gas turbine engine to drive the aircraft's propellers. What the Special Committee could not know was that Whittle had chosen not to use the more complicated axial configuration for his turbojet engine.

By the May 8 meeting, Arnold had returned to the United States, and the Special Committee expected to be briefed on the latest developments. Instead, because of the British imposition of a "most secret" classification on the project, the committee was merely asked to suggest the names of two engineers to be sent to England to "make contact" with British developments in jet propulsion. Durand, betraying his mistaken belief that the new British propulsion system used the axial compressor, suggested D.R. Shoults of General Electric, "an expert in matters relating to axial-turbo compressors, which type of equipment forms the core of the British development."[36] At the same meeting, Lewis, sharing the same prejudice in favor of the axial-flow compressor, referred to the the eight-stage compressor developed by Eastman Jacobs and Eugene Wasielewski intended primarily as a supercharger. He revealed that General Electric "was interested in developing this compressor to its full capacity since the Committee's tests had been limited to low speeds and the use of only six of the eight stages which had been provided." At this point, all the signs indicated that an axial compressor would be a significant component of any jet propulsion scheme, a presumption shaped by the influence of Jacobs and the knowledge of the publications of the British aerodynamicists, Griffith and Constant. Future engineering practice would vindicate this decision, since the axial compressor did eventually prevail over the centrifugal.[37] For short-term wartime needs, however, Jacobs underestimated the axial-compressor's recalcitrant problems. The NACA would pay dearly in terms of lowered prestige for its early commitment to axial compressor development and its failure to recognize the definite advantage of the compressor-turbine combination embodied in Whittle's turbojet.

In early June Arnold sent a brief but significant memorandum to Bush. It contained as attachments a picture of the Whittle engine and a short description that had been sent by diplomatic pouch from Lieutenant Colonel J. T. C. Moore-Brabizon of the Ministry of Aircraft Production. Item one of the description stated: "The Whittle jet propulsion engine consists of 10 combustion chambers (equivalent to the cylinders of a normal engine), an exhaust gas turbine, a supercharger, and an exhaust jet or nozzle."[38] Notably absent from the description was a key element. Was the "supercharger" (i.e., the compressor) axial or centrifugal?

By the end of the month, Arnold appears to have recognized the possible superiority of the compressor-combustor-turbine combination to the hybrid piston engine-compressor-combustor combination of Jacobs's conception. In a letter dated 25 June 1941, Arnold wrote to Bush, concerning the Jacobs project: "As regards the 'Jacobs' engine, the Air Corps will stand ready to assist this project to the maximum extent possible; however, further conferences with N.A.C.A. personnel and further investigation of the project as a whole indicate that this development is far from ready for a test installation." Speaking in the context of his personal knowledge of the British success with the Whittle engine, Arnold urged the Special Committee to consider not only jet-assisted take-off, but also jet engines as "primary sources of power."[39]

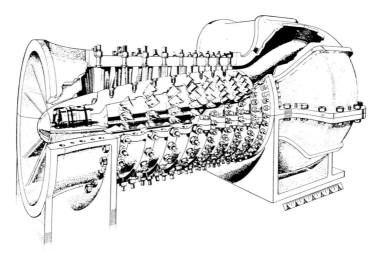

The NACA eight-stage axial-flow compressor designed by Eastman Jacobs and Eugene Wasielewski.

In June Durand informed the committee of the Whittle project, but only in general terms because of the classification of the project. The inquiries of Wright Aeronautical to obtain the license to the Whittle engine from Power Jets, Ltd., however, caused a brief diplomatic flurry, since it created the impression that the British-American agreement on the Whittle was common knowledge. As a memorandum from Bush to Arnold indicated, they had been extremely careful about what had been communicated:

> I have checked with Dr. Durand this morning. Neither he nor I have communicated any of the explicit [sic] information regarding the Whittle engine to any individual. Dr. Durand in particular tells me that when his Jet Propulsion Committee met he told them only that the British had a development along jet propulsion lines without giving them any explicit [sic] information. In fact, he did not have this information at the time himself... I am quite sure that explicit information placed in the hands of Dr. Durand and myself has not gone elsewhere.[40]

It now began to dawn on Bush that development of the Whittle engine was far ahead of the NACA project. In July he wrote to Arnold: "It becomes evident that the Whittle engine is a satisfactory development and that it is approaching production, although we yet do not know just how satisfactory it is. Certainly if it is now in such state that the British plans call for large production in five months, it is extraordinarily advanced and no time should be lost on the matter." Bush recommended that arrangements for production of the British engine in the United States should be expedited by the selection of a suitable company. He suggested either A.R. Stevenson of General Electric or R.G. Allen of Allis-Chalmers, both of whom had representatives on Durand's Special Committee. The choice would depend on which company they selected to develop the Whittle. The committee as a whole, Bush reminded him, "on account of British wishes," could not be privy to full information about the Whittle engine. Bush now qualified his support for the Jacobs project. If the Whittle engine was as advanced as it appeared, it deserved to be expedited, regardless of the promise of the Jacobs project over the long term:

I am inclined to believe personally that in the long run the Jacobs development will prove to be equally or more interesting. It is certainly true, however, that the Whittle development is much further advanced. If it is really serviceable, and if it will really produce a relatively inexpensive power plant for pursuit craft which can be rapidly put into production, I feel that no time should be lost in expediting the matter.[41]

By July Arnold had selected General Electric to copy the Whittle engine. D. Roy Shoults, then in England to oversee the British use of General Electric's turbosupercharger, became General Electric's representative, assisted by Alfred J. Lyon, the Army's technical liaison officer in Great Britain. In August Colonel Donald Keirn, the engineer from Wright Field who brought the news to the Cleveland laboratory two years later, took off for England to bring back the Whittle engine. Later Keirn joined the Special Committee so that he was fully informed of all the jet propulsion projects, both the "most secret" Whittle project and the "secret" projects of the Special Committee.

While Bush and Durand steadfastly supported the NACA project, from the time of his visit to England in April, Arnold had become a believer in the future of the Whittle engine. His letter to Colonel Lyon, 2 October 1941, reveals the first discussions of a possible future Army effort to preempt the jet propulsion field and thereby end the NACA hegemony over basic aeronautical research. However, with characteristic restraint, he refused to commit himself on this issue. Clearly, he saw the turbojet as a possible answer to the problem of obtaining higher speeds for pursuit aircraft, but he stopped short of predicting that the piston engine would be obsolete in ten years. The letter reveals Arnold's astute assessment of the possible dawning of a new era of jet propulsion.

> I was told in England in April that in ten years there wouldn't be any more poppet valves or, as a matter of fact, any type of gas [piston] engine as we now have in pursuit airplanes, and another five years would see the end of that type of engine in all types of aircraft. I must admit that I was not as enthusiastic about such a proposition as the advocates in England were. In my 30 years in aviation I have seen too many of these things come up that are going to completely revolutionize everything and do away with all heretofore existing forms of aircraft, so while I am enthusiastic, I am not super-enthusiastic...
>
> I do not believe that we are ready at this time to start a development program tending towards the production of the jet propulsion engine on the same scale as we now have for the conventional type of gas engine. I am of the opinion, however, that it will be much easier to reach the 4,000 to 5,000 horsepower with the jet propulsion and gas turbine than it will be with the conventional type of engine. Everything points in that direction. The turbine has everything to its advantage.[42]

Although not privy to the full Whittle story, the Durand committee had enough information on the Whittle engine to see the potential of the compressor-turbine combination. The committee set up a Special Compressor-Turbine Panel, chaired by R. C. Allen, manager of the Allis-Chalmers Steam-Turbine Department. It should be noted that Jacobs and his team were obviously informed of the conclusion of the panel, but persisted in their belief that the hybrid scheme would work. A letter to the panel from Henry Reid, Engineer-in-Charge at Langley, indicated that "jet propulsion can better be accomplished at present with the use of the conventional engine."[43] Reid conceded that a more radical approach to aircraft propulsion might prevail in the long run.

Although they had at last hit upon the compressor-turbine combination, the panel considered only the axial-flow compressor. Whether the simpler centrifugal compressor was considered at all is difficult to determine, since all the minutes for the compressor-turbine panel have not been found. The axial compressor, because of its smaller frontal area and higher potential pressure ratio, looked more promising on paper. However, if the axial compressor was lighter and more compact, it demanded a knowledge of aerodynamics. The complex movement of air across the blades of several stages presented a challenge to the designer. The fabrication of the complicated compressor was a nightmare. Vibrations created the danger that compressor blades might fly off in all directions. The simpler solution found by Whittle and von Ohain—the centrifugal compressor—eluded the steam turbine experts on the committee.

The same month that the compressor panel was formed, representatives of Allis-Chalmers visited Langley. "Their particular interest was the axial-flow compressor, which has been constructed at Langley Field," George Lewis wrote to Durand. Lewis revealed that the results of a joint investigation with General Electric would be made available. This was obviously a reference to the eight-stage axial-flow compressor of Jacobs and Wasielewski. All three of the companies selected axial-flow compressors, but they decided not to attempt as many stages.[44] Although the NACA directly influenced the axial compressors in the General Electric and Allis-Chalmers designs, influence on the Westinghouse turbojet is less clear. The Westinghouse design team may have decided to use a Brown-Boveri compressor as its model. In any case, the company was familiar with the axial configuration through experience with axial compressors in Navy surface vessels.[45]

When the Durand Committee met at Langley Field in September, they recommended that Jacobs begin design studies to explore "the most suitable means for applying this system of jet propulsion to actual aircraft." They also decided that the preliminary studies of the companies could be made into actual proposals for submission to the Army or Navy.[46] The Navy approved designs for a turbojet by Westinghouse and for a type of ducted fan by Allis-Chalmers. The Army agreed to support General Electric's proposal for a turboprop.

Up to the time of the submission of the proposals, the committee had allowed considerable cooperation and exchange of information among the three companies, and the NACA was a clearinghouse for information. After the September meeting each company began to work independently, and although the upper management of each company represented on the Special Committee was aware of the parallel development of General Electric's Whittle turbojet, the design teams actually working on the respective projects were kept in the dark. Moreover, they were not allowed to exchange information with designers working on the other projects sponsored by the Special Committee until Durand wrote to General O. P. Echols for permission for greater cooperation. In recalling the "helpful attitude regarding mutual conference and interchange of data and suggestions" that the companies had enjoyed prior to the awarding of specific design contracts, he urged that it be allowed to continue.[47]

While the members of the Special Committee knew about the "Whittle matter," as did selected high-level individuals at General Electric, Arnold would not allow the Whittle engine to be tested at Langley Field because of the British "most secret" classification. Nevertheless, Oliver P. Echols, Chief of the Material Division, was aware of the development problems that the West Lynn team was encountering and urged Arnold to let General Electric send the Whittle engine for testing in NACA wind tunnels. In a memorandum addressed to General Arnold, 13 November 1941, he wrote: "As we get deeper into the Bell XP-59A and GE Type I Supercharger Projects, we find that in order to exploit the fullest possibilities of this engine-airplane combination... it is highly desirable that we initiate wind tunnel studies as soon as possible... " Echols suggested either the 16-foot tunnel at Moffet Field (Ames) or the 19-foot pressure tunnel at Langley. Noted in large letters on the memo was "Decision is *NO!*" with the appended note: "General Echols advised that he had discussed this matter with Gen. A, this date, and that Gen. A did not wish to tunnel test at NACA in view of the 'secrecy' of project. Therefore it will be necessary to proceed without tunnel tests planning on testing for 2nd attack if first attempt is a 'bust'."[48]

If the committee had encouraged at least one American design based on the centrifugal compressor, more rapid progress would have been apparent. Kept in the dark, those making the initial decisions did not know that part of the success of the Whittle engine depended on its simple centrifugal compressor. Progress on all four of the projects of Durand's Special Committee was slow. In June 1942, Vannevar Bush raised doubts about the wisdom of exclusive reliance on the axial compressor. Referring to "the secret development being carried on by the General Electric Company on compressors for use in jet propulsion," he wanted to know whether the special panel that "had previously provided for the interchange of information on compressor design" should be reconvened. Durand responded that A. R. Stevenson, Jr., General Electric's representative on the committee "had expressed the view that the time had passed for such an interchange of views."[49] In November Stevenson reassured the committee that, although it was behind schedule, their "troubles" were routine. These "troubles" were directly related to the compressor: "We are becoming quite worried about vibration of the blades on the axial-flow compressor." He reported that their experimental four-stage compressor, like the one at Langley, had lost its blades. "We believe it was due to fatigue caused by pulsating air force."[50] General Electric's turboprop, the TG-100/T31, reached the test stand by 1943. Although a turboprop provides more efficient propulsion at modest speeds, the gearing to connect the gas turbine to the propeller adds mechanical complexity. The simplicity of the turbojet probably induced General Electric engineers to design the succeeding model, the TG-180/J35, as a turbojet. Nevertheless, its tricky axial compressor made significant progress slow. Support for the Allis-Chalmers design for a ducted fan with double paths of cool and hot air was dropped by the Navy in 1943, when the company obtained the license to build a British Havilland-Halford jet propulsion unit.

Centrifugal compressor.

Of the three designs submitted by the steam turbine manufacturers, only the Westinghouse 19B turbojet actually reached flight testing before the end of World War II. The company proudly called it the "Yankee" because it was the product of American engineering. It appears that R. P. Kroon, head of the team that actually built the "Yankee," did not know of the British developments prior to 1943. However, even in the Westinghouse unit, a British idea for a ring of individual combustors around the central shaft of the engine did find its way into the design. The "Yankee" engine had 24 combustor "cans." A company history relates that in July 1942, during the time that Westinghouse was struggling with its design, Stuart Way mentioned their problems in a meeting of a NACA combustion subcommittee. "It so happened that a GE man said that the problem was very simple—'all you have to do was take a tin can and punch some holes in it and you will have a combustion chamber.' "[51] The story also belies the view that the two divisions within General Electric worked in complete ignorance of what the other was doing. At some point the engineers at West Lynn and Schenectady may have exchanged information, because the TG-100, the General Electric project at Schenectady, also used multiple combustor cans. Glenn Warren, one of its designers, called the idea one of the most important aspects of British-American cooperation.[52]

Jacobs never had the benefit of the British solution to the combustion problem. Unaware that turbojets had already passed their bench tests in England and Germany, Langley engineers struggled to perfect Jacobs's hybrid scheme. The problem of achieving stable combustion in a continuous airstream without creating a flame that was so hot it would melt the metal sides of the apparatus was particularly recalcitrant. Jacobs tried to get the fuel to vaporize within a tubular boiler. However, he could not get his system to operate satisfactorily, and he agreed to enlist the assistance of Kemper's Power Plants Division. The "burner" problem was turned over to Ben Pinkel's Engine Analysis Section. Durand strongly supported the idea that a series of fuel jets should be tried. Pinkel assigned Kervork Nahigyan the task of redesigning the burner. Durand noted on a visit to Langley in March 1942 that both Jacobs's approach and that of the Power Plants Division appeared promising. He encouraged the rivalry between the two groups and set a deadline for an actual demonstration to the entire committee for July 15.[53] The demonstration, featuring Jacobs's solution, looked promising enough for the committee to encourage the work to be continued.

While Durand still strongly supported the Jacobs project, he realized that the NACA had a great deal at stake. As the first test flight of the General Electric 1-A engine neared, he became apprehensive. If Jake's Jeep failed, it would seriously affect the prestige of his committee, perhaps that of the entire NACA. In late September, he revealed his anxiety over the NACA project to George Lewis. In a letter to Lewis from California, written several days before he was to witness the flight over Muroc Dry Lake, Durand urged Lewis to "feel quite free to take hold of and direct the work of Jacobs along the lines agreed upon earlier." There was not a great deal that they could do about the projects that were in the hands of the private companies, but, he wrote, "I have,

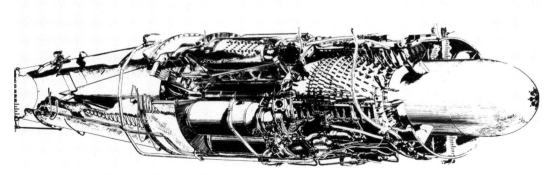

Schematic view of General Electric's TG-180 shows the axial compressor influenced by the NACA eight-stage compressor.

however, felt a little anxious about Jacobs's work, due to the fact that the Committee is directly interested in that particular project in the sense that its success or failure will react directly on the reputation of the Committee—at least in connection with this particular work."[54] Two General Electric 1-A engines powered the Bell Airacomet (P-59A) into the sky several days later.

There can be no question that once the Whittle engine was successfully flown, it became clearer that the outlines of future development would favor the far simpler compressor and turbine combination over the unwieldy piston engine and fan combination of Jacobs's conception. Durand was enthusiastic about the "splendid results" of the tests at Muroc. He wrote to Keirn, "It really begins to look as though a definite start has been made along the lines we have been thinking about so long."[55]

Durand informed members of the Special Committee that "resulting from entirely different causes" a meeting had been called "on the initiative of Army aviation" to take place in Washington, D.C., on November 13. Although no direct reference was made to the Whittle project, there could have been no question in any member's mind as to what Durand was talking about when he wrote that representatives of the Army, Navy, the Chairman of NACA, and the Chairman of the Special Committee on Jet Propulsion "take a broad general view, with an attempt to evaluate its significance as a factor in our present war effort, and, if possible, to reach some decision as to the extent to which the subject merits immediate support and development." He revealed that a report on the Langley project would be presented at that time.[56] Thus, the committee was placed for the first time in a position to judge the relative merits of the two systems, Jacobs's ducted fan and Whittle's turbojet. Obviously, the Whittle turbojet was the winner because it was at a point of development well beyond that of the NACA project. Although it was not clear at the time, ultimately the complexity and the excessive amount of weight in comparison to its low thrust meant that the ducted fan could not compete with the simplicity, efficiency, and low maintenance of future turbojets. The Jeep, nevertheless, played an important role in future American turbojet development because it stimulated both axial-compressor research and pioneering work on afterburners—work that was continued after the move of the Power Plants Division to Cleveland.

There is little doubt that after the November meeting of the Special Committee, as far as the Army was concerned, the NACA project was dead. The failure of the Jeep to win the continuing support of the Army directly affected the research program of the Cleveland laboratory. Ben Pinkel recalled that some time prior to his departure for Cleveland in December 1942, he was called to Henry Reid's office, where George Lewis reported that "officers of the military echelon" had informed him that "the war would be fought" with five reciprocating engines currently under production and "that all work on jet propulsion should be stopped in order that all effort should be directed toward those reciprocating engines."[57]

Even after the Army's decision, Jacobs continued to believe in his ducted-fan design. In January 1943, after his transfer to Cleveland, Nahigyan perfected his design for a burner employing a series of liquid-injection spray nozzles, located within bell-shaped flame holders.[58] This experience made him the natural choice to head the Jet Propulsion Section when Keirn brought the plans for the Static Test Laboratory from General Electric.

In late January, Jacobs himself visited the Cleveland Laboratory and, accompanied by Henry Reid, called on the Army officers at Wright Field. In a memorandum written after this visit, Reid noted the apparent lack of general overview of the jet propulsion situation. It was impossible to compare the various schemes to decide which ones were worthy of vigorous development

A technician uses a micrometer to determine possible distortion of the turbine blades of General Electric's I-40 turbojet engine. The ring of combustor cans, immediately behind the turbine, was Whittle's solution to the combustion problem.

because no one individual, with the exception of Durand, was fully informed of both the American and British developments.[59] Clearly, Reid and Jacobs still believed that the NACA's project was viable. However, the successful test flight of the General Electric 1-A engines in the Bell Airacomet the previous fall had sealed the fate of the Jacobs project. On 15 April 1943 the Special Committee officially resolved to drop "without prejudice" the project they had so wholeheartedly supported.[60] As Alex Roland has cogently argued in *Model Research*, the NACA never fully recovered from the blow to its prestige from the failure of the United States to develop aircraft jet propulsion before the Europeans.[61]

Viewed in the context of the abortive effort to develop the Jeep at Langley, Arnold's decision to assign the Cleveland laboratory the task of solving the mechanical problems of existing piston engines takes on new meaning. He had lost confidence in the NACA's technical leadership in the propulsion field. The cancellation of the Jeep took the creative, experimental work on jet propulsion away from the NACA for the duration of the war. Arnold chose to promote General Electric, a company previously only marginally involved in the development of aircraft engines, to a place on the cutting edge of jet propulsion development in the United States. Although the piston engine companies bore the brunt of Arnold's wrath for the dismal engine situation, he also punished the NACA for its belated and rather minimal efforts prior to 1941 to develop a jet propulsion scheme.

Arnold's decision to focus on developing existing piston engines to fight the war was a gamble. By 1944 the Germans were mass-producing a turbojet with an axial-flow compressor, the Jumo 004 for the Messerschmitt 262. Fortunately, Hitler did not appreciate the strategic importance of the superior speed of the turbojet, and production of the Jumo 004 came too late to make a difference in the outcome of the war. The Germans made only limited use of jet aircraft to shoot down Allied reconnaissance planes and to attack bomber missions. How close the jet engine came to making the difference in the war is revealed by a remark in a memo from Arnold in May 1944: "The jet propelled airplane has one idea and mission in life and that is to get at the bombers, and he is going by our fighters so fast that they will barely see him, much less throw out a sky hook and slow him up."[62]

When Colonel Donald Keirn unveiled the plans for a Jet Propulsion Static Test Laboratory for the Cleveland laboratory, the Army again assigned a role in the development of jet propulsion to the NACA. This visit, however, clearly underscored the Army's intention to limit this involvement to the testing of engines already developed by private companies such as General Electric and Westinghouse. Jacobs's Jeep briefly gave the NACA license to develop a jet prototype. The Cleveland laboratory would continue to feel the repercussions of its cancellation.

By August 1943 it was clear to the leaders of the Cleveland laboratory that jet propulsion would play an increasingly important role in the future. After a survey of existing facilities, George Lewis pointed out that "when the Committee's Cleveland laboratory was laid out, no thought was given to the provision of facilities for testing jet propulsion units."[63] This omission revealed an astounding lack of vision.

Jacobs himself spent several months at the laboratory in 1944 and made such an impression on several clean-shaven young engineers that they grew beards in his honor. The precise nature of Jacobs's work in Cleveland is not clear. It appears that he continued work on his jet propulsion scheme despite the Army's cancellation. It was now "bootleg" work, carried on without official sanction. "Nothing was so secret," one of the technicians at the laboratory recalled, "as Jacobs's jet rotor." His friend Henry Melzer cut the blades for a turbojet in the machine shop. He was told that Jacobs designed the engine from information gathered by two agents in a German Bavarian Motor Works plant. Melzer recalled that Jacobs often came to the shop to watch his painstaking labor, cutting the blades to conform to the so-called German configurations. One afternoon Jacobs called Meltzer to let him know that they were going to start the unit in a test cell. "While it was running, we stepped over it and felt for vibrations. About a year later, we heard that another engine had exploded, and the blades had gone off in all directions. We were lucky taking that chance."[64]

Secret jet propulsion tests of General Electric's I-16 were carried out in the Static Test Jet Propulstion Laboratory, completed in September 1943.

By March 1944 Lewis reported on the "change in character of the Committee's research program" brought about by the "success of the Whittle jet-propulsion engine."[65] Staff working under Kervork Nahigyan in the special Jet Propulsion Static Test Laboratory built and tested the first afterburner in October 1943, a direct result of the earlier work on the burner for Jake's Jeep. Abe Silverstein's group adapted the Altitude Wind Tunnel to test the new jet propulsion units. General Electric and Westinghouse sent experimental models of their engines for tests in the new tunnel. Although denied work on their own experimental engine of NACA design, the staff of the Cleveland laboratory acquired a unique, hands on, experience in jet technology. They would build on this early experience to become the government's experts in jet propulsion in the early postwar years.

NOTES

[1] Letter from Ben Pinkel to V. Dawson, 2 September 1984.

[2] Trip to England, 9 April-1 May 1941, Container 271, H. H. Arnold Papers, Manuscript Division, Library of Congress. Lord Beaverbrook's full name was William Maxwell Aitken Lord Beaverbrook.

[3] The best primary source for the history of the General Electric Whittle project is "Case History of Whittle Engine," Historical Study no. 93, Air Force Logistical Command History Office, Wright Patterson Air Force Base. This consists of Army correspondence and contains a wealth of information waiting to be mined. General Electric's company history, *Seven Decades of Progress* (Fallbrook, Calif.: Aero Publishers, Inc., 1979) is somewhat disappointing. An unpublished study by William Travers, The General Electric Aircraft Engine Story, is more detailed. General Electric Company papers from the West Lynn plant have recently been acquired by the National Air and Space Museum. "Jet Propulsion Engine Technical Data," Colonel Donald Keirn's Personal Data, Book, 1945, Part I, Air Force Central Museum, Dayton, Ohio, includes the performances of all of the American turbojet projects.

[4] Statement by Dan Walker, *An Encounter Between the Jet Engine Inventors, Sir Frank Whittle and Dr. Hans von Ohain, 3-4 May 1978,* History Office, Aeronautical Systems Division Air Force Systems Command, Wright-Patterson Air Force Base, Historical Publication, 1978, p. 47.

[5] On turbosupercharger development, see Robert Schlaifer, *Development of Aircraft Engines* (Boston: Graduate School of Business Administration, Harvard University, 1950),p. 328-329. Also, Leslie E. Neville and Nathaniel F. Silsbee, *Jet Propulsion Progress: The Development of Aircraft Gas Turbines* (New York: McGraw Hill, 1948], p. 98-102.

[6] Ben Pinkel, "Smoker Talk to AERL Staff," History looseleaf, NASA Lewis Records.

[7] Ben Pinkel to V. Dawson, 2 September 1984.

[8] A. H. R. Fedden, "Next Decade's Aero Engines Will Be Advanced But Not Radical." *Transactions of the Society of Automotive Engineers* 28(1933):379.

[9] Oscar W. Schey, Benjamin Pinkel, and Herman H. Ellerbrock, Jr., "Correction of Temperatures of Air-Cooled Engine Cylinders for Variation in Engine and Cooling Conditions," Technical Report 645, *NACA 1939 Annual Report*.

[10] Frank Whittle, "The Early History of the Whittle Jet Propulsion Gas Turbine," *Inst. Mech. Engr. Proceedings* 152(1945):419.

[11] In addition to studies mentioned in note 5, for the history of jet propulsion, see Edward W. Constant II, *The Origins of the Turbojet Revolution* (Baltimore: The Johns Hopkins University Press, 1980). See also G. Geoffrey Smith, *Gas Turbines and Jet Propulsion* (London: Iliffe & Sons, 1955), 6th ed., and Walter J. Boyne and Donald S. Lopez, *The Jet Age: Forty Years of Jet Aviation* (Washington, D.C.: National Air and Space Museum, 1979).

[12] On the science-technology relationship, see Edwin Layton, "Mirror-Image Twins: The communities of science and technology in 19th-Century America." *Technology and Culture* 12:562-580.

[13] Edgar Buckingham, "Jet Propulsion for Airplanes," Technical Report 159, *NACA 1923 Annual Report*, p. 75-90. Buckingham's scheme probably consisted of a compressor with afterburner, the compressor driven by a reciprocating gasoline engine. (Comments courtesy of Hans von Ohain, 5 June 1987.) See also Rexmond C. Cochrane, *Measures for Progress: A History of the National Bureau of Standards* (U.S. Department of Commerce, 1966), p. 282-283.

[14] James Hansen, *Engineer in Charge*, NASA SP-4305, 1987, p. 225; and John Becker, *The High-Speed Frontier*, NASA SP-445 (Washington, D.C.: U.S. Government Printing Office, 1980), p. 30.

[15] See Theodore von Kármán's description of the conference in *The Wind and Beyond* (Boston: Little, Brown and Co., 1967), p. 216-218.

[16] "Walker, *An Encounter Between the Jet Engine Inventors, Sir Frank Whittle and Dr. Hans von Ohain,* p. 28.

[17] See Edward Constant's analysis, *The Origins of the Turbojet Revolution,* p. 15-18 and chapter 7. To an earlier draft of this chapter, Dr. Hans von Ohain responded by letter 5 June 1987: "I fully agree with you that the first success of jet engines was more a result of the simplicity of a radial jet engine with respect to structure, performance characteristics of the engine components and matching, rather than superior

scientific insights in aerothermodynamics. (One could add that the radial engine also has inherently a favorable thrust to weight ratio, which is a necessary condition for high-speed flight.)"

[18] Hans von Ohain, "The Evolution and Future of Aeropropulsion Systems,"in Boyne and Lopez, *The Jet Age*, p. 29.

[19] Ibid.

[20] Interview with Hans von Ohain, 11 February 1985, at the National Air and Space Museum.

[21] Bush to Arnold, 2 July 1941, 47/208, Papers of H. H. Arnold, Manuscript Division, Library of Congress. On the Tizard mission, see Daniel J. Kevles, *The Physicists* (New York: Vantage Books, 1979), p. 302-303.

[22] Arnold to Bush, 25 February 1941, Records of NACA Committees and Subcommittees, National Archives, Record Group 255, 117.15. On the rocket work of the Guggenheim Aeronautical Laboratory, California Institute of Technology, see also Clayton Koppes, *The JPL and the American Space Program* (New Haven: Yale University Press, 1982).

[23] Kevles, *The Physicists*, p. 296.

[24] Bush to Arnold, 10 March 1941, Records of NACA Committees and Subcommittees, National Archives, Record Group 255, 117.15.

[25] Towers to Bush, 17 March 1941, NACA Committees and Subcommittees, National Archives, Record Group 255, 117.15.

[26] Frank B. Jewett, President of the National Academy of Science, on the occasion of Durand's 85th birthday, National Archives, Record Group 255, Durand biographical file. See also Walter G. Vincenti, "The Air-Propeller Tests of W. F. Durand and E. P. Lesley: A Case Study in Technological Methodology." *Technology and Culture* 20:712-751.

[27] Bush to Durand, 18 March 1941, Records of Committees and Subcommittees, National Archives, Record Group 225, 117.15.

[28] Ibid. This opinion was also shared by Towers. See Tower's letter to Bush, 17 March 1941, and Bush to Charles Abbot, 29 March 1941, National Archives, Record Group 225. The full committee consisted of Durand, Soderberg, R. C. Allen (Allis-Chalmers), L. W. Chubb (Westinghouse), A. G. Christie, Hugh L. Dryden, Brig. Gen. O. P. Echols, Jerome Hunsaker (ex officio), Capt. S. M. Kraus, U.S.N., G. W. Lewis (ex officio), and A. R. Stevenson, Jr. (General Electric).

[29] L. S. Hobbs to Jerome Hunsaker, 12 December 1941, NASA History Office, Washington, D.C., copied from J. C. Hunsaker Papers, Smithsonian Institution. See also Schlaifer, *Development of Aircraft Engines*, p. 453.

[30] Minutes of Meeting of Special Committee on Jet Propulsion, 10 April 1941, NASA History Office. My discussion relies on the minutes of the Special Committee April 10, 22, May 2, 8, 28 (July 25 missing); Compressor-Turbine Panel: July 25, September 22, 1941, February 3, 1942; Compressor-Turbine Panel, February 3, 1942, July 31, 1942, and December 1, 1942, located in the NASA History Office. Minutes of February 20, 1942, July 31, 1942, April 2, 1943, August 18, 1943, October 29, 1943 are in National Archives, Record Group 225. See also correspondence and Durand's reports in Records of NACA Committees and Subcommittees, National Archives, Record Group 225, 117.15. My account is supplemented by correspondence between Bush, Durand, and Arnold found in H. H. Arnold Papers, Manuscript Division, Library of Congress. For information on the Westinghouse project, I have also consulted the New Papers and the Westinghouse file, National Air and Space Musuem, Washington, D.C. Goddard's rocket work is compared to the far more practical work of the group at the California Institute of Technology by Clayton Koppes, *JPL and the American Space Program* (New Haven: Yale University Press, 1982), chapter 1.

[31] Bush to Durand, 18 March 1941, Records of Committees and Subcommittees, National Archives, Record Group 225, 117.15.

[32] James Hansen has shed new light on the NACA project at Langley in *Engineer in Charge*, chapter 8. Hansen's account relies on extensive documents in the Langley archives. See also Brian J. Nichelson, "Early Jet Engines and the Transition from Centrifugal to Axial Compressors: A Case Study in Technological Change," Ph.D. Dissertation, University of Minnesota, 1988. The work of the Durand committee is discussed briefly in Schlaifer, *The Development of Aircraft Engines*, p. 457-460. The Jacobs project received only a passing reference in George Gray's *Frontiers of Flight* (New York: Alfred A. Knopf, 1948), p. 278, a work commissioned by the NACA. For a reliable account of early jet propulsion

work in Europe and the United States, see Leslie E. Neville and Nathaniel F. Silsbee, *Jet Propulsion Progress* (New York: McGraw-Hill, 1948).

[33] In a letter to the author, Ben Pinkel wrote, 2 September 1984:

> Jacobs enlisted the aid of Eugene Wasielewski (a member of the Supercharger Section of the Power Plant Division) in the design of the compressor, and it proved to provide good performance. They built a vaporizing type burner for this system on the assumption that vaporization of the fuel was required to achieve efficient combustion.
>
> Jacobs could not get the burner to function properly. The "jeep," as this system was called, was turned over to the Engine Analysis Section for further development and testing. I assigned K. K. (Nick) Nahigyan the task of designing the burner. He employed about 40 spray type liquid injection nozzles each located at the apex of individual bell-shaped shells. The bells were oriented with their open ends down-stream and served as flame holders.
>
> The engine cycle consisted of the following steps. Air entered the front of the nacelle, was compressed by the engine-driven compressor, then passed into the combustion chamber where fuel was injected and ignited and finally, the products were discharged through the variable area nozzle.

[34] Clinton E. Brown to V. Dawson, 11 September 1989. On the ducted fan, see James Hansen, *Engineer in Charge*, p. 222. See also Jonathan W. Thompson, *Italian Civil and Military Aircraft 1930–1945* (Fallbrook, Calif.: Aero Publishing, 1963), p. 95–96.

[35] Macon C. Ellis, Jr., and Clinton E. Brown, "NACA Investigation of a Jet-Propulsion System Applicable to Flight." Technical Report 802, *NACA 1943 Annual Report*, p. 491–501. This is the only published NACA report on the Jeep.

[36] Durand to Arnold, 9 May 1941, 43/102, Manuscript Division, Library of Congress. The work of Hayne Constant and A. A. Griffith led to an agreement in 1937 between the Royal Aircraft Establishment and Metropolitan Vickers Company to design an engine with an axial compressor. This engine was flight tested 13 November 1943. For further information on the development of British turbojet engines, see Harold Roxbee Cox, "The Beginnings of Jet Propulsion." *The Royal Society of Arts Journal*, September 1985, p. 705–723.

[37] Minutes of the Special Committee on Jet Propulsion, 8 May 1941, p. 4, NASA History Office. The report on Jacobs's compressor work was published after he left Langley by John T. Sinnette, Jr., Oscar W. Schey, and J. Austin King, "Performance of NACA Eight-Stage Axial-Flow Compressor Designed on the Basis of Airfoil Theory," Technical Report 758, *NACA 1943 Annual Report*. For a case study of early axial-compressor development, see Brian J. Nichelson, "Early Jet Engines and the Transition from Centrifugal to Axial Compressors: A Case Study in Technological Change," Ph.D. Dissertation, University of Minnesota, 1988.

[38] Arnold to Bush, 2 June 1941, Picture and description have no date and were separated from the memo routed from Bush to Durand and then returned. H. H. Arnold Papers, 47/208, Manuscript Division, Library of Congress.

[39] Arnold to Bush, 25 June 1941, H. H. Arnold Papers, 44/124, Manuscript Division, Library of Congress.

[40] Bush to Arnold, 2 July 1941, H. H. Arnold Papers, 47/208, Manuscript Division, Library of Congress.

[41] Bush to Arnold, 11 July 1941, H. H. Arnold Papers, 47/208, Manuscript Division, Library of Congress.

[42] Arnold to Alfred J. Lyon, 2 October 1941, H. H. Arnold Papers, 43/102, Manuscript Division, Library of Congress.

[43] Minutes of Meeting of Turbine Panel of Jet Propulsion Committee, 25 July 1941, p. 2, NASA History Office. A company history of General Electric, *Seven Decades of Progress* (Fallbrook,Calif.: Aero Publishers, 1979), p. 41, says that by June all three companies were committed to the axial compressor.

[44] Alan Howard, who worked on General Electric's turboprop, the TG-100, based his design for an axial-flow compressor on a 1934 NACA paper by O'Brien and Folsom, "The Design of Propeller Pumps and Fans." He gave the specifications based on data relating to airflow over a NACA airfoil to the Peerless Pump Company (now part of Food Machinery Corporation) "with the proviso that the pump be built exactly to the design calculations." Letter to the author from William Travers, 22 August 1985. However, a G.E. company history relates that Howard, Glenn Warren, and Bruce Buckland, who worked on the project, were convinced by tests of an axial compressor carried out in Cleveland, undoubtedly a reference to

the eight-stage axial compressor, tested in Cleveland and used in the TG-180, a turbojet designed after the TG-100. See *Seven Decades of Progress*, p. 39. See also A. R. Stevenson to Durand, 27 November 1942, NACA Committees and Subcommittees, National Archives, Record Group 225, 117.15.

[45] Neville and Silsbee, *Jet Propulsion Progress*, p. 147. The Brown-Boveri compressor, mentioned in the W.R. New Papers, National Air and Space Museum, may have been the basis for their compressor design. See also Kroon to Durand, 24 April 1944, Records of NACA Committees and Subcommittees, National Archives, Record Group 225, 117.15

[46] Minutes of the Executive Committee of the NACA, 24 October 1941, National Archives, Record Group 225, Box 8.

[47] Durand to Echols, 27 February 1942, Records of NACA Committees and Subcommittees, National Archives, Record Group 225, 117.15.

[48] "Case History of Whittle Engine," Historical Study no. 93, vol. I, document 24, AFLC History Office, Wright-Patterson Air Force Base, Dayton, Ohio. Classification of the Whittle project was downgraded from "supersecret" to "secret" in summer 1943.

[49] Minutes of the Executive Committee of the NACA, 16 June 1942, National Archives, Record Group 225, Box 8.

[50] A. R. Stevenson to Durand, 27 November 1942, NACA Committees and Subcommittees, National Archives, Record Group 225, 117.15.

[51] For the development of the Westinghouse "Yankee" engine, see "The History of Westinghouse in the War," Aviation Gas Turbine Division, Engineering Department, Westinghouse, in the W. R. New Papers, Special Collections of Air and Space Museum, Washington, D.C., p. 20. Charles Edward Chapel, ed., *Aircraft Power Plants* ed, (New York: McGraw-Hill, 1948), p. 353–363. See also Neville and Silsbee, *Jet Propulsion Progress*, p. 145–50; John Foster, Jr., "Design Analysis of Westinghouse 19-B Turbojet." *Aviation*, January 1946, p. 60–68; Robert B. Meyer, Jr. "Classic Turbine Engines," in *Casting About* (Howmet Turbine Components Corp. magazine, 1985), p. 12–15.

[52] Neville and Silsbee, *Seven Decades of Progress*, p. 55. Arnold authorized discussion "of the Whittle matter" with Glenn Warren, one of G.E.'s designers at Schenectady. Arnold to D. R. Shoults, 27 August 1941, reproduced in *Seven Decades of Progress*, p. 45.

[53] Durand's "Notes on Visit to Langley Field," 31 March 1942, and Minutes of Executive Committee of NACA, 16 June 1942, National Archives, Record Group 255, Box 8; Ben Pinkel to author, 26 October 1984.

[54] Durand to Lewis, 29 September 1942, National Archives, Group Record 255, 117.15.

[55] Durand to Stevenson, 16 October 1942; Durand to Keirn, 29 October 1942, National Archives, Record Group 255, 117.15. Hansen discusses the continuation of the Campini project, in *Engineer in Charge*, p. 238–247.

[56] Durand to Members of Special Committee on Jet Propulsion: Soderberg, Allen, Chubb, Christie, Dryden, Keirn, Kraus, Spangler, Stevenson, Taylor, 6 November 1942, Records of NACA Committees and Subcommittees, National Archives, Record Group 255, 117.15.

[57] Letter to V. Dawson, 2 September 1984. Pinkel did not give the author an exact date. Arnold's letter to the NACA informing it of his decision to fight the war with the piston engine is dated 14 October 1942. It was reported in the Minutes of the Power Plants Committee, 11 December 1942, Records of NACA Committees and Subcommittees, National Archives, Record Group 255, 112.02. This seems consistent with Pinkel's recollection that he heard of Arnold's decision prior to his departure for Cleveland. It is not entirely clear what tests on the Jeep he is referring to here.

[58] Pinkel to V. Dawson, 2 September 1984. A sketch of Nahigyan's design can be found in Records of NACA Committees and Subcommittees, National Archives, Record Group 255, 117.15.

[59] Memorandum for files, "Visit to Wright Field to discuss NACA jet-propulsion airplane design," 20 January 1943, Jacobs file, National Archives, Record Group 255, Box 131, 23–25.

[60] Minutes of Meeting of Special Committee on Jet Propulsion, 2 April 1943, National Archives, Record Group 255, 117.15.

[61] Roland, *Model Research*, p. 185.

[62] Arnold to Craig, "Defense Against Enemy Jet Propelled Aircraft," 24 May 1944, Papers of H. H. Arnold, Carton 43, file 102, Manuscript Division, Library of Congress. See also I. B. Holley, Jr., "Jet Lag in the Army Air Corps," *Military Planning in the Twentieth Century, Proceedings of the Eleventh Military History Symposium, 10–12 October 1984,* Office of Air Force History, p. 123–153.

[63] Minutes of Meeting of Special Committee on Jet Propulsion, 18 August 1943, National Archives, Record Group 255, 11.

[64] Telephone conversation with Henry Meltzer, 17 September 1984. Meltzer later became head of the turbine blade section. Also interview with Rudy Beheim, 11 July 1984.

[65] Report to the Executive Committee, 16 March 1944, NACA Executive Committee Minutes, National Archives, Record Group 255, Box 9.

CHAPTER FOUR

TESTING THEIR METTLE

When journalists who belonged to the Aviation Writers Association visited the Cleveland laboratory in June 1945, they witnessed a carefully orchestrated display of the arcane world of aircraft propulsion. This was the laboratory's public debut—the first time the NACA could partially pull back the shroud of wartime secrecy. The writers for the country's major newspapers gawked at demonstrations of methods used to cool the cylinders of radial engines, "sniffed newly-developed fuels," and saw how a new spray bar for the carburetor of the huge B-29 "Super-fortress" could prevent overheating.

The laboratory's contributions to the old piston engine technology, however, told only part of the story. Demonstrations of jet propulsion, now suddenly part of aviation's new vocabulary, held the writers spellbound. They experienced the earsplitting roar of a ramjet and other "jet propulsion performances," presented by "a staff of efficient and capable-looking engineers." The high point of the tour was the first press showing of the Lockheed P-80 Shooting Star, powered by the General Electric I-40 turbojet engine, reputed to be the fastest plane in the world. The staff's lucid explanations convinced the writers, as well as special guest, Frances P. Bolton, Ohio's 22nd District Congresswoman, of the need for continuing government support for engine research. Bolton "urged the tour be made a 'required subject' for every person having anything to do with research appropriations."[1]

The journalists came away impressed that research at the Cleveland laboratory was being "carried on by the best aeronautical brains available, provided with the best equipment obtainable."[2] This was, in fact, an overstatement. More than 62 percent of its engineers had less than two years experience; the laboratory's research staff was young and untried.[3] In addition, although the laboratory had hastily shifted gears in 1944 to add turbojets, rockets, and ramjets to its research arsenal, its major facilities had been designed to meet the needs of the piston engine.

The wartime technology of jet propulsion represented peacetime opportunity. The laboratory's leaders were ready to take charge of the research agenda. They were impatient to terminate work on short-term development problems. They could not wait for the slow-moving Washington office to set their priorities. Trouble-shooting for the engine companies had served as an apprenticeship for the laboratory's youthful staff. Now they were ready to harness their energy and intelligence to tackle problems of a more fundamental nature. It was clear that the staff would need to hone its analytical skills. They were eager to launch a strong program in the new field of jet propulsion.

In the early euphoria at the end of World War II in Europe, few staff of the Cleveland laboratory, like the members of the press, were aware that the American development of the turbojet was late and on a considerably smaller scale than in Germany and Great Britain. Companies in Great Britain had benefited from the exchange of information facilitated by the Gas Turbine Collaboration Committee. They included Armstrong Siddeley, Bristol, De Havilland, Metropolitan-Vickers, Power Jets, Rolls Royce, and Rover. In the United States, secrecy had prevented the fruitful technical exchanges enjoyed by the British. With the American aircraft engine companies, Wright Aeronautical and Pratt & Whitney, kept out of the picture altogether and the Allis-Chalmers project dropped, the only American companies involved in turbojet development at the end of the war were General Electric and Westinghouse. What impressed an American Delegation to Great Britain in early 1944 was the "magnitude of the British effort." With as many as 30,000 British workers in the general field of jet propulsion, it was clear that the British had a "strong faith in the future of the turbine as a prime mover," a sentiment that seems to have come as a surprise to the American visitors.[4] With the aircraft engine industry in Germany eliminated, competition in the commercial development of the turbojet would come from the British.

When military technical missions to Europe revealed the extent of the German commitment to jet propulsion, it became increasingly clear that the policy of concentrating most of the American technical resources on the piston engine had been dubious, and possibly dangerous. In 1944, as Germany was falling, the Alsos Mission under Lieutenant Colonel Boris Pash and Samuel Goudsmit, its civilian scientist, gathered information on all aspects of Germany's advanced technology, particularly the development of atomic energy. The mission found that the Germans working on an atomic bomb under Werner Heisenberg were far behind the United States. Their reports also revealed the strong emphasis on jet propulsion in Germany. An early report described the gas turbine research at the Deutsche Versuchsanstalt für Luftfahrt (DVL), near Berlin, and that of the Junkers and Heinkel-Hirth Companies. The DVL had concentrated on thermodynamics and the metallurgy of turbine blades, while intensive aerodynamics studies were carried out by other government laboratories. "Germany was literally sprinkled with high Mach number wind tunnels" that appeared "to have been used extensively for jet work." In the field of jet propulsion, the report bluntly stated, "we are very much behind the Nazis." The report revealed that the Germans had developed jet engines with both centrifugal (von Ohain's turbojet) and axial compressors (the Jumo 004, designed by Anslem Franz).[5]

In 1945 the NACA dispatched Russell Robinson and Henry Reid from the Langley Laboratory to join the Alsos mission with the specific objective to uncover and assess the extent of German aeronautical advances during World War II. They were joined by William Ebert, also of Langley, and Carlton Kemper

The P-80 Shooting Star powered by the General Electric I–40 set up for testing in the Altitude Wind Tunnel.

from Cleveland. In May, Robinson, bypassing the normal channels of communication, wrote directly to George Lewis. He downplayed the extent of German superiority in aeronautical research, describing two proposed wind tunnels near Innsbruck, Austria, as "the only research equipment and plans that have come to light that are definitely beyond our own." The first was to be used for testing full-scale propellers, jet engines, rockets, and model aircraft "up to sonic velocities." The other tunnel, he guessed, was to be a supersonic tunnel. In addition, the Germans had planned a "propulsion laboratory for research at full scale on the elements of jet and gas turbine propulsion." No doubt reflecting on the innovative design of the Altitude Wind Tunnel at the Aircraft Engine Research Laboratory, he reported that the Germans had only begun to realize that they would need some way to produce low pressures and refrigerated air in their altitude facilities.[6]

The impressive facilities of Nazi Germany were only part of the story. When Robinson presented his final report to the NACA, he described in greater detail the research contributions that the Germans had made to the field of high-speed aerodynamics and jet propulsion. He stressed the "emphasis and liberal support that had been given to aeronautical research by the German Government, as measured by the number of workers, the number of laboratories, and the modern nature of their equipment, and particularly the construction under way to provide research facilities in advance of those possessed by any other nation."[7] In addition to the extensive German laboratory for applied research, the DVL (not visited by the Alsos Mission because Berlin was under the control of the Russian Army), the Germans had built a laboratory for advanced research on aerodynamics, engines, solid mechanics, and armaments—the Luftfahrtforschungsanstalt (LFA) at Braunschweig. The laboratory and the nearby Technical Institute at Braunschweig shared a fruitful exchange of personnel, among whom were Adolf Busemann, Herman Schlichting, and Theodor Zobel, renowned for their work in supersonic aerodynamics. In the engine research division at Braunschweig, pioneering work in heat transfer by Ernst Schmidt and his student, Ernst Eckert, had resulted in some of the first efforts in turbine cooling, an area that would receive considerable emphasis at the Cleveland laboratory in the late 1940s.

In addition to the physical evidence of these German research centers, the quantity and quality of research reports indicated the advanced nature of the German aeronautical research program. The Alsos team also interrogated hundreds of German scientists and employees of aircraft and engine companies, summarized in short NACA reports.[8] Members of the Alsos and other technical missions confiscated tons of German documents. They were sent to Wright Field, where the laborious process of cataloging and translating began immediately. The Cleveland laboratory hired an extremely able translator, Sam Reiss, to expedite the process of assimilation of German research, and the laboratory assisted the Army in the preparation of an index.[9] George Mandel and Dorothy Morris helped to create a technical library to put the most up-to-date reports and information in the hands of the laboratory's staff. The library became an important support of engineering activity, a change from the days when George Lewis thought engineers should spend their time monitoring tests, not reading articles in the library stacks.

Even before they had digested the wealth of information gathered by the Alsos Mission, Cleveland engineers had the opportunity to study captured enemy hardware sent from Wright Field. The first jet-propelled device that Cleveland engineers encountered was the German "pulse-jet," also called the V-1, or "buzz bomb." The Germans had shot this ingenious and terrifying pilotless aircraft across the English Channel to bomb the civilian population. In Cleveland, the buzz bomb was carefully taken apart. It consisted of a single cylinder with a system of organ-like flapper valves in the front end to control the discontinuous, or intermittent, combustion that caused its loud, pulsating noise. Air entered the combustion chamber at the front end. With the explosion of the fuel, the valves closed. As the hot gases were pushed out the rear, the loss of pressure caused the valves to open to receive a new charge of air. During testing, this work could hardly be kept secret. The noise rattled the windows of nearby houses like that of the Guerin family, who lived in the valley below the laboratory on what is now the southwest portion of the laboratory property.

Shortly after the first explorations of the pulse jet carried out by a group under Eugene Manganiello, the laboratory launched an effort with General Electric to develop simpler jet-propelled devices called ramjets.[10] The ramjet, known as the "flying stovepipe," consisted of a tube or cylinder open at both ends. Thrust was created by the combustion of fuel within the cylinder. Conceived by the Frenchman René Lorin in 1913, it was at first viewed as impractical because it only became efficient at high speeds.[11]

The Army also made available for study the Junkers Jumo 004—the engine that had powered the Messerschmidt 262. With Anselm Franz, the Jumo 004's designer, available for consultation at Wright Field, this engine received close scrutiny. Clearly impressed by evidence of German work in jet propulsion and by British postwar plans gleaned through the visits of British missions to Cleveland, the laboratory's leaders recognized the need to reorganize its entire research program.

German buzz bomb (V-1) set up in the Engine-Propeller Research Building.

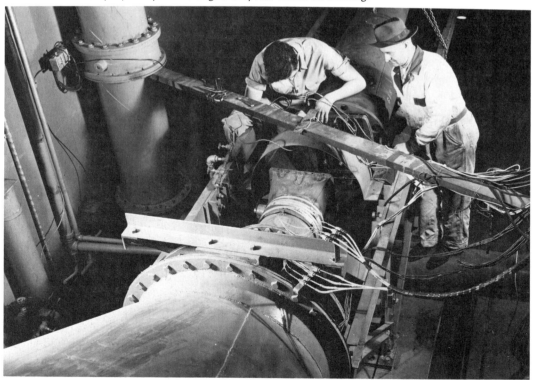

THE BIG SWITCH

The transition from the piston engine to jet propulsion was so sudden and sweeping that it caught not only the staff, but also the lower-level supervisors, completely by surprise. As one engineer recalled, he went home one evening in late September "deeply engaged in writing a report on spark plug fouling" to discover upon his return the next morning that his desk had been moved to another building and that henceforth he was to be engaged in rocket-engine cooling research.[12] However, if the institutionalization of the revolution in jet propulsion may have seemed abrupt and revolutionary to individuals at the lower levels of the laboratory's management, to leaders seasoned from their years at Langley, it was liberating and not unexpected. As early as 1944 they had looked forward to the time when they could lay aside the immediate and pressing development problems of existing engines and return to the basic problems that had characterized NACA research before World War II.

The staff forwarded to the Washington office in December 1945 its "Survey of Fundamental Problems Requiring Research." The survey was the product of a careful analysis of the present utility and future purpose of the laboratory. It showed that the laboratory's leaders were eager to expand research into new swaths freshly cut by wartime propulsion advances: the immature technologies of turbojets, ramjets, and rockets, and the virgin territory of aircraft nuclear propulsion. They rued the European origins of jet propulsion and the peripheral role that the NACA had played in its development. The "Survey of Fundamental Problems" reflected the frustration of the staff with the wartime program of research focused exclusively on trouble-shooting:

> While there is no doubt that the developmental work carried forward at the laboratory during the war was of great value to the military services, the effort put forth in this work was at the expense of fundamental research. The stringent requirement for accomplishing certain types of specific tests within a minimum period of time made it impossible to obtain basic data which are sorely needed for the continued development and improvement of aircraft propulsion systems.

Lewis staff intensively studied the axial compressor of the German Jumo 004.

With clear awareness that they were on the threshold of a new era, the planning document stated, "The simultaneous development of aerodynamic shapes for high-speed flight, and the use of jet-reaction power systems has suddenly placed the aeronautical engineer in position to attain supersonic speeds, but as yet only the outer fringes of research on this mode of transportation have been touched."[13] Postwar research would return to fundamental problems in aircraft propulsion.

In the December 1945 plan, there were nine research categories, each devoted to a specific engine type and assigned a percentage of effort:

Turbojet engines (20 percent); turbo-propeller engines (20 percent); continuous ramjet engines (12.5 percent); intermittent ramjet engines (5.5 percent); rocket engines (4.0 percent); reciprocating engines (13 percent); compound engines (15 percent); icing research (5 percent); and engines for supersonic flight (5 percent).

The proposed reduction of piston engine effort from about 95 percent to 28 percent was pared down even further in the revised plan of May 1946 to a mere 5 percent. In response to criticism by the engine companies that the projected research was not fundamental enough, general categories, such as compressor, turbine, combustion, fuels, materials, lubrication, super-sonics, and nuclear, were substituted for specific engine types. Two new categories that appeared in the revised plan—nuclear energy and "unconventional engines"—revealed the laboratory's eagerness to practice on the frontiers of propulsion technology. The turbojet—a compressor driven by a turbine—had not yet emerged as the clear winner among jet propulsion schemes. In the new research plan the compressor-turbine-propeller (turboprop) combination and the turbojet each commanded 20 percent of the research effort, with the compound engine (reciprocating engine plus turbosupercharger) claiming 15 percent.[14]

In the context of the 1946 "Survey of Fundamental Problems," fundamental research did not refer to science or theoretical work as opposed to engineering. Rather, fundamental research covered a spectrum of research stretching from basic scientific investigations to applied research in the form of testing and component development investigations. Engineering remained the heart of the NACA research. Funding depended on the laboratory's ability to demonstrate its substantive contributions to aviation. Theoretical research often complemented the more practical aspects of a particular engine problem, but it could never be viewed as an end in itself. What the NACA regarded as fundamental research was the opportunity to tackle general problems common to a particular class of engines. The new program envisioned by the Cleveland staff symbolized their liberation from narrow development problems of existing engines. They were determined to transcend current technical practice and to keep the demands of industry for immediate answers to their development problems at a minimum. This ordering of priorities was consistent with the National Aeronautical Research Policy approved in March 1946. Neglect of fundamental research before World War II had created an opportunity for aggression the Germans had exploited. The NACA's mandate included basic scientific investigations and testing of both components and full-scale engines. Development of specific hardware for production models would remain the responsibility of industry.[15]

The swing of the laboratory away from wartime trouble-shooting to long-term fundamental research goals was not unique among government research organizations after the war. The Jet Propulsion Laboratory of the California Institute of Technology and the Naval Research Laboratory, despite their explicit ties to the military, made similar efforts to redefine their research programs to embrace more general, all-encompassing definitions of what constituted basic, or fundamental, research.[16]

Concern over national security played a role in promoting fundamental research in government laboratories. The drive for profits made it unlikely that private corporations would be willing to invest in research whose long-term benefits were not sufficiently clear. Because national security required advanced technology, the government's role was to assume the risk for investigations in which there was chance for failure. Fundamental or basic research was, in the view of Vannevar Bush, "the pacemaker of technological progress." It was the intellectual capital on which future applications were drawn. Government research institutions had to be able to step out of the straight-jacket of current technical practice. They needed the freedom to pursue promising technology regardless of cost. "New products and new processes do not appear full-grown," Bush stressed. "They are founded on new principles and new conceptions, which in turn are painstakingly developed by research in the purest realms of science."[17]

When British Air Ministry representative F. Rodwell Banks visited the laboratory in summer 1945, he projected a "healthy obsolescence of reciprocating engines." Nevertheless, the British still planned to allocate roughly one-quarter of their research to the piston engine. Half of their research would be directed to developing the turbine-propeller combination, with the remaining 25 percent to be devoted to the turbojet.[18] The Cleveland laboratory paid close attention to British postwar planning, and its 1945 plan was roughly equivalent.

The strong commitment to jet propulsion shown in the reorganization of the Cleveland laboratory contrasted with the more conservative attitudes of university, military, and engine company representatives expressed at a meeting of the NACA Power Plants Committee in September 1945. Edward Taylor of the Massachusetts Institute of the Technology warned that the reciprocating engine should not be made artificially obsolete by cutting off research prematurely. Seemingly unimpressed with the success of the P-80 Shooting Star, he claimed that there was "not yet one successful airplane flying with a turbine engine." Colonel Donald Keirn, who remained in the thick of issues relating to the application of gas turbines to aircraft, felt that, while gas turbines would "undoubtedly come into their own," they were not at that point yet. He observed that "the manufacturers of really excellent reciprocating engines could hardly be expected to bear the cost of developing turbines with a view to making their present products obsolete." Pratt & Whitney's representative, Leonard Hobbs, claimed that his company planned to invest 50 percent of its funds for research and development of jet engines. Nevertheless, he wanted research on the piston engine to continue. After considerable debate, the members passed a resolution that piston engine research should not be terminated.[19]

Laboratory leaders ignored the Power Plants Committee's hesitant pronouncements. With Executive Engineer Carlton Kemper in Europe on the Alsos Mission, Addison Rothrock took responsibility for the technical leadership of the laboratory. The other division heads enthusiastically supported his decision to move strongly into the field of jet propulsion. The natural choice to implement the reorganization, he became the new Chief of Research. He created four new research divisions to reflect the new reality of jet propulsion. Ben Pinkel became the head of Fuels and Thermodynamics. John Collins took over as chief of Engine Performance and Materials. Underscoring the continuity between the supercharger and the turbojet, Oscar Schey assumed leadership of the Compressor and Turbine Division, while Abe Silverstein became chief of a consolidated Wind Tunnels and Flight Division. With the new division heads solidly behind the decision, Ray Sharp informed the Washington office. One of the important transitions in the corporate memory of Lewis Laboratory, the 1945 reorganization is remembered by former staff as an engineering decision made by engineers. Moreover, it was a decision reached at the laboratory level and communicated to the Washington office, not imposed from above.[20] This early expression of the laboratory's autonomy left an indelible impression on the character of the laboratory. Autonomy became a permanent aspect of its institutional identity.

The big switch assumed the flexibility of engineers to respond to the demands of a new technology. Nevertheless, for some engineers the transition was painful, particularly for those whose major research interests had been shaped by the piston engine. Despite the difficulty of adjusting to a new technology, the choice was simple—either fall into step or leave. As Walter Olson recalled:

> Any of our reorganizations cause a certain amount of trauma. There were people who wouldn't give up the piston engine. They were extruded out. Some of them stayed here and they were pushed down into the lower regions of the center and weren't allowed much help. They were out of step.[21]

The new technology forced a realignment of power relationships in the management structure. Oscar Schey's Compressor and Turbine Division became the premier division of the laboratory, claiming the largest number of staff and the highest output of research papers. Because the jet engine could run on almost any fuel, knowledge of chemistry was less important than an understanding of aerodynamics—how air flowed into and through the engine. When the octane-sensitive piston engine had been the focus of laboratory research, Addison Rothrock's Fuels and Lubricants Division had commanded the greatest resources in terms of facilities and personnel. After the reorganization, fuels no longer occupied the top of the research hierarchy. Many seasoned engineers from Rothrock's division left during the trauma of the reorganization. Cearcy D. Miller, for example, whose reputation rested on his high-speed camera to study the phenomenon of knock in the piston engine, left to go to the Battelle Institute in Columbus, Ohio, where he could continue his work on fuels. Nevertheless, the camera techniques that he pioneered would become standard research tools of the laboratory.[22] Young engineers hired by Rothrock during World War II moved into positions of greater responsibility. John Evvard, Walter Olson, Irving Pinkel, Wolfgang Moeckel, Edmond Bisson, all future leaders of the laboratory, learned the traditions of the NACA under Rothrock.

STAKING OUT A PLACE IN SUPERSONICS

After the flight of the V-2 at speeds greater than the speed of sound, supersonic aerodynamics could no longer be viewed as a visionary enterprise more suited to Buck Rogers than a responsible government research organization. Supersonic flight now fit securely within the province of the NACA's duty to find practical solutions to the problems of flight. Because the nature of the aerodynamics changes dramatically and the drag of an object in flight greatly increases as its speed passes beyond the speed of sound, flight at supersonic speeds created new engine problems that researchers at the Cleveland laboratory were eager to explore. For Cleveland staff from Langley, it was through a course taught by the Italian Antonio Ferri, once in charge of the high-speed tunnel at Guidonia, that they first learned of European advances in supersonics.[23] George Lewis, at last fully aware of the importance of the European research in supersonics, convened an interlaboratory High-Speed Panel to coordinate new research in this area. Lewis declared that he "wanted the panel to be the most forward-thinking group in this field." NACA luminaries Russell Robinson, Harvey Allen, Eastman Jacobs, John Stack, and Robert Littell (secretary) attended the first meeting of the panel, held at Langley in March 1944. Shortly afterwards, probably by 1945, Abe Silverstein had joined the panel as the representative from Cleveland; in January 1946 the panel met in Cleveland.[24]

In April 1945, possibly unaware of the High-Speed Panel, Cleveland engineer Bruce Ayer went over the heads of his superiors. He wrote directly to George Lewis to point out the inadequacy of the NACA's wind tunnels for supersonic research. He proposed a large national supersonic facility to be located in the West near one of the new hydroelectric dams. Ayer's grandiose scheme for an "Altitude and Supersonic Research Laboratory" was not taken seriously at first, but when the Alsos mission returned with reports of a water-driven 100,000-

Addison M. Rothrock, Acting Executive Engineer, took charge the "big switch" from the piston engine to jet propulsion in 1945.

horsepower supersonic tunnel under construction near Munich, the NACA set in motion plans for a large-scale supersonic facility.[25] In November Ray Sharp submitted a formal proposal for a national high-speed laboratory. He urged the Committee to *"preempt this field of high-speed research."*[26] Rather than preempting the field, however, the NACA slowly became aware of similar ambitious plans on the part of the Army Air Forces for a large-scale "engineering development center." This competition with the Army Air Forces for scarce postwar resources ended in 1949 in the Unitary Wind Tunnels Plan. The plan enabled the NACA to build supersonic tunnels at each of its three centers, with a lion's share of the appropriations going to the Air Force's Arnold Engineering Center in Tullahoma, Tenn. Plans for a NACA supersonic research center never materialized.

Silverstein's approach to supersonic research facilities was far more down to earth. On one of George Lewis's weekly trips to Cleveland in the last months of World War II, Silverstein broached the subject of a large supersonic tunnel. Lewis encouraged early design studies for the $9 million, 8-foot x 6-foot supersonic tunnel completed in 1949.[27]

Silverstein wanted research in supersonics to begin at once. In spring 1945 he called Demarquis D. Wyatt, a bright, articulate, but inexperienced engineer, into his office. He bluntly asked him if he would be interested in working on a supersonic wind tunnel. Wyatt admitted he had not the slightest idea what supersonics was, but he agreed with youthful bravado to head the design team to build several small supersonic tunnels.[28]

Given Abe Silverstein's background in the design and running of wind tunnels at Langley, the speed with which these tunnels were built was not surprising. If Wyatt was yet a novice, Silverstein brought a solid background in wind tunnels from Langley. Silverstein's colleagues credited him with an unerring feel for design. His approach to engineering was visual, intuitive, and practical. "He always maintained philosophically that if something doesn't look right, it wasn't right... If it is good, sound, proper design, your eye will detect it as good design."[29] An anecdote reflects what is often referred to as Silverstein's engineering intuition. One of his young engineers assigned to design a supersonic tunnel had reached an impasse. With knowledge of supersonics still in its infancy, he had calculated the shape for the upstream, subsonic side of the throat and for the downstream, supersonic part, which expands beyond the throat into the test section, but he lacked equations for the transonic section between these two parts, where the flow passed from subsonic to supersonic. Silverstein "eyeballed" the design. Picking up a pencil, he pared the shape of the curve. Despite the freehand addition, the tunnel worked perfectly. James Hansen has pointed out in *Engineer in Charge* that this ability to visualize an engineering problem was typical of some of the best engineers at Langley. It was an aspect of a unique engineering creativity encouraged by the NACA.[30] However, Silverstein's ego sometimes interfered with his engineering judgment. He had little patience for any point of view but his own.

This did not matter to the young Wyatt, for whom Silverstein was a model and an inspiration. Wyatt and his group groped empirically for the best configuration to explore the uncharted territory of supersonics. They built two tunnels, an 18-inch x 18-inch square tunnel and a 20-inch diameter round tunnel, both capable of speeds up to about Mach 2. Called the "stack tunnels," they were built one on top of the other above the Altitude Wind Tunnel and shared its exhaust system. They were run at night when the Altitude Wind Tunnel was not in operation. Additional supersonic wind tunnels, called "duct tunnels," were built in an underground passage connecting the Altitude Wind Tunnel and the Engine Research Building. The research program for these tunnels focused on the study of inlets and diffusers for supersonic ramjets.[31]

As soon as they ran tests in the new tunnels in summer 1945, researchers under Silverstein encountered shock waves, typical of supersonic aerodynamics. The discovery of shock waves

experimentally in the stack tunnels coincided with the group's first awareness of outstanding theoretical work by the British and Germans in supersonics. Members of Silverstein's division studied papers published in British journals as well as the work of Adolf Busemann, Klemens Oswatitsch, Albert Betz, and Hermann Kurzweg, translated and published as NACA Memoranda. Later they would have more direct access to Busemann, when the Army's Operation Paperclip assigned him to Langley.[32]

The NACA's High-Speed Panel met in Cleveland on January 21, 1946. Left to right: Addison Rothrock, John Stack, Langley; H. Julian Allen, Ames; Russell G. Robinson, Washington office; Abe Silverstein, and Carlton Kemper.

With the new supersonic tunnels in operation, Silverstein reorganized his Wind Tunnels and Flight Division. He placed John

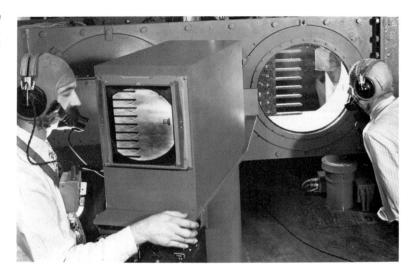

A camera (foreground) records shock waves during supersonic test in the duct tunnels, 1949.

Evvard in charge of a Special Projects Panel. The use of "panels" to cross division and disciplinary lines was one of the distinguishing marks of Silverstein's management style. By drawing talent from the entire laboratory, Silverstein encouraged greater flexibility and interaction between groups. Demarquis Wyatt became the section head in charge of the stack tunnels, and John Disher took charge of the development of an unconventional ramjet concept carried out on the hangar apron.

THE ROCKET FRONTIER

Like the group in supersonics, members of the small rocket section at the Cleveland laboratory started with little knowledge of previous work in rocketry. In the 1930s the Cleveland Rocket Society had nurtured an enthusiastic group of amateurs, but it had vanished without trace. Reports of the firing of the V-2 across the English channel in summer 1944 awakened a more serious and lasting interest in rockets among the laboratory staff. In December the Navy complained that "progress being made on high-speed research is not as rapid as military necessity now demands" and urged that jet-propelled aircraft and missiles be given the "highest practicable priority."[33] Cleveland researchers were eager to comply. While the NACA debated how best to coordinate work on guided missiles, the laboratory's rocket group jumped into research on small solid-fuel rockets.[34] After some "prodding" by the Army Air Forces in 1944, George Lewis authorized the Cleveland laboratory to build four rocket test cells.[35] Responding particularly to new information on the V-2, in June 1945 the Cleveland laboratory submitted a formal proposal that included research on turbojets, ramjets, and rockets for applications as power plants for guided missiles. The mood among government engine researchers was "to catch up and not ever fall behind again in advanced propulsion."[36]

Walter Olson brought back news of successful rocket experiments at the Jet Propulsion Laboratory (JPL) in Pasadena, Calif. Olson's reports fired the imaginations of members of the Fuels and Lubricants Division. Late in World War II, the NACA had sent Olson to the Santa Ana Air Force Base to recruit men with technical backgrounds as they returned from active duty. With a Ph.D. in chemistry, Olson did not like to let his analytic skills grow dull. He took the opportunity to meet with Theodore von Kármán, Frank Malina, and Martin Summerfield. He was intrigued by their stories of the development of jet-assisted take-off devices, although he did not visit Aerojet, JPL's commercial spinoff, where these JATOs were mass-produced. Olson recognized the risks Malina's small band of rocket enthusiasts had taken before the war when they mixed asphalt and the fertilizer ammonium nitrate at CalTech's primitive rocket facilities. The NACA was too conservative to have allowed dangerous tests like the ones carried out in the Arroyo Seco, the future site of JPL. Olson could hardly wait to get back to Cleveland to discuss this new work, which immediately fired the imaginations of the young staff in the Fuel and Lubricants Division.[37] When the laboratory reorganized shortly after Olson's return, Ben Pinkel selected Olson to head the Combustion Branch within the new Fuels and Thermodynamics Division. The Rocket Section headed by Joseph Dietrich took shape under Olson's enthusiastic leadership.

At first the laboratory's rocket program had to be disguised as "high-pressure combustion" because the chairman of the NACA's Main Committee, Jerome Hunsaker, did not approve of rocket research. He thought that rocket research was outside the NACA's mandate to improve aircraft. Undaunted, the rocket group intensely studied the Alsos reports of German work and the publications of the Jet Propulsion Laboratory. John Sloop, later head of the Rocket Section, recalled that they were acutely aware that they "had a lot of catching up to do." Because of their feeling that they were latecomers, they decided to direct their attention to "lesser ploughed fields" of rocketry. Research on solid rockets they could leave to others.[38]

With minimal support for personnel, the section decided to focus on high-energy liquid propellants. The group studied combustion and rocket-engine cooling and evaluated the performance of these propellants both theoretically and through experiments. A team working under Vearl Huff developed a method to calculate theoretical performance that greatly simplified the process of propellant selection. Riley Miller and Paul Ordin made a systematic study of various combinations of hydrogen, nitrogen, and oxygen atoms. Despite the lack of official sanction, work on rocket fuels slowly increased, pushed by the technical interests of the group rather than external demands for specific applications. With the same spirit shown by those who were pushing the frontiers of supersonics, the members of the rocket section enjoyed the adventure of an entirely new field. They took great risks to obtain small quantities of exotic chemicals. One determined researcher brought pure hydrogen peroxide from Buffalo, N.Y., on the all-night train clamped in a container between his legs. The potential of hydrazine and diborane also received close scrutiny. In the late 1940s, experiments on diborane, which was also being studied as a potential high-performance fuel for jet engines, revealed that it left oxide deposits that impaired performance. When diborane was combined with fluorine, the deposits disappeared, but no satisfactory method of cooling could be found. Researchers studied the effects of using pentaborane as a fuel by testing it in the five-foot diameter Navaho ramjet in the Propulsion Systems Laboratory. By 1948 the group had formed a high opinion of liquid hydrogen.[39]

The initiative for the laboratory's work in rockets came from the staff in the Fuels and Thermodynamics Division. This work was neither inspired nor encouraged by the Washington office and received surprisingly little support from Addison Rothrock, then in charge of the laboratory's research program. Understaffed, underfunded, but undeterred, the rocket group slowly built a technical competence in rocketry that would serve as an important base for future achievements in liquid propellants. However, the group would wait many years for adequate facilities for their research.

NUCLEAR PROPULSION

Initiative from within the laboratory can also be seen in nuclear propulsion. The attraction of a nuclear power plant for aircraft was the potential for long-range flight without refueling. Former Langley staff were no doubt familiar with the work of Eastman Jacobs and Arthur Kantrowitz at Langley, where they made the first attempt in the United States to achieve a controlled fusion reaction.[40] Engineers at the Cleveland laboratory immediately connected the breakthrough in jet propulsion with the potential of nuclear-propelled aircraft and missiles. If the feasibility of a new propulsion system for aircraft could be demonstrated, it would represent a "breakthrough" in propulsion similar to that of jet propulsion during World War II.

Although nuclear propulsion received only a brief statement in the "Survey of Fundamental Problems," serious thinking in Cleveland about nuclear propulsion began two months prior to the bombing of Hiroshima and Nagasaki. Bruce Hicks, a physicist, and Sidney Simon, a chemist, both recent Ph.D.s, were unaware of the Manhattan Project. However, they were both certain of the technical feasibility of splitting the atom. They urged headquarters to allow them to begin to explore the potential of nuclear energy for aircraft propulsion. They pointed out in a memo to the Washington office that before the war the process of nuclear fission was beginning to be understood. They stated that in the early years of the war a great deal of work had focused on producing a self-sustaining nuclear reaction. Publication had then ceased. "It is a matter of common belief among physicists," they wrote," that every major power in the world has been devoting a tremendous amount of effort to the solution of this and similar problems." They stressed the need to train a team from the Cleveland laboratory. They thought that it would take 12 months for a physicist or chemist with a Ph.D. to become a nuclear physicist and about two to three years to turn an outstanding individual with an undergraduate degree in physics or chemistry into an expert in nuclear fuels. Hicks and Simon suggested that the laboratory hire three nuclear physicists who had worked on wartime projects to assist in setting up the program. Drawing on their expertise, the laboratory could then hire about 50 new staff to design, construct, and operate nuclear equipment, such as cyclotrons.[41]

Several days after the announcement that the United States had dropped two nuclear bombs on Japan, laboratory personnel suggested that four or five NACA scientists be sent to the "inner sanctum" of Los Alamos, N.M. John Evvard pointed out the new vulnerability of the United States in a world with long-range, possibly nuclear, rockets for the delivery of nuclear bombs. As a point to be raised in discussions of nuclear propulsion in Washington, he wrote:

> The Germans had a modified V-2 rocket on the drawing boards equipped with collapsible wings. Using a skipping technique in the outer atmosphere, this rocket was reported to be capable of bombing New York from Germany within a radius of ten miles from the point target. Combine this implement of war with the potential applications of the atomic bomb principles, and you get a missile which could destroy any point on the earth's surface from any other point. THERE IS NO SUCH THING AS SAFETY OF DISTANCES![42]

Access to the nuclear inner circle proved difficult for the NACA. Vannevar Bush, Director of the Office of Scientific Research and Development, suggested they wait until Congress had set up the Atomic Energy Commission. Six months later, a Cleveland memo warned headquarters that "unless the Committee sets up an active and farsighted group in this field, we will be 'left at the post.' "[43]

While the Cleveland laboratory enthusiastically formulated its plans to tap into the mainstream of nuclear propulsion research, the Washington office demurred. In May 1946 the Army Air Forces initiated the Nuclear Energy Propulsion for Aircraft (NEPA) under Donald Keirn, now on the staff of Leslie Groves, former director of the Manhattan Project. Although denied a leading role in this work, the NACA was placed on a board of consultants for NEPA along with nine companies and the Navy. Soon the Army was anxious to tap its growing nuclear expertise.[44]

The Cleveland laboratory staff persevered in the pursuit of a larger piece of the national nuclear propulsion program and succeeded in winning the support of Farrington Daniels, head of the metallurgical laboratory at the University of Chicago and a key member of the Manhattan Project. They proposed a program of basic research in high temperature–heat transfer and materials to support the development of Daniels' design for a gas-cooled nuclear reactor.[45] By the next year the NEPA project was foundering. It was clear that the Army project needed the NACA. Andrew Kalitinsky, Chief Engineer of the NEPA division of Fairchild, was anxious to use NACA research data. For example, after a meeting with Cleveland laboratory engineers, he wrote:

> In the course of these discussions it became apparent that the analytical and experimental heat-transfer studies now under way at Cleveland may be of great immediate value to NEPA. In the analytical studies, a method of calculating heat transfer and pressure drop has been devised which appears to be far simpler and more accurate than anything we now have available.[46]

With increased emphasis on heat-transfer problems related to nuclear propulsion by members of Ben Pinkel's Fuels and Thermodynamics Division, the NACA and the Atomic Energy Commission came to a formal agreement on a joint research program on 15 July 1948. Various Lewis personnel were assigned to Oak Ridge National Laboratory for training, the beginning of a long and, in hindsight, misdirected commitment to nuclear propulsion that continued until 1972, when the dismantling of the nuclear effort would nearly bring about the closing of the laboratory.

THE ENGINE INDUSTRY AND THE NACA

It was critical that the Cleveland laboratory find and occupy a niche in the transformed economic and political environment of the early post–World War II period. Even with a

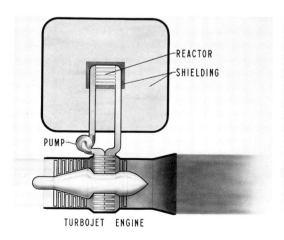
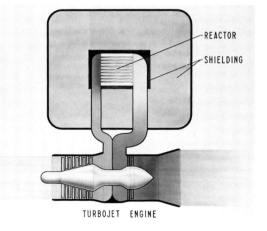

Two approaches to aircraft nuclear propulsion.

well-defined research agenda, its role in the emerging propulsion community would be a difficult one. It had to avoid being used by industry to clean up its immediate development problems; however, unlike disinterested university research, scientific and engineering knowledge generated by a government laboratory had to serve the national interest.

Historically, the NACA had prided itself on its contributions to the kinds of basic knowledge that took concrete expression in the design of aircraft. Basic research, made available to the entire aircraft industry, stimulated innovation. The NACA did research that industry could not afford to undertake. Between the two world wars the air-frame industry had come to rely on the NACA. Small innovations like the change in the configuration of wing, tail, or propeller—discovered through testing in the NACA's wind tunnels—could dramatically improve aircraft performance. Often redesign of a particular component could be introduced without major revamping of the assembly line. In contrast, even a small change in an engine usually affected the entire system. Engine innovations were costly because of the watch-like precision and interrelationship of the engine's complex components.

Would the new laboratory ever enjoy the same easy relationship with the engine companies the NACA had enjoyed with air-frame designers? Conservative, intensely competitive, and resistant to any kind of government interference, the engine companies were not sure whether development of the turbojet would ever be profitable. The existence of the new engine laboratory seemed to threaten their independence. With sufficient expertise in the new field of jet propulsion, the laboratory could influence the demands the military put on the engine companies. Government research could assist the United States in catching up and surpassing the British in turbojet development, but only if the engine companies would accept government research and the government's right to disseminate it as widely as possible to competitors. Because of the intense rivalry among the engine companies, the laboratory found itself in a delicate position. Research in the national interest could not benefit a single company, but must be freely available to the entire industry.

In 1945 the turbojet was by no means a finished, or mature, technology. Moreover, it was not clear whether the turbojet could be mass-produced for a commercial market. For fighter aircraft, where speed outweighed other considerations, such as fuel consumption and length of service, the compressor-turbine combination held great promise, but how much emphasis should military hardware receive in peacetime? Many design questions remained to be solved. Would the axial or centrifugal compressor prevail? What form should the combustor take, and how would the designer overcome the problem of the high temperatures of the combustor and turbine? Would it require the development of new materials? Should methods of turbine cooling be investigated? Mechanically, the gas-turbine engine was simpler than the piston engine, but the complexity of the physical processes involved in passing air through a compressor, combustor, and turbine required a level of theoretical sophistication far above what had been necessary during World War II. To grapple with these problems demanded more formal training for engineers and a gradual accumulation of experience.

The first opportunity for the Cleveland laboratory to demonstrate the potential benefits of government engine research in the new field of jet propulsion came in May 1945. Ben Pinkel, Oscar Schey, Abe Silverstein, and William Fleming from Cleveland and John Becker from Langley attended the first American conference on aircraft gas turbine engineering, sponsored jointly by General Electric and the Army Air Forces. Held in Swampscott, Mass., the conference attracted nearly 200 members of the aeronautical community, including representatives from Great

1954 cartoon refers to the NACA's role in aircraft nuclear propulsion. Reproduced by permission of The Cleveland Plain Dealer.

Britain.[47] While General Electric engineers and their British colleagues presented the bulk of the 27 papers, Silverstein had the distinction of describing the NACA's contribution, the test program in the Altitude Wind Tunnel. He described how late in the war, his staff had increased the air exhaust capacity of the tunnel from 8 pounds per second to 80 pounds per second. Testing had enabled General Electric to improve its prototype from the balky I-16 to the more reliable I-40. By the end of the war, the I-40 was actually superior to Rolls Royce engines based on Whittle's design, although this superiority was not to last.

Silverstein's paper used a valuable comparative perspective to evaluate the engine performance of five different engines.[48] In addition to data on General Electric I-16 and the I-40, with their centrifugal compressors, the laboratory made available comparable data for other American designs—the General Electric TG-180 and the Westinghouse 19-B and 19-XB, with their axial compressors. Silverstein's paper symbolized the laboratory's new commitment to defining and solving problems for the benefit of the entire engine industry. For example, he described "combustion blowout" at low speeds and the effect of Reynolds number, which might impair the efficiency of the compressor and turbine at high altitudes.[49]

The NACA paper demonstrated the developing expertise of the laboratory in the new field of jet propulsion. However, winning the cooperation of the engine companies would not be easy. As early as 1944, Jerome Hunsaker, Chairman of the NACA, anticipated trouble with the established engine companies, Pratt & Whitney and Wright Aeronautical. In a "Memorandum on Postwar Research Policy for NACA," he reported that one of the questions that industry had raised during his trip across the country in mid-1944 was "whether or not the Cleveland laboratory constitutes a potential threat to the engine industry." He explained, "The idea here is that private enterprise has already developed very superior engines and fuels and does not need government competition in research, invention, and development."[50] Hunsaker reported that industry management argued that they could make better use of public funds than a government laboratory and wanted government engine research stopped. In particular, the engine companies complained that the Cleveland laboratory's extensive work on the Allison engine interfered with the impersonal forces of the market. They were also bitter about the Army's decision to set up the Packard Company in the aircraft engine business through their license from the Rolls Royce Company to manufacture the British Merlin engine. However, their major complaint was that the NACA was taking the lead in jet propulsion "in collaboration with firms previously outside the aeronautical engine field."[51]

The engine companies had reason to worry. General Electric appeared to be a potentially powerful new competitor, with a head start in the gas-turbine field, and Westinghouse, tasting its first success with its small turbojet for use on aircraft carriers, had captured the Navy's interest and investment. Moreover, the Army had licensed the Allison Division of General Motors to take over the manufacture of the I-40. Pratt & Whitney and Wright Aeronautical still dominated the piston-engine field, but, in the postwar environment, how long would the piston engine continue to be commercially viable? The engine companies were aware of their precarious position in the new peacetime economy. As a result of the war, they had enormously expanded facilities. Now they were faced with the possibility that the market for their engines might cease to exist. The very day that President Harry S. Truman announced victory over Japan, the government canceled more than $414 million in contracts with Pratt & Whitney, and the machinery of its vast production empire fell silent.[52] With a radically new power plant on the horizon, the engine companies could anticipate the costly replacement of the entire set of machine tools necessary to mass produce aircraft engines.

Vannevar Bush and other members of the NACA's Executive Committee, however, had little sympathy for the plight of the companies that made piston engines. Bush retorted, "Inasmuch as the Germans have just sprung a clever, new engine on us, which our industry never thought of, their attitude does not strike me forcibly."[53] Bush blamed not the NACA but the engine companies for the tardiness of the American effort to develop the turbojet. Recalling with displeasure their predictable attitudes toward developing any unusual engine, he commented, "If we brought new people into the engine field I think we have done a public service."[54] The new companies ended the domination of Pratt & Whitney and Wright Aeronautical.

Competition encouraged innovation. Once a strong company prevailed over its weaker competitors, innovation ceased. It was always more profitable to market a production engine than to undertake the costly development of new ideas. Another NACA Executive Committee member commented that, although the aircraft industry might be just as able to conduct fundamental research as the NACA, it was not interested in the "general progress of the art." What industry objected to and feared was the publication of new knowledge, thus eliminating the competitive advantage a company might win through its own efforts. The committee thought that government research would encourage competition. It would force industry to keep up by performing at higher technical levels. This research dynamic needed to be sustained because the industry could anticipate strenuous competition with the British, who were looking forward to the expansion of the aircraft industry and were proposing to build new facilities. Hunsaker observed:

> They are going throughout the United States, and they are frank in saying that what we have now is what they propose to build, only larger and better. We have a 20-foot-altitude wind tunnel at Cleveland. They will have a 25-foot-altitude tunnel. Their program now calls for the construction of 12 wind tunnels, which will constitute a great national research organization for the British empire.[55]

In the same way that the Russian Sputnik raised national security fears almost 15 years later and galvanized public opinion for the outlay of tax money for technology research, the superiority of British engines and the perceived danger of this technology in the hands of the Russians was a recurring theme in the late 1940s to justify expansion of government facilities.

THE COMPOUND ENGINE

Ben Pinkel, respected for his analytic ability, led the laboratory's effort to evaluate the potential of the different types of propulsion systems in terms of weight, altitude, range, and fuel consumption. The results of this analysis were first presented at the second annual Flight Propulsion Meeting of the Institute for Aeronautical Sciences held in Cleveland in March 1947.[56] This type of systems analysis was an important aspect of the work of the laboratory because it was the one institution in the United States that could attempt an overview of the entire propulsion picture. The group evaluated six engines: the compound engine by Eugene J. Manganiello and Leroy V. Humble; the turbine-propeller engine by John C. Sanders and Gerald W. Englert; the turbojet engine by Newell D. Sanders and John Palasics; the turbo-ramjet engine by Bruce T. Lundin; the ramjet engine by George F. Klinghorn; and the rocket engine by Everett Bernardo, Walter T. Olson, and Clyde S. Calvert. By weighing different parameters, such as thrust in relation to engine weight, engine frontal area and the rate of fuel consumption, speed, and altitude, Pinkel's group

Ben Pinkel, chief of the Fuels and Thermodynamics Division, sits with staff who presented papers at the propulsion meeting of the Institute of Aeronautical Sciences (I.A.S.) March 28, 1947. Left to right: Everett Bernardo, Newell D. Sanders, Bruce Lundin, Benjamin Pinkel, George F. Klinghorn, John C. Sanders, and Eugene J. Manganiello.

assessed the advantages and disadvantages of each system. On the basis of the NACA's analysis, engine companies could more realistically plan development of different engine types.

In the late 1940s, the turbojet seemed an unlikely candidate for commercial development because of its high fuel consumption and lack of reliability. As Ben Pinkel recalled, the aircraft industry could not imagine a passenger airplane flying at speeds of 500 miles per hour because of the buffeting the aircraft would receive. "There was a general feeling that the human body just could not stand to go that fast. It was just beyond the point of human endurance." Few could imagine pressurization of passenger cabins to make flight at high altitudes in less turbulent air possible. Pinkel, who served on the NACA Subcommittee for Propulsion Systems with William Littlewood, director of research for United Aircraft, vividly recalled Littlewood's assertion that his company had decided, after considerable study, that the jet engine had no future for commercial applications.[57]

There seemed little doubt that for military applications, the turbojet would remain a strong candidate for continued development. However, the engine companies had their eyes on the commercial market where fuel consumption was an important consideration. The group under Pinkel concluded that the compound engine and the turboprop were about equal in terms of altitude and range. Because of their relatively lower fuel consumption, both were superior to the turbojet at speeds of less than 550 miles per hour. For commercial applications, they concluded the compound engine was superior to the turboprop because it exploited the known technology of the piston engine and exhaust gas turbine or turbosupercharger. Now more or less forgotten because of the current domination of the turbojet for all aircraft engine applications, between 1945 and the early 1950s the compound engine seemed to hold great promise for commercial planes. It consisted of a piston engine and propeller with an exhaust gas turbine to drive an auxiliary supercharger. The turbine delivered excess power to the engine shaft through gearing. There may have been a hint of national pride in its short popularity. While the turbojet was a European development, the compound engine had secure roots in American turbosupercharger innovations. Ben Pinkel's analysis encouraged the engine companies to develop the compound engine, which became for a short time the engine of preference for long-range passenger flight. The development of the compound engine was the beginning of a new positive working relationship between the NACA and Pratt & Whitney.[58]

The reorganization of the laboratory in 1945 to emphasize fundamental research reflected the assumptions of leaders like Vannevar Bush that research was the key to national survival, both from a military point of view and in the commercial arena. World War II was waged in the research laboratory as well as on the battlefields of Europe. Planning for the next war on the part of the Army Air Forces began before World War II had ended. This planning emphasized the need for continued support for science and technology. Technical superiority could be a deterrent to future enemy aggression.[59] By carefully distinguishing fundamental research—the presumed province of the government—from development—the arena of private enterprise—National Aeronautical Research Policy expressly avoided leaving the nation's aircraft-engine requirements exclusively in the hands of private industry. But where was the line between research and development to be drawn? The supposed connection between fundamental research and national defense in the event of future wars mandated close ties between the Cleveland laboratory and the Army, Navy, and later the Air Force. These ties strengthened in the postwar period.

With the reorganization, the basic outline of the management structure of Lewis was fixed until the advent of the National Aeronautics and Space Administration in 1958. The "Survey of Fundamental Problems" set the research course of the laboratory through the mid-1950s. Gradually the superiority of the turbojet over the turboprop and the compound engine was demonstrated. The turbojet demanded focus on the problem of developing materials such as alloys and ceramic and metal compounds to withstand the temperatures of the hot gases. The early effort in high-energy liquid propellants for rockets and missiles would later culminate in the success of the Centaur rocket. Work on the supersonic ramjet played an important role in stimulating basic research in aerodynamics and heat transfer. The ramjet work was applied in the Navaho program, the Bomarc program, and the so-called "T" series of missiles for the Navy, including the Terrier and Talos missiles. The early promise of nuclear propulsion, never realized, nurtured basic research in materials.

In April 1947 the Cleveland laboratory was renamed the Flight Propulsion Research Laboratory to mark its transition from an engine laboratory, charged with assisting industry with its wartime development problems, to a laboratory with the freedom to explore areas in propulsion research that seemed to hold promise for the future. The following year, after the death of George W. Lewis, the laboratory became the Lewis Flight Propulsion Laboratory. Lewis's name, more than any other, had stood behind the NACA's reputation for basic research in the prewar period. He had guided its work from the 1920s through World War II, winning the backing of key members of Congress through the force of his personality and his single-minded dedication to the institution he served. He had taken an active part in every decision, never losing sight of the enabling legislation that had established the NACA: the duty "to supervise and direct the scientific study of the problems of flight with a view to their practical solution." Although his background was in engineering, his approach to the problems of aviation had been practical and down-to-earth. In his view, testing was the path to useful knowledge—the careful gathering and interpretation of data—to save industry designers unnecessary steps. Wind tunnels, not libraries, were where NACA staff did basic research. However, World War II and the turbojet revolution that George Lewis had only belatedly recognized had changed the practice of engineering. The dramatic breakthroughs of World War II in jet propulsion, nuclear fission, radar, and guided missiles increased the need for engineering more firmly grounded in science. The NACA's engineering traditions, nurtured by Lewis, would have to be leavened with a stronger dose of analytical talent.

NOTES

[1] *The Cleveland News,* 23 June 1945.

[2] Quotations from *Aviation News,* 25 June 1945, and *New York Mirror,* 24 June 1945. The articles were reproduced in *Wing Tips,* 18 July 1945.

[3] "Memorandum for Manager, Report of trip by C. T. Perin, January 19 to January 28, 1946," 18 February 1946, NASA Lewis Records, 34/200.

[4] Minutes of the Executive Committee, January–June 1944, National Archives, Record Group 255, Box 9.

[5] Alsos Mission Report, 4 March 1944, National Archives, Intelligence Division Alsos Mission File 1944–1945, Entry 187, Box 137. On the Alsos Mission, see Samuel A. Goudsmit, *Alsos* (Los Angeles: Tomash, History of Modern Physics Series, 1947); Clarence Lasby, *Project Paperclip: German Scientists and the Cold War* (New York: Atheneum, 1971); and Boris T. Pash, *The Alsos Mission* (New York: Award House, 1969). Less reliable are Tom Bowler, *The Paperclip Conspiracy: The Hunt for the Nazi Scientists* (Boston: Little, Brown, 1987); and Michel Bar-Zohar, *The Hunt for the German Scientists* (New York: Hawthorne, 1967).

[6] Russell Robinson to George Lewis, 14 May 1945, National Advisory Committee for Aeronautics 490, National Archives, Intelligence Division Alsos Mission File, 1944–1945, Entry 187, Box 138.

[7] Minutes of the Executive Committee, January–June 1945, National Archives, Record Group 255, Box 9.

[8] Kemper's Alsos reports are listed in the Langley file, although not all were obtainable through NASA Technical Services and may have been destroyed. The Langley file is an index of NACA reports kept at Langley Research Center and obtainable on microfilm at the Lewis Technical Library. To use it requires clearance. "Report upon the war work of the institute for the development of instruments and of the department for measuring instruments," by Kemper and Betz-Klein (Translation of a German report) 23 July 1946, 5301/174. "Inspection of the jet engine test stands and interrogation of the chief test pilot, Ing. Kuhn, at the Walter Werke, Keil," 27 July 1945, 7818, 01113, Walter/2. "Visit to dispersal plants of the Dornier Company at Brieurichshafen/Lowenthal, Ravensberg . . . ," 25 May 1945, KR/157. "Report on Luftfahrtforschungsanstalt, Munchen (LFW) . . . " 13 May 1945, KR/174. "Report on interrogation of Peter Dornier . . . ," 24 May 1945, KR/178. "Report on Flugtechnisches Institute of the Techn. Hochschule, Stuttgart . . . ," 26 May 1945. "Report on aircraft engines and jet propulsion research at Luftfahrtforschungsanstalt (LFA) Herman Goering," 22 June 1945, CK/215. "Report on inspection of mock-up Junkers 262 . . . " 22 June 1945, CK/212. "Interrogation of Ing. Hans Becker and inspection of the reciprocating engine research and test facilities of the Junkers Flugseug and Motoren-Werke, Dessau," 27 July 1945, CK/245. "Interrogation of Dr. Heinz Schmitt in charge of the jet engine research and development of the Junkers works at Dessau," 6 June 1945, CK/233. "Interrogation of Dr. Ing. Alfred Grumbt in charge of Flugs. Trauen and inspection of the laboratory equipment," 14 August 1945, CK/263. "Inspection of Daimler-Benz dispersal plant at Kulbermoor," 27 July 1945, CK/243. "German establishment for aerodynamic research on missiles; cover names Wasserbau Versuchsanstalt (WVA)," 23 May 1945, RK/180.

[9] Although this index is listed in Cunliffe and Godlbeck, "Special Study on the Records of the National Advisory Committee for Aeronautics," p. 35, it could not be located in National Archives, Record Group 255. See Lois Walker and Shelby Wickham, *From Huffman Prairie to the Moon* (Washington, D.C.: U.S. Government Printing Office, 1986), p. 169–170. Many of the reports prepared at Wright Field by the Material Command are still not available to historians. For example, I was unable to obtain the release of Fritz Zwicky's, "Report on Certain Phases of War Research in Germany," 1947, ADB-953510.

[10] See Russ Murray, "The Navaho Inheritance." *American Aviation Historical Society Journal* 19:17–21; Kenneth P. Werrell, "The Cruise Missile: Precursors and Problems." *Air University Review* 32:36–50. John Evvard to V. Dawson, 18 March 1985.

[11] Minutes of Special Meeting of Executive Committee, 18 May 1944, January–June 1944, National Archives, Record Group 255, Box 9.

[12] John Sloop, "NACA High Energy Rocket Propellant Research in the Fifties," AIAA 8th Annual Meeting, Washington, D.C., 28 October 1971. The reorganization occurred 1 October 1945.

[13] "A Survey of Fundamental Problems Requiring Research at the Aircraft Engine Research Laboratory," December 1945. NASA Lewis Records, 34/376.

[14] "A Survey of Fundamental Problems Requiring Research at the Aircraft Engine Research Laboratory," May 1946. NASA Lewis Records, 34/376.

[15] For text of "National Aeronautical Research Policy," see Alex Roland, *Model Research*, vol. 2, NASA SP-4103 (Washington, D.C.: U.S. Government Printing Office, 1985), p. 693–695.

[16] Bruce Hevly, "Basic Research Within a Military Context: The Naval Research Laboratory and the Foundations of Extreme Ultraviolet and X-Ray," Ph.D. Dissertation, The Johns Hopkins University, 1987. University Microfilms 8716611, p. 73. See also Paul Forman, "Behind Quantum Electronics: National Security as Basis for Physical Research in the United States, 1940–1960." *Historical Studies in the Physical and Biological Sciences* 18(1):149–229. For analysis of the contributions of JPL, see Clayton Koppes, *JPL and the American Space Program* (New Haven: Yale University Press, 1982).

[17] Vannevar Bush, *Endless Horizons* (Washington, D.C.: U.S. Government Printing Office, 1946), p. 52–53. Quoted in Edwin Layton, "Mirror-Image Twins: The Communities of Science and Technology in 19th-Century America." *Technology and Culture* 12:563.

[18] Power Plants Committee Minutes, 20 September 1945, National Archives, Record Group 255, 112.02.

[19] Ibid.

[20] Interview by V. Dawson with Abe Silverstein, 5 October 1984; letter from John Evvard to V. Dawson, February 1987.

[21] Interview with Walter Olson by V. Dawson, 16 July 1984.

[22] Interview with Carl David Miller (Cearcy D. Miller) by V. Dawson, 12 October 1984.

[23] Interview with Carl Schueller by V. Dawson, 12 October 1984.

[24] Minutes of High-Speed Panel, National Archives, Record Group 255, 111.52. Cleveland was not represented and did not receive copies of the minutes of the first meeting. Minutes of meetings between 1944 and 1947 are missing from National Archives, Record Group 255.

[25] Roland, *Model Research*, vol. 1, p. 211.

[26] Quoted by Roland, *Model Research*, vol. 1, p. 212.

[27] W. T. Bonney interview with Abe Silverstein, transcript, 20 September 1973.

[28] Transcript of interview with D. D. Wyatt by Eugene Emme, 21 June 1973, NASA History Office, Washington, D.C.

[29] Ibid.

[30] Ibid. Also interview with W. Olson, 16 July 1984. In *Engineer in Charge*, NASA SP-4305 (Washington, D.C.: U.S. Government Printing Office, 1987), James Hansen connected this visual, intuitive approach to design to a discussion by Eugene S. Ferguson in "The Mind's Eye: Nonverbal Thought in Technology." *Science* 197:836. Hansen's insightful discussions can be found principally on p. 311, 334–335, 341, and in note 2 (chapter 4), p. 526, and note 2 (chapter 11), p. 556.

[31] See Carlton Kemper to NACA, "Outline of research projects for the 18- by 18-inch and 20-inch supersonic tunnels at the Cleveland laboratory," 4 October 1946, 34/521, NASA Lewis Records. Lewis researchers also applied ramjet technology to the improvement of afterburners in turbojet engines. See Russ Murray, "The Navaho Inheritance." *American Aviation Historical Society Journal* 19:17–21; Kenneth P. Werrell, "The Cruise Missile: Precursors and Problems." *Air University Review* 32:36–50.

[32] Interview with D. D. Wyatt by Eugene Emme, 21 June 1973. On Busemann at Langley see Hansen, *Engineer in Charge*, p. 282, 285, and 322.

[33] Chief, BuAer to NACA, December 1944, National Archives, Record Group 255, 118.25.

[34] Interview with Paul Ordin by V. Dawson, 19 March 1986.

[35] John Sloop, *Liquid Hydrogen*, NASA SP-4404 (Washington, D.C.: U.S. Government Printing Office, 1978), p. 74.

[36] Ibid, p. 3.

[37] Transcript of interview by V. Dawson with Walter Olson, 16 July 1984, p. 38. Sloop, *Liquid Hydrogen*, p. 74.

[38] John Sloop, "NACA High Energy Rocket Propellant Research in the Fifties," AIAA 8th Annual Meeting, 28 October 1971, p. 2–3. This paper includes an inclusive bibliography of NACA/NASA Lewis research reports on rocket engines, 1948–1960.

[39] Sloop, *Liquid Hydrogen*, p. 74–75.

[40] On the work of Jacobs and Kantrowitz, see Hansen, *Engineer in Charge*, p. 39.

[41] Hicks and Simon to Acting Executive Engineer (Rothrock), "Nature of AERL Research on Nuclear Energy Fuels," 11 June 1945, 34/17112, NASA Lewis Records.

[42] John Evvard to Acting Engineer, "Points Which Might Be of Interest to You for Your Washington Discussions," 9 August 1945, 34/17112, NASA Lewis Records. See also J. F. Victory to Cleveland, "Utilization of Atomic Energy," 10 December 1945, 34/17112, NASA Lewis Records; J. R. Dietrich to Executive Engineer, "Atomic-Power Aircraft Engines," 7 August 1945, 34/17112, NASA Lewis Records.

[43] Cleveland to NACA, "Recommendations Concerning the Application of Nuclear Energy to Aircraft Power Plants," 24 May 1946, 34/17112, NASA Lewis Records.

[44] Robert Seldon to Manager, "Comments on Nuclear Energy Aircraft Propulsion Laboratory,"21 September 1946, 34/17112, NASA Lewis Records. Under NEPA, the Air Force studied both nuclear aircraft and rocket propulsion between 1946 and 1951 when NEPA was superseded by a joint program with the Atomic Energy Commission called the Aircraft Nuclear Propulsion Program (ANP). See Richard G. Hewlett and Francis Duncan, *Atomic Shield, 1947/1952*, vol. 2 of *A History of the United States Atomic Energy Commission* (University Park: Pennsylvania State University, 1969), p. 70–78. See also R. W. Bussard and R. D. DeLauer, *Fundamentals of Nuclear Flight* (New York: McGraw-Hill, 1965).

[45] E. R. Sharp to Director of Aeronautical Research, 29 October 1946, 34/376, NASA Lewis Records.

[46] A. Kalitinsky Memo, 1 October 1947, Transactions/Communications 63 A 250, National Archives, Record Group 255, Box 14, C-2-8. I have requested declassification of the Addison Rothrock files, Record Group 255, believed to contain detailed information on the NACA nuclear program.

[47] The proceedings of the conference were published by General Electric in *Aircraft Gas Turbine Engineering Conference*, 1945; the conference is also mentioned in Neville and Silsbee, *Jet Propulsion Progress*, p. 113.

[48] Abe Silverstein, "Investigations of Jet-Propulsion Engines in the NACA Altitude Wind Tunnel," in *Aircraft Gas Turbine Engineering Conference* (West Lynn, Mass.: General Electric Company, Limited edition, No. 538, 1945), p. 255–270.

[49] Interview with William Fleming by V. Dawson, 19 November 1986.

[50] Jerome Hunsaker, "Memorandum on Postwar Research Policy for NACA," full text in Roland, *Model Research*, vol. 2, appendix H, p. 684–686.

[51] " 'Notes on discussion at meeting of NACA,' July 27, 1944," 8 August 1944, in Roland, *Model Research*, vol. 2, appendix H, p. 689.

[52] *The Pratt & Whitney Aircraft Story* (West Hartford: Pratt & Whitney Aircraft Division of United Aircraft Corporation, 1950), p. 152.

[53] " 'Notes on discussion at meeting of NACA,' July 27, 1944," 8 August 1944 in Roland, *Model Research*, vol. 2, appendix H, p. 687.

[54] Ibid, p. 688.

[55] Ibid, p. 689.

[56] Cleveland Laboratory Staff, "Performance and Ranges of Application of Various Types of Aircraft-Propulsion System," Technical Note 1349, August 1947.

[57] Interview with Ben Pinkel by V. Dawson, 4 August 1985.

[58] This is evident in Eugene Manganiello, "Visit to Wright Field on February 20, 1946 in Connection with a Proposed Investigation of Composite Operation of the Pratt & Whitney R-4360 Engine," NASA Lewis Records. As late as 1948 the compound engine was considered an "outstanding development" in Neville and Silsbee, *Jet Propulsion Progress*, p. 101.

[59] See Michael S. Sherry, *Preparing for the Next War* (New Haven: Yale University Press, 1977), p. 128.

CHAPTER FIVE

NEW EDUCATIONAL DEMANDS

Although the NACA had very capable engineers, it had few men and women with advanced training in science and engineering. The disparity between the NACA professional staff, generally with undergraduate degrees in mechanical engineering, and the availability of superior research facilities had increased with the physical expansion of the NACA during World War II. The relatively low salaries paid to civil servants made it difficult to attract staff with advanced degrees in science and engineering, who found their skills in high demand after the war. Edwin P. Hartman, head of the NACA's Coordinating Office on the West Coast, wrote to headquarters to prod it to action. To Hartman, the construction of new facilities seemed profligate without a comparable effort to recruit scientific talent. "While spending millions of dollars and exerting the highest scientific skill in the design and construction of modern research facilities," Hartman stated, "the Committee appears penurious and juvenile in its apathetic efforts to provide research brains."[1]. Between 1945 and 1958 the NACA would struggle with the problem of recruiting highly trained individuals in a particular field and retaining its most experienced staff.

Hugh L. Dryden, named in 1947 to succeed George Lewis, symbolized the postwar effort on the part of the NACA to recruit outstanding scientific talent. He had formidable qualifications. After earning two Ph.D.'s at The Johns Hopkins University—one in physics in 1919 and the other in mathematics in 1920—he had spent the first 30 years of his career as head of the Aerodynamics Section of the National Bureau of Standards. He had published widely on boundary layer theory and wind tunnel turbulence. As one of the country's leading aerodynamicists, he had attended the Volta Congress on High-Speed Aeronautics in 1935 with Eastman Jacobs. During World War II he had been appointed to both the National Defense Research Committee (NDRC) and to William Durand's Special Committee on Jet Propulsion. Deputy to Theodore von Kármán on the Science Advisory Board's technical mission to Europe at the close of the war, he was well acquainted with the British and German contributions to basic research in high-speed aerodynamics and jet propulsion.[2]

Dryden shared Vannevar Bush's presumption that technology was applied science. Bush had emphatically stated in *Science, the Endless Frontier*: "*A nation which depends upon others for its new basic scientific knowledge will be slow in its industrial progress and weak in its competitive position in world trade, regardless of its mechanical skill.*"[3] This statement was made with the awareness of the enormous contributions of British and German theoreticians before World War II. It was this intellectual capital which Americans, in both universities and government laboratories, were beginning to tap in the postwar period. Dryden knew that it was not enough to live off European capital. The research laboratory provided Americans with the tools to contribute to the country's store of basic and applied science. Research was capital, a reserve, for the future. The integrity of the NACA laboratories had to be protected from undue influence from industry, whose drive for profits required them to focus on short-term problems. Dryden was a quiet, religious man who believed intensely that his job was to protect the creativity and independence of the NACA laboratories under his stewardship.

NACA Director Hugh L. Dryden succeeded the ailing George Lewis in 1947.

Dryden knew that, without highly trained staff, it would be difficult to continue the NACA's commitment "to supervise and direct the scientific study of the problems of flight with a view to their practical solution." Missile development, the atom bomb, and radar had created a new generation of scientists. It had brought into being new national laboratories, like Oak Ridge and Los Alamos, as well as the important university-affiliated laboratories—the Radiation Laboratory at the Massachusetts Institute of Technology and the Applied Physics Laboratory at The Johns Hopkins University. After World War II, many of the national laboratories began to lose staff, who were attracted to prestigious positions in universities or higher paying jobs in industry. With a national shortage of scientists and engineers, the NACA found it hard to compete. In the 1920s and 1930s the mystique of flight had attracted talented engineers. During the Depression the security of a civil service position gave the NACA the leverage to select the cream of its applicants. Neither aviation nor the civil service had the same appeal after the war.

Addison Rothrock and other NACA staff worried about the implications of these changes. In a 1946 memo Rothrock informed Sharp that the Ford Motor Company, Standard Oil of New Jersey, General Motors, DuPont, and other companies had announced large-scale expansion of their research facilities. Locally, entry-level salaries were comparable to those of Cleveland-area firms, such as Standard Oil of Ohio, Brush Development Company, Dupont, Thompson Products (later TRW), and the Weatherhead Company. However, these companies could offer appreciably better salaries to attract NACA engineers in the higher professional grades.[4] Between 1945 and 1956 this problem would plague their efforts to recruit and retain personnel. In 1951 John Victory submitted the first draft bill to the Bureau of Budget to alleviate this problem by exempting the NACA from some Civil Service regulations. The response of the Civil Service Commission was not sympathetic. It argued that the preferential treatment of the NACA would allow it to pirate personnel from industry and other agencies, a practice that might jeopardize the programs of the Department of Defense. In 1955 Dryden gained the support of the Industry Consulting Committee by pointing out that the staffing of NACA wind tunnels (completed under the Unitary Wind

Tunnels Plan) was inadequate because of the personnel ceiling fixed by Congress. In Dryden's view, however, the ceiling on salaries in the civil service categories was even more damaging to the NACA, which was losing key personnel and could not find replacements without salaries commensurate with those of industry. Not until 1956, as the NACA period was drawing to a close, would the NACA finally obtain legislation for competitive compensation.[5]

In the early postwar period the laboratory had to cope with this shortage of research brains by falling back on its own resources. Its strategy was to ferret out talent from within. The "big switch" of 1945 to research in jet propulsion hastened the exodus of experienced staff, but they were the very men who had been tied to the old piston engine technology. Because turbojet, nuclear, and rocket propulsion required the shaping of a new community of practice, the relative inexperience and youth of the remaining staff was an advantage. They were flexible and eager to prove themselves, and reorganization caught their imaginations. Walter Olson recalled, "A number of us did not think that we were even going to stay and work for the government. The war was over. What were we going to do now? But then we reorganized. You get a new responsibility and some new challenges and you say, 'Well, I will try that.' Next thing you know you've spent a lifetime."[6]

Jet propulsion represented an educational challenge. Surprisingly, in the early postwar years, the Case School of Applied Science, located on the east side of Cleveland about 20 miles from the laboratory, played only a minor role in the effort to prepare the staff for the new theoretical demands of jet propulsion. The reputation of Case (renamed Case Institute of Technology in 1947) had been one of the selling points in the NACA's acceptance of the Cleveland Chamber of Commerce invitation in 1940. However, unlike the close connection between the California Institute of Technology (CalTech) and the Jet Propulsion Laboratory, or the NACA Ames laboratory with Stanford University, the intended bonding between Case and Lewis Laboratory had only partial success. Work in aeronautics had begun auspiciously at Case in the 1930s under Paul E. Hemke, a Ph.D. from The Johns Hopkins University. He came to Cleveland from Langley after the unpleasant experience of attempting to work under the autocratic German theoretician Max Munk. During Hemke's tenure in Cleveland, Case had built a low-speed subsonic wind tunnel. In 1935 Hemke recruited John R. Weske to found a graduate program stressing fluid mechanics and aeronautics. Weske, a student of Lionel S. Marks at Harvard University, had worked with his professor to produce the first axial-flow compressor based on the isolated airfoil design theory, an approach that later came into standard use by American designers.[7] During World War II, Hemke left Case to found Rensselaer Polytechnic Institute's program in aeronautics and later became Dean of Faculty. Weske hung on at Case with minimal support for new facilities until 1944, when Case temporarily abandoned work in aeronautics because of the loss of students and faculty swept up by the draft or lured by new opportunities offered by the expansion of industry and government laboratories.

The Cleveland laboratory could not wait for Case to rebuild its aeronautics program. Within the Wind Tunnels and Flight Division, Abe Silverstein created a Special Projects Panel to attract badly needed analytical talent from other divisions. Although theoretical aerodynamics could not be strictly viewed as related to propulsion, Silverstein recognized that the problems of jet engines were also related to supersonic aerodynamics, where the design of the inlet was particularly susceptible to the special conditions created by flight at supersonic speeds. According to former staff member Eli Reshotko, who later joined the Case faculty, Silverstein strongly believed that, in addition to the more applied work, research at more fundamental levels ought to be supported.[8]

Silverstein asked John Evvard to head the Special Projects Panel because he was one of the few staff with an advanced degree in physics. Evvard had written his Ph.D. thesis at CalTech on ion bombardment using mass spectroscopy. Within the division, Silverstein organized study groups that met weekly, often on Sunday evenings. One group humorously called itself *Brutsag*, the reverse abbreviation of gas turbine. The other group claimed the name of *Cinosrepus*, or supersonics spelled backward. A staff member selected a research topic and reported to the others "so that he could bring the others up to the level that he had reached."[9]

Silverstein asked Evvard to begin his work in supersonics by preparing a report on Allen Puckett's linearized theory for three-dimensional supersonic wings. When Evvard objected that he did not know anything about supersonics, Silverstein replied that it was new to everyone else too. He handed Evvard a copy of Pucketts' paper as Evvard left for a laboratory-sponsored trip. Evvard read it on the plane. After the presentation of his report to the members of the Special Projects Panel, Evvard continued to think about Puckett's theory. It appeared to be superior to that of the German aerodynamicist Ackeret, who had dealt with two-dimensional wings at angle of attack. Puckett's supersonic wing theory allowed the wing to be contoured; it could have any plane shape, but required supersonic leading edges. Evvard thought that the theory could be extended to include wing tip regions with subsonic leading edges. He was able to set up an integral equation that greatly simplified the original theory. This paper established his reputation and was the foundation for the future work of Lewis Laboratory in supersonic aerodynamics. "After I came up with my wing tip theory for supersonic wings," Evvard recalled, "we mustered a sizeable effort in supersonic aerodynamics to capitalize on the breakthrough."[10]

Evvard's simple but elegant solution to the problem of thin, finite wings stimulated other members of the division. Wolfgang Moeckel, who later took charge of the Theoretical Section of the Supersonic Propulsion Division, tackled the design of a supersonic inlet. What was the best aerodynamic shape to ensure the smooth passage of air into the engine? He carefully studied the work of Herman Oswatitsch on the spike inlet before beginning his own work, which soon went beyond that of the Germans. In general, early supersonic work at Lewis Laboratory focused on various types of diffusers and the inlets for supersonic ramjets.[11] By 1947 the workers had developed from a group of novices in the field into a research team that made significant contributions to supersonic wing theory, despite complaints from Langley that the Cleveland laboratory should stick to propulsion.

In the late 1940s, through its own efforts, the laboratory had established a reputation in areas such as supersonic aerodynamics. In 1949 Evvard was able to persuade Franklin K. Moore to join his staff. Moore had worked at CalTech under William Sears, one of Theodore von Kármán's outstanding students. Moore's contributions to three-dimensional and unsteady boundary layer theory stimulated others to tackle theoretical problems. By the early 1950s, papers by Leroy Turner, Herbert Ribner, William Perl, Clarence B. Cohen, Wolfgang Moeckel, Harold Mirels, and others established Lewis Laboratory's reputation for basic work in supersonic aerodynamics.

The basic outlines of some fields necessary to advance engine development were only beginning to take shape in the 1940s. For example, tribology—the study of friction, lubrication, and wear—did not yet exist as an engineering discipline when Langley hired Edmond Bisson in 1939. Bisson moved with the Power Plants Division to Lewis Laboratory in 1943. During World War II, work focused on quick fixes for piston rings and cylinder barrels. However, in 1945 Bisson and his staff were able to turn to more fundamental problems. When the nature of the work began to change, some of his staff, hired during the war, lost interest and left the NACA. Bisson wanted research people for his division. It was not sufficient to solve friction problems, for example, simply by coating a surface and testing to see how it worked. He needed people who would ask, what is physically occurring when two metal surfaces, separated by a thin film, interact? His staff needed knowledge of boundary layer theory and chemistry to understand the problems of lubrication, friction, and wear. Most of the group who made the transition from the piston engine to the gas turbine engine had degrees in mechanical engineering. Bisson saw the need to make the Division of Lubrication, Friction, and Wear more interdisciplinary. He looked for people with different backgrounds in science, and he hired carefully.

> We usually had to get someone from another field and train him in our field: what we were doing, why we were doing it and what was involved technically. We were always looking for the creative types... My own philosophy was that you hire the creative people, the people who have inquisitive minds, and you encourage them to come up with ideas. You tell them, now here is the problem. Now what can we do to solve it?... Again the interdisciplinary concept was all important because we would kick around some of these ideas with [people with] different backgrounds and it is amazing what the comments would be from the other people and the contribution that the other people could give to such an idea... We had tremendous morale and tremendous output.[12]

John C. Evvard, appointed Chief of the Supersonic Propulsion Division in 1949, took charge of the Lewis Non-Credit Graduate Study Program.

Bisson's division had two branches, one for lubrication fundamentals headed by Robert L. Johnson and the other to study bearings and seals under William J. Anderson. They approached lubrication problems using both analysis and experiment. From the late 1940s through the 1960s, this division worked to establish the basic outlines of tribology. The publication of one of the first texts in the field, *Advanced Bearing Technology,* in 1965 by Bisson and Anderson marked tribology's coming of age as an engineering discipline.[13]

LEWIS LABORATORY AND CASE INSTITUTE OF TECHNOLOGY

Between 1946 and 1952, the very years that the new fields of supersonics and jet propulsion made the Cleveland laboratory's educational needs most pressing, the aeronautics program at

Case Institute of Technology languished without support for facilities or new faculty.[14] The "make-shift" equipment at Case stood in striking contrast to the impressive new facilities for research at Lewis Laboratory. In 1947, to compensate for the weakness of its program, Case offered evening extension courses leading to a masters degree. These courses were taught at Harding Junior High School in Lakewood, a suburb on Cleveland's west side close to the laboratory. This saved NACA employees the trip to the Case campus. The courses were taught by either laboratory personnel (who were designated as adjunct professors) or by Case faculty members. So highly regarded were these extension courses that some Case students were motivated to drive to the west side to attend. Research for masters theses (and in a few cases the doctoral dissertations) was done using the superior facilities that Lewis Laboratory could provide. Evening courses were offered on the Case campus in mathematical foundations of fluid mechanics, taught by one of the members of the mathematics department. Eugene Manganiello assumed a strong role in the organization and teaching of these courses. Manganiello had earned his bachelors degree in electrical engineering from the City College of New York (CCNY) in 1934 and his masters degree in 1935, at a time when the CCNY was extremely selective. He was typical of the bright and articulate engineering students from middle- and lower-income families that the NACA attracted in the late 1930s.

The inadequacies of the Case offerings in aeronautics were not unusual by American standards. In contrast to German technical institutes, only a handful of American universities offered formal courses in either aircraft gas turbine technology or supersonics during World War II. Suitable English texts for these subjects were not available until the late 1940s. *Introduction to Aerodynamics of a Compressible Fluid* by W. H. Liepmann and A. E. Puckett was published in 1947, about the time that courses in supersonics in a few universities (like CalTech) began to be offered. For the study of gas turbine technology, Aurel Stodola's *Steam and Gas Turbines*, published in translation in 1927 and reprinted many times up to 1945, was all that was available. This was a comprehensive work on all facets of steam turbine technology; it included some theoretical discussion of the subject, but focused on turbines made by specific companies in the field. The section on gas turbines was short because of the lack of interest at the time the book was written. Despite its limitations, before 1948, when the *Principles of Jet Propulsion and Gas Turbines* by M. J. Zucrow of Purdue University filled this gap, Stodola was a basic reference for engineers. Abe Silverstein recalled studying Stodola, and a well-thumbed copy of this two-volume work in the laboratory library attests to its usefulness to the first generation of jet propulsion students. They taught themselves what they needed to know.

The continuing national shortage of engineers in the early 1950s tantalized Case Institute of Technology with the promise of new opportunities in graduate education. Case had a solid undergraduate program in engineering, but to become a first-rate engineering institution, it needed to strengthen its graduate offerings. This new direction affected its relationship with Lewis Laboratory. In 1947 the university trustees chose T. Keith Glennan to take the reins of the presidency. From humble origins, Glennan had a solid engineering and business background. The son of a train dispatcher, Glennan attended elementary, high school, and college at the state normal school in Eau Clair, Wisc. With the railroad in his blood, he aspired to a career as a railroad electrical engineer. He transferred to the Sheffield Scientific School at Yale University, where he married the daughter of a well-known professor of economics. After graduation *cum laude* in 1927, Glennan worked for the motion picture industry for ten years as an operations and studio manager. During World War II, he concentrated on the development of sonar as head of the

Underwater Sound Laboratory at New London, Conn., operated by Columbia University for the Office of Scientific Research and Development.[15]

Glennan's presidency transformed Case from a small regional technical school focused on undergraduate training to a major engineering institution with strong graduate programs. He set in motion plans to overhaul the engineering curriculum and sparked a drive for faculty that ended in a 60 percent increase. Hard driving, gregarious, with a retentive memory for facts and figures, he raised $40 million for ten additional academic buildings, as well as additional dormitories.[16] Glennan's vision included a strong program in the humanities to supplement the more narrow engineering disciplines. He supported interdisciplinary programs, including graduate programs in the history of science and the history of technology, and the founding of the journal *Technology and Culture* by former Case professor Melvin Kranzberg. To attract an impressive faculty for these programs, he won a substantial grant from the Ford Foundation.

In 1950 Glennan recruited Ray Bolz from Lewis Laboratory to head an Aeronautics Division to be set up within the Department of Mechanical Engineering. A graduate of Case, Bolz had begun his career with the NACA in 1940, first at Langley and later in Cleveland. In 1946 he enrolled in the Ph.D. program at Yale University. He taught under Hemke at Rensselaer while he was completing his dissertation. Bolz was the first of several Lewis staff to be drawn to the Case faculty, a group that included Louis Green, Paul Guenther, Stan Manson, Alexander Mendelssohn, Harry Mergler, Simon Ostrach, and Eli Reshotko. The presence of the NACA laboratory in Cleveland thus contributed to raising Case's standards and reputation in aeronautics. By 1950, Case had awarded 25 degrees to Lewis employees, and Lewis had provided employment for 150 graduates of Case.

In 1951, to upgrade the graduate program in aircraft propulsion, aerodynamics, and general fluid mechanics, Bolz and others at Case decided that their program could not depend on part-time students, provided to a large extent by the NACA.[17] Bolz worked to build a resident program centered on the Case campus with full-time faculty teaching full-time students. Requirements for the Ph.D. were to include one year of residency.

To continue to teach extension courses on the west side would have divided the efforts of the small faculty, since any course would have to be taught twice. The Case faculty in charge of planning the new propulsion curriculum criticized the past practice of using Lewis Laboratory personnel to teach courses: "The men teaching were competent, but full-time research jobs left little time for development of good graduate courses."[18] This statement requires some scrutiny. Evvard, a Ph.D. from CalTech, for example, had credentials equal or superior to those of the Case faculty. Lewis Laboratory personnel could teach the new principles of jet propulsion with the benefit of specialized knowledge acquired through the study of theory and experimentally in the laboratory's wind tunnels. NACA engineers and scientists had studied the German documents available through Wright Field, and they had the benefit of interaction with the German pioneers of the caliber of Hans von Ohain and Anselm Franz. In contrast to this large and supportive engineering community at Lewis Laboratory, in 1952 Case had an Aero Division that consisted of only three full-time faculty members. Facilities for research were also lacking until the late 1950s, when Case completed a Jet Propulsion Laboratory.

Although it wanted to drop the west side extension courses, Case hoped to keep its talented pool of part-time students from Lewis Laboratory. It instituted a program of late afternoon classes on the Case campus that full-time resident students, as well as NACA, Thompson Products, and other industry employees could attend after work. The laboratory personnel who had previously taught the extension courses turned over their lecture notes and course outlines to the Case faculty. The end of their formal connection with Case, in Eugene Manganiello's view, marked the end of the school's dependence on the NACA for the most advanced knowledge in the field. "This is an example where the schools, partially because of the national security restrictions, were unable to keep pace with a rapidly advancing technology. Our efforts in this regard were designed to assist the college until such time as it was able to incorporate this advanced material into its own curriculum."[19]

On a graduate level, Case now could offer five courses in incompressible, compressible, and viscous flow theory; three aircraft propulsion courses: aircraft propulsion principles, compressor and turbine theory, and advanced gas turbine power plant design; and one course on the dynamics of aircraft and missiles.[20] The new arrangement meant that Lewis employees now had a 45-minute commute after a day of work. Although some laboratory personnel did make the journey to the Case campus to complete their degrees, the new, more stringent Case policies had the effect of encouraging Lewis personnel to look to more prestigious institutions when they considered graduate work. When a division head encouraged a staff member to go to graduate school, he (or, in very rare cases, she) often passed over Case in favor of Brown, Columbia, CalTech, Rensselaer, Cornell, the Massachusetts Institute of Technology, or Cambridge University in England to spend the required year of residency. They brought the benefits of contact with faculty in these schools back to Lewis Laboratory.

The first engineers to seek advanced training did not receive any financial support from the NACA. They took leaves of absence and paid their tuition out-of-pocket, with the expectation of a higher civil service grade when they returned. In 1950, with the passage of the NACA-Graduate Study Leave Act, it was possible to partially compensate employees for their loss of salary. However, tuition still had to be paid by the employee. In the first year the act went into effect, the laboratory had a training budget of $10,000 for seven participants. By 1958 it had 51 participants and a budget of $31,000. Other personnel took graduate courses at their own expense. During the same period the Department of Defense could offer much more generous financing for the training of its scientists and engineers. The laboratory had to wait until Sputnik forced the passage of the government Employees Training Act in July 1958. This act provided a uniform government-wide training program. Only then was it possible to cover all the expenses of graduate education for Lewis employees.[21]

When Case discontinued its extension courses on the west side, Lewis formalized the seminar approach practiced since the days of *Brutsag* and *Cinosrepus*. It began a program of free, non-credit, in-house courses. These courses had the advantage of focusing on areas related to general aspects of current work at the laboratory. They fostered communication among divisions, thus strengthening an interdisciplinary approach to common problems. "Courses taught at the Lewis Center," Manganiello pointed out, "also offered an excellent means of communicating advanced concepts developed by one particular research group to others whose research activities were in broadly related fields."[22].

In its first year the course attracted 150 employees. John Evvard took charge of the curriculum. In 1951 the laboratory offered courses on heat transfer, taught by Robert Deissler and Simon Ostrach, who later joined the Case faculty. John Livingood, a Ph.D. from the University of Pennsylvania, taught mathematical analysis. Dr. Robert B. Spooner's course in theoretical physics, originally a Case course, also became part of the non-credit offerings. Members of the staff of the Compressor and Turbine Division used a team approach in their courses in that subject, and chemical background for combustion research was taught by members of the Fuels and Thermodynamics Division. With weekly meetings of two hours, one on the employee's own time, the courses were regarded as an important supplement to the experimental work of the laboratory. They were rigorous, with required mid-term and final exams.[23]

The imprimatur of an advanced degree did not necessarily guarantee that a particular individual could be useful to the laboratory. As Walter Olson, then chief of the Combustion Branch, explained, "A professor nurtured in academia would likely not have encountered and diagnosed the physical problems involved in the new types of propulsion systems."[24] Educated at Case at the end of the Depression, Olson had gone to work for Lubrizol, a Cleveland-based company that made oil additives. Since much of the Lubrizol research was being carried on at Case in Carl Prutton's laboratory, Olson remained at Case to earn his Ph.D. in chemistry and chemical engineering in 1941. He was well acquainted with the pace and prerogatives of academe. When he looked back on the engine situation after World War II, he explained that a formal degree program did not always meet the needs of those who were deeply immersed in the perplexing problems of jet propulsion. His remarks highlight the sense of urgency and impatience to get results in the Cold War atmosphere of the late 1940s. National security concerns shaped the research programs of government laboratories. "We were trying to get into specialties fast. We needed to get out to the cutting edge and sometimes it was more useful to bring in a specialist in a particular field."[25]

ERNST ECKERT AND THE HEAT TRANSFER FRONTIER

Ernst Eckert was just such a specialist in heat transfer—a scientist who had worked at the Luftfahrtforschungsanstalt (LFA), the German laboratory for basic research at Braunschweig during World War II. Presented with the opportunity to bring him to Lewis Laboratory, Abe Silverstein, the laboratory's new Chief of Research, lost no time in seizing it. Eckert accepted a generous offer from the NACA and left Wright Field for Cleveland in 1949. He brought to Lewis Laboratory knowledge and experience of basic work in Germany in jet propulsion and, more important, a new approach to the problems of heat transfer. It was through his role as a teacher at the laboratory and later at the University of Minnesota that Eckert personally reinforced the American synthesis of advanced German work in heat transfer begun by Wilhelm Nusselt and his successor, Ernst Schmidt, at the University of Munich.[26]

By training and experience, Eckert's background contrasted with that of his American colleagues, who struggled to find ways to acquire advanced training comparable to that available in Germany before World War II. He completed a Ph.D. in mechanical engineering at the German Institute of Technology in Prague in 1931. Intrigued by photographs of turbulence and separation of flow of heat, in 1934 he chanced upon *Abriss der Strömungslehre*, Ludwig Prandtl's introduction to fluid mechanics. This was a turning point in his intellectual development. It required a leap of the imagination to see that Prandtl's boundary layer theory could be applied not only to the flow of air over the wing of an airplane but also to the complex processes involved in the transfer of heat. After study with the well-known expert in radiative heat transfer, Ernst Schmidt, at the Institute of Technology in Danzig, in 1937 Eckert followed Schmidt to Braunschweig, where Schmidt was head of engine research.

In Germany basic and applied research were kept physically separate. Applied research was carried on near Berlin at the Deutsche Versuchsanstalt für Luftfahrt (DVL). The concentration of more basic research at Braunschweig allowed considerable interaction between theoreticians involved in engine research and those in other disciplines, particularly fluid mechanics. In contrast, the NACA had isolated its engine research at one location, preventing the fruitful exchanges with aerodynamicists that Eckert had enjoyed at Braunschweig. Adolf Busemann, Herman Schlichting, and Ludwig Prandtl (at nearby Goettingen) were his colleagues. These associations reinforced his awareness of the importance of fluid mechanics in the study of heat transfer. His book, *Wärme und Stoffaustausch,* applied Prandtl's boundary layer concept to heat transfer problems; it was not published in 1944 as he had expected, because Allied bombing repeatedly destroyed the plates for the book. In 1940, almost immediately after Hans von Ohain had demonstrated the feasibility of jet propulsion, Eckert's Division of Thermodynamics dropped piston engine research and began to focus on the problems of turbojet engines. Through his research using an optical instrument developed in the late 19th century—the Mach-Zehnder interferometer—to study heat transfer, Eckert began to lay the theoretical basis for turbine cooling.[27]

"We are trying to get into specialties fast," declared Walter T. Olson, Chief of the Combustion and Fuels Division.

Eckert was among the 260 scientists and engineers invited by the Army Air Forces to come to the United States under "Operation Paperclip" in 1945.[28] At Wright Field Eckert joined Hans von Ohain, Theodor Zobel, Anselm Franz, Helmut Schelp, Alexander Lippisch, Eugen Ryschkewitsch, and others who had been doing advanced work in high-speed aerodynamics and jet propulsion in Germany. At the expiration of his one-year contract with the Army in 1946, it was renewed for an additional five years.

Because Eckert was the first to recognize the usefulness of the Mach-Zehnder interferometer for basic studies of heat transfer, he was anxious to have one built at Wright Field so that he could continue work begun in Germany.[29] The success of the American-built interferometer made it a model for other interferometers at universities such as Rutgers, Ohio State, and the University of California at Berkeley in the late 1940s.

The Air Force appears to have viewed Eckert as too valuable to lose prematurely to a university. Eckert was denied permission to join L. M. K. Boelter's heat transfer group at the University of California at Los Angeles.[30] However, the Air Force had a keen interest in assisting the research in jet propulsion in Cleveland, and with the funds for expensive experimental apparatus more available to the NACA than the Power Plants Laboratory at Wright Field, Eckert was allowed to become a consultant for the Cleveland laboratory. He was assigned to the Turbine Cooling Branch under Herman Ellerbrock to complete the last two years of his contract. Eckert's presence stimulated the group in turbine cooling to move beyond the foundations of heat transfer laid by W. H. McAdams in his book *Heat Transmission,* published in 1933.[31]

When the laboratory embarked on a study of the solid and air-cooled turbine blades of the Junkers Jumo 004, Eckert pointed out the limitations of Franz's method of internal air cooling. Heat had to penetrate the metal blade to reach to cooling air in the interior, a slow and inefficient process. He encouraged the laboratory to consider other methods of turbine cooling. At Braunschweig he had begun to explore potentially more effective approaches like transpiration, film, and natural convection liquid cooling. At Lewis Laboratory he continued this work. "I developed, together with members of the Turbine Cooling Branch [at Lewis], the theory of these cooling methods by analysis and furthered their development by experiments."[32] Film cooling, now in general use, particularly attracted him, and he spent much of his time advocating further basic research on this method. While at Lewis Laboratory, he also worked out the theories for transpiration cooling and natural convection liquid cooling. He had begun to experiment with various methods of applying these new theories.[33]

ADVOCACY OF BASIC RESEARCH

Eckert's efforts to turn the opinion of the Viscous Flow Panel in favor of basic research were only partly successful. He suggested that more precise values of Prandtl numbers were necessary for high-temperature investigations and proposed a method to measure these numbers based on work he had done at Braunschweig. In a memo prepared for the panel, he suggested that a test set-up, based on the analytical relation for a flat plate, could use a cylinder to investigate the temperature relations in the gas flow. After considerable discussion, the panel agreed that Eckert's proposal demonstrated a "pressing" need, but recommended that this research be undertaken by a university.[34] Exactly why Eckert failed to receive support for this basic work is unclear, but it appears that Lewis's leadership was skeptical that research at such a fundamental level would yield tangible results.

Eckert chafed at the emphasis on applications at Lewis Laboratory. Unlike the clear-cut German organization of research, which kept basic research and applications separate, at Lewis there was a shifting, never quite defined, line between them. Those who practiced on the most analytic levels were never allowed to lose sight of the connection of their research to the improvement of American engine technology. The organizational structure, which usually included fundamental and applied branches within divisions, reflected this supposition.

Testing of full-scale turbojet engines was, in Eckert's view, less valuable than work on isolated problems using scale models of components. He advocated a careful, systematic approach, working from simple to more complex experimental rigs. Eckert viewed Silverstein as a man "too eager for quick results, and not patient or meticulous enough" to allow research to proceed in a careful and rational manner from simple turbine wheels consisting of one stage, through models of several stages up to full-scale testing.[35] Silverstein was willing to skip steps to reach the hardware stage, where full-scale testing took over. He could never see research as an end in itself. Eckert did not feel that the role of a research laboratory was to design engines or components. Although Eckert was allowed to set his own research agenda, he did not have an entirely free hand. He was frustrated in his desire to address the entire range of basic heat transfer problems. For example, Eckert could not work on the problem of aerodynamic heating, an interest that he had developed at Braunschweig in connection with the supersonic flight of the V-2.

Silverstein appears to have preferred Eckert to work on calculations, rather than build expensive experimental apparatus, although he did authorize the construction of several large turbine wheels for Eckert to continue his work on natural convection liquid cooling after Eckert had

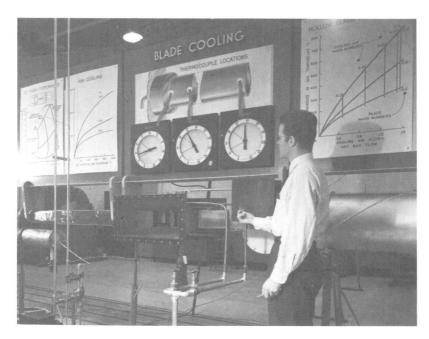

An engineer explains apparatus for studying how to air cool hollow turbine blades, 1946.

Test rig to study film cooling in the rocket laboratory, 1952.

worked out the theory with a Lewis mathematician, Thomas W. Jackson. Why a Mach-Zehnder interferometer for heat transfer studies was not built at Lewis Laboratory is not entirely clear, but it seems that Eckert's personal research interests were viewed by Silverstein as subordinate to his role as mentor to the capable, but not as highly trained staff at Lewis. Robert Deissler, a quiet giant in the heat transfer field who spent his professional career at Lewis, recalled Eckert's helpful attitude and his ability as a teacher to make extremely complex subjects appear simple.[36] George Low, later Deputy Administrator of NASA, worked with Eckert on a heat transfer problem in connection with the design of nuclear reactors.[37]

Eckert stimulated the work of others both directly through work on specific problems and through his course in heat transfer. He used his text, *Introduction to the Transfer of Heat and Mass*, translated at Wright Field with the help of Robert Drake, to teach a seminar in heat transfer.[38] After Eckert left in 1952, his book continued to serve as a text for courses in heat transfer.

Why Eckert did not press to have a Mach-Zehnder interferometer built for heat transfer studies at Lewis is not clear, but it seems that Eckert's energies were directed toward fostering analytical talent. Members of the Instruments Division built an interferometer for studies in supersonic aerodynamics, but Eckert had no contact with this work. Donald R. Buchele and Walton Howes recalled that they used the early papers of H. Shardin as a guide in building their first interferometer. By the time they could take advantage of the presence of Eckert and Zobel at Wright Field, they had perfected their instrument to a point that rivaled Zobel's German-built interferometer.[39]

Eckert's impatience with the applied emphasis of the laboratory, his interest in teaching, and his desire to see the field of heat transfer established as a coherent body of knowledge pulled him toward university research. When he left Lewis in 1952, after turning down an offer of an endowed professorship at Case, he established his own heat transfer laboratory at the University of Minnesota. There he built his second Mach-Zehnder interferometer.

Although his tenure at the laboratory was brief, Eckert's association laid the foundation for an extremely creative and productive group in the field of heat transfer. By the 1960s German work in heat transfer had become integrated into the general curricula of the best schools. When the strength of the heat transfer group at Lewis Laboratory was at its height, graduate schools like the Massachusetts Institute of Technology, Cornell, and Purdue had active programs in heat transfer, and Lewis staff were recruited from these programs. Robert Siegel, for example, worked under Warren Rohsenow at the Massachusetts Institute of Technology. He wrote, with John Howell, *Thermal Radiation and Heat Transfer;* this basic text, now in its second printing, has been translated into twelve languages.

In terms of basic research, the heat transfer group seems to have come close to the Braunschweig model. Robert Deissler recalled that it remained the philosophy of the group in fundamental heat transfer that problems should be "approached in such a way that results might have some lasting value, independent of a particular application." Although the group took up problems that could apply to aircraft nuclear propulsion, "the fact that nuclear propulsion never quite materialized as a viable scheme did not lessen the value of the research, which aided in understanding heat transfer in a variety of situations."[40] The Analytical Section at Lewis Laboratory became a center for basic research on the problems of radiation, convection, and conduction, a distinction it held until the early 1970s, when government support was drastically reduced.[41]

"HELL, MAN, WE'RE NOT INTERESTED IN HOME HEATING!"

Simon Ostrach's career at Lewis sheds light on how the laboratory encouraged basic research within an institutional framework whose main focus was the improvement of turbojet engines. Ostrach graduated from the University of Rhode Island with a degree in mechanical engineering in 1944. At Lewis Laboratory he went to work under John Sanders to find quick fixes for the burned-out pistons of the Pratt & Whitney R-2800 and the exhaust valves of the Wright R-3350. William Perl, a theoretical aerodynamicist who transferred from Langley in 1944, was the laboratory's "resident genius." He served as the role model for aspiring theorists like Ostrach. Perl had designed one of the early supersonic duct tunnels at the laboratory. In 1946 he took a leave of absence to study under Theodor von Kármán at CalTech. By chance, Alexander Mendelssohn, a branch chief, noticed his analytical ability. In 1947 Sanders suggested that Ostrach get a Ph.D.

Ostrach went to Brown University to study in the Graduate Division of Applied Mathematics, at that time one of the outstanding programs in the country. George F. Carrier was his thesis advisor and mentor. He studied fluid mechanics under Sydney Goldstein, C.C. Lin, and Wallace D. Hayes. Ostrach recalled that his professors rejected one thesis topic after another until he heard about the thesis topic of a fellow student: the problem of gas bubbles dispersed throughout a solid material. It was a problem in heat transfer by natural convection, an individual bubble treated as a horizontal cylinder of circular cross-section and infinite length. Ostrach suggested a second approach to the problem, allowing him to treat it as a boundary layer problem. This appealed to his professors because boundary layer theory was only beginning to be applied in the study of heat transfer.[42] Ostrach completed his thesis, "A Boundary Layer Problem in the Theory of Free Convection," in 1950.

After graduation he was offered an assistantship at Harvard University, but the salary was low. Abe Silverstein promised him a double jump in civil service professional grade if he would come back to Lewis Laboratory. Ostrach was assigned to work under John Evvard, who informed him that workers with doctoral degrees were expected to produce 2.34 reports per year, which filled Ostrach with trepidation. Evvard gave Ostrach permission to work on buoyancy flows, still virgin territory for theoretical investigation in the United States. He decided to simplify the problem he had tackled in his thesis by examining free convection about a vertical flat plate. He solved the problem deductively with the help of a colleague from another division, Lynn U. Albers, using a Card Programmed Electronic Calculator.

At one of the periodic research reviews, Ostrach presented a summary of his flat-plate theory; Silverstein exploded, "Hell, man, we're not interested in home heating!" Evvard was hardly more sympathetic. He never missed the opportunity to scoff good naturedly that Ostrach was "becoming the world's expert in a field in which no one was interested."[43] Fortunately, Eckert was making his weekly visits to Lewis Laboratory at this time. Eckert encouraged Ostrach to continue. He told him that Ernst Schmidt and W. Beckmann had solved the identical problem in 1930! Ostrach needed a justification for his work, and Eckert may have told him that Ernst Schmidt had used natural convection to circulate a fluid to cool turbine blades. Ostrach began to refer to the paper he was preparing as "natural convection parallel to a generating body force" to imply a relationship to turbine cooling. "But anyhow," Ostrach recalled, "I started making all this noise about the importance of it, and I tried like hell to justify it."[44] Shortly afterward, the American Society of Mechanical Engineers (ASME) accepted Ostrach's paper describing work on buoyancy flows. Coincidentally, Ernst Schmidt, then on a visit to the United States, planned to attend the meeting. Eckert asked Ostrach to accompany Schmidt on the train from Cleveland to Chicago. Ostrach described his work and gave Schmidt a copy of his paper, not knowing what to expect. After Ostrach's presentation, Schmidt rose and introduced himself as a "pioneer in this field." He commented on the soundness of Ostrach's calculations and his approach to the problem. The Chicago meeting, Ostrach recalled, was the "beginning of a long, friendly, and stimulating relationship between us."[45]

Fortunately, Ostrach found another justification for his work when Ben Pinkel flagged him down for a ride on his way to the laboratory when Pinkel had a flat tire. Since Pinkel knew that Ostrach was working on heat transfer problems, he invited Ostrach to attend a meeting with Admiral Hyman Rickover. Rickover described how the early sodium-cooled nuclear reactor for submarines produced greater heat transfer in the control rods than they had expected. Thinking over the problem, Ostrach suggested that natural convection could be the cause. "I was told, in no uncertain terms, that that could not be the case since natural convection was an innocuous process and could not possibly result in such large heat transfer."[46] Knolls Atomic Power Laboratory later verified Ostrach's prediction. Rickover's reactor problem provided Ostrach with material for his next paper, "Laminar Natural-Convection Flow and Heat Transfer of Fluids With and Without Heat Sources in Channels with Constant Wall Temperatures."[47]

Few people were interested in natural convection in the early 1950s. However, Ephraim M. Sparrow, a young Harvard University student working at the Raytheon Corporation, had noticed some of Ostrach's papers and wrote that he was interested in verifying some of his solutions experimentally. Ostrach encouraged him to come to Lewis Laboratory to work with him. Sparrow returned to Harvard for a Ph.D. and later joined Eckert and another former Lewis colleague, Perry Blackshear, at the University of Minnesota.

In the mid-1950s Silverstein created the Applied Mechanics Group within Evvard's division. This group consisted of Ostrach, Steven Maslen, Franklin Moore, and Harold Mirels, who shared the same office. Moore and Ostrach contributed to three-dimensional, unsteady boundary layer theory. Mirels and Maslen focused on acoustic screaming. In 1987 all four had achieved the highest professional distinction conferred on an engineer, membership in the National Academy of Engineering.[48]

Although they were generally left alone to pursue their own work, from time to time Abe Silverstein would call on his "academicians" to tackle a problem related to the real world of engines, where problems were still generally approached empirically. For example, in the late 1950s research had turned to helicopter ramjets.

> So, of course, the first thing that they did was build them. And they were having a lot of trouble with them. Frank [Moore] and I asked for a briefing or something. We asked what was the problem? They answered that they were getting very bad combustion. So Frank and I went back (it was primarily I, because I was looking for justification for doing these buoyancy kind of flows) . . . and we showed that the flow would break up in these big vortices. It is most likely the finest piece of work that Frank and I did, but I don't think that anybody knows about it. And shortly thereafter they stopped building those helicopter ramjets for a long period of time.[49]

It is doubtful that the theoretical work of the Special Projects Panel, the Applied Mechanics Group, and the Heat Transfer Group had a great impact on the work of the laboratory as a whole. Commitment to basic research was probably never more than 5 to 10 percent of the laboratory's resources.[50] Relative to the costs of testing, which took a lion's share of the laboratory's budget, it was not expensive. A room, a pencil, a slide rule, and computing facilities, when available, were often all that basic research required.

The influence of these men lay outside the laboratory through their NACA reports and papers in the *Transactions of the ASME*. Their presence at the laboratory was due in no small measure to Abe Silverstein's commitment to basic research. Like Dryden and Vannevar Bush, he believed that basic research was the nation's technical capital. Although Silverstein was more comfortable with creativity expressed in tangible objects—a new compressor or afterburner—he usually recognized the value of the theoretical contributions of people like Ostrach. A new theory was like a new piece of hardware, something on the shelf, ready if it was needed in the future.

> Our function is to lead the military services into the most favorable set of actions that we can. They're always interested in an airplane that will fly faster, farther, higher. And they are always looking for this, and they come initially to you to see whether you have something in your pocket now that you have created that would make something possible that wasn't possible before.[51]

The significance of the laboratory's theoreticians in the history of the laboratory does not lie in what they contributed to on-going work. During this period the bread and butter of the laboratory still remained full-scale testing of turbojet engines and components. Rather, what the laboratory provided to young theoreticians at a formative time in their careers was incentive to continue their educations and a nurturing environment for creative work. They stimulated each other. Beyond the publication of their papers and the recognition of their engineering peers, they were free from the demands of teaching or tangible product. Their theoretical skills were complemented by comparable mechanical ingenuity on the part of the laboratory's support services personnel. They could build a small supersonic tunnel or a test rig, or modify a computer to test their results experimentally. They were at Lewis Laboratory at a time when engineering was becoming more scientific. Ernst Eckert had modestly written in the preface to his important text, "It is the opinion of the author that a physical process is understood thoroughly only where it is possible to calculate the occurrences from basic knowledge and when these calculated results are checked by experiments."[52] American engineers did not yet have sufficient theoretical tools to understand what happens inside engines as predictable physical processes. Innovation in gas turbine engines in the 1950s still came more from systematic testing of full-scale engines than the theoretical approach of Lewis Laboratory's academicians.

NOTES

[1] Edwin P. Hartman to R. G. Robinson, "NACA Personnel Program," 6 May 1946, NASA Lewis Records, Box 34, file 200. The problem of a shortage of engineers between 1949 and 1955 is documented in Paul Forman, "Behind Quantum Electronics: National Security as Basis for Physical Research in the United States, 1940-1960." *Historical Studies in the Physical and Biological Sciences*, vol. 18, part 1, p. 166-167.

[2] See discussion of NACA's effort to strengthen science influence in Arthur L. Levine, "United States Aeronautical Research Policy, 1945-1958: A Study of the Major Policy Decisions of the National Advisory Committee for Aeronautics," Ph.D. Dissertation, Columbia University, 1963, p. 92-103. For biographical information on Dryden, see Alex Roland, *Model Research*, NASA SP-4103 (Washington, D.C.: U.S. Government Printing Office, 1985), vol. 1, p. 225-226.

[3] Quoted by Edwin T. Layton, Jr., "American Ideologies of Science and Engineering." *Technology and Culture* 17:689.

[4] Addison Rothrock to Manager, "Comparison of Professional Salaries at Cleveland Laboratory of NACA with Corresponding Industrial Salaries," 12 February 1946, NASA Lewis Records 34/200. "Memorandum for Manager, Report of Trip by C. T. Perin, January 19 to January 28, 1946," 18 February 1946, PB 34/200. See also Robert Seldon for Manager, "Comments on Nuclear Energy Aircraft Propulsion Laboratory," 21 September 1946, NASA Lewis Records, Box 34. Overall, national laboratories lost nearly 20 percent of their staffs. See Clarence Lasby, *Project Paperclip: German Scientists and the Cold War* (New York: Atheneum, 1971), p. 150 and note 8, p. 308.

[5] Documents describing the effort for legislation for Competitive Compensation Proposals can be found in a carton designated "NACA Documents 1913-1960," located in the NASA History Office, Washington, D.C.

[6] Interview with Walter Olson, 16 July 1984. I am indebted to Edward Constant, *The Origins of the Turbojet Revolution* (Baltimore: The Johns Hopkins University Press, 1980) for defining an engineering "community of practice," and for calling attention to the discontinuity between the piston engine and turbojet engine communities.

[7] Brian J. Nichelson, "Early Jet Engines and the Transition from Centrifugal to Axial Compressors: A Case Study in Technological Change," Ph.D. Dissertation, University of Minnesota, 1988. On Hemke, see James R. Hansen, *Engineer in Charge* NASA SP-4305 (Washington, D.C.: U.S Government Printing Office, 1987) p. 93.

[8] Eli Reshotko, telephone interview, 30 January 1987.

[9] Interview with Abe Silverstein, 5 October 1984. Interview with Irving Pinkel, 30 January 1985.

[10] Letter from John Evvard to V. Dawson, 18 March 1985. See John C. Evvard, "Distribution of Wave Drag and Lift in the Vicinity of Wing Tips at Supersonic Speeds," NACA TN 1382, 1947, and "Use of Source Distributions for Evaluating Theoretical Aerodynamics of Thin Finite Wings at Supersonic Speeds," NACA TR 951, 1950. See also Allen E. Puckett, "Supersonic Wave Drag of Thin Airfoils." *J. Aero. Sci.* 13:475-84 and papers by Lewis personnel L. Turner, Clarence B. Cohen, Wolfgang Moeckel, and Harold Mirels, among others

[11] Carlton Kemper to NACA, "Outline of Research Projects for the 18- by 18-inch and 20-inch Supersonic Tunnels at the Cleveland Laboratory," 4 October 1946, NASA Lewis Records.

[12] Interview with Edmond E. Bisson by V. Dawson, 22 March 1985. See also *Tribology in the 80s*, NASA Conference Publication 2300, 1984

[13] Edmond E. Bisson, *Advanced Bearing Technology*, NASA SP-38, (Washington, D.C.: U.S. Government Printing Office, 1965). For a detailed description of Lewis Laboratory's contributions to the field of tribology, see "LeRC Contributions to Aeronautics in the Field of Tribology," undated typescript. Files of the author.

[14] "Planning and Goals for Instruction and Research in the Fields of Aircraft Propulsion, Aerodynamics, and General Fluid Mechanics at Case Institute of Technology," 1952, Case Western Reserve University Archives, Case Institute of Technology Engineering Department Records, 19FL, 2:1.

[15] C.H. Cramer, *Case Western Reserve: A History of the University, 1826-1976* (Boston: Little Brown and Company, 1976), p. 262, Glennan served as President of Case from 1947 to 1966. He took a leave of

absence from Case to serve as NASA's first administrator for 29 months, from August 1958 through December 1960.

[16] Cramer, *Case Western*, p. 63–70

[17] Telephone interview with Ray Bolz, September 1987. See also "Planning and Goals for Instruction and Research in the Fields of Aircraft Propulsion, Aerodynamics, and General Fluid Mechanics at Case Institute of Technology," 1952, CWRU Archives, CIT Engineering Department Records, 19FL, 2:1

[18] "Planning and Goals," CWRU Archives, 19FL, 2:1.

[19] Eugene J. Manganiello and Vincent F. Hlavin, "Post University On-the-Job Training for Engineers." Presentation at 1961 Annual Meeting of the Society of Automotive Engineers, 11 January 1961. 221, NASA Lewis Records.

[20] "Planning and Goals," CWRU Archives, 19FL, 2:1.

[21] Manganiello and Hlavin, "Post University On-the-job Training."

[22] Ibid.

[23] Syllibi for courses between 1952 and 1957, 296/116.1, NASA Lewis Records.

[24] Telephone conversation with Walter Olson, 12 September 1986.

[25] Ibid.

[26] On Ernst Eckert, see V. Dawson, "From Braunschweig to Ohio: Ernst Eckert and Government Heat Transfer Research," in *History of Heat Transfer*, Edwin T. Layton, Jr., and John H. Lienhard, eds. (New York: American Society of Mechanical Engineers, 1988), p. 125–37.

[27] See Dawson, "From Braunschweig to Ohio: Ernst Eckert and Government Heat Transfer Research," p. 125–137. E. R. G. Eckert, "Gas Turbine Research at the Aeronautical Research Center, Braunschweig, during 1940–1945," *Atomkerenergie* (ATKE) Bd. 23 (1978) Lfg 4: 208–211. Braunschweig is described in Leslie E. Simon, *German Research in World War II: An Analysis of the Conduct of Research* (New York: John Wiley & Sons, 1947).

[28] For the story of the importing of German scientists, see Clarence Lasby, *Project Paperclip and the Cold War.* Lasby incorrectly identifies Eckert as an "expert in jet motor fuels," (p. 29). Tom Bower, *The Paperclip Conspiracy* (Boston: Little Brown and Company, 1987) also contains inaccuracies.

[29] E. R. G. Eckert, R. M. Drake, Jr., and E. Soehngen, "Manufacture of a Zehnder-Mach interferometer," *Wright-Patterson Air Force Base Technical Report* 5721 (1948).

[30] On L. M. K. Boelter, see John H. Lienhard, "Notes on the Origins and Evolution of the Subject of Heat Transfer." *Mechanical Engineering* 105(6):26.

[31] William H. McAdams, *Heat Transmission*, 2nd ed. (New York: McGraw Hill, 1942). Nine NACA memoranda on turbine cooling were published as RM E7Blla-h and RM E8HO3. Authors included W. B. Brown, Lincoln Wolfenstein, Gene Meyer, John Livingood, and John Sanders.

[32] Anselm Franz, the designer of the Jumo 004, used hollow blades in which the cooling air was ducted through passages in the blade. His Cromadur sheet metal blades contained less than five pounds of chromium and no nickel at all, an achievement that particularly pleased him. They reached production in Germany in 1944 in the Jumo 004B. See Anselm Franz, "The Development of the 'Jumo 004' Turbojet Engine," in *The Jet Age: Forty Years of Jet Aviation*, Walter J. Boyne and Donald S. Lopez, eds. (Washington, D.C.: Smithsonian Institution Press, 1979), p. 73.
E. R. G. Eckert, "Comments to the Draft by Dr. Virginia Dawson on the History of Lewis Research Center," 9 January 1987; and E. R. G. Eckert's notes appended to "Interview with Dr. Ernst Eckert," 13 January 1987, by Edwin T. Layton, Jr.

[33] See E. R. G. Eckert and John N. Livingood, "Method for Calculation of Heat Transfer in Laminar Region of Air Flow Around Cylinders of Arbitrary Cross Section (Including Large Temperature Differences and Transpiration Cooling)," NACA TN 2733, June 1952. See also E. R. G. Eckert, Martin R. Kinsler, and Reeves P. Cochran, "Wire Cloth as Porous Material for Transpiration-Cooled Walls," NACA RM E51H23, November 1951.

[34] This work, carried out with W. Weise, was published in *Forschung auf dem Gebiete des Ingenieurwesens*, vol. 13 (1942). See "Memorandum to Dr. John Evvard, Chairman of the Viscous Flow Panel at the Lewis Laboratory," 1950, 295/100.71, NASA Lewis Records.

[35] "Interview with Dr. Ernst Eckert," 13 January 1987, by Edwin T. Layton, Jr.

[36] Personal communications by Robert Deissler, John Livingood, and Robert Hickel.

[37] E. R. G. Eckert and George M. Low, "Temperature Distribution in Internally Heated Walls of Heat Exchangers Composed of Noncircular Flow Passages," NACA Report (1951) 1022, superseded TN 2257.

[38] Ernst Eckert, *Introduction to the Transfer of Heat and Mass* (New York: McGraw-Hill 1950); published in German in 1949; revised English edition, 1963.

[39] Interview with Donald Buchele and Walton Howes, 8 July 1986. I am indebted to Mr. Howes for providing me with a copy of "Visit to Wright-Patterson Air Force Base on April 26, 1949 to Discuss Interferogram Evaluation in Supersonic Airflow." See also H. Shardin, "Theorie und Anwendungen des Mach-Zehnderchen Interferenz-Refraktometers," *Zeitschrift für instrumentenkunde*, vol. 53, p. 396–403 and 424–436.

[40] Personal communication from Robert Deissler, October 1986.

[41] See J. H. Lienhard, "Notes on the Origins and Evolution of the Subject of Heat Transfer." *Mechanical Engineering* 105(6):20–26. See work by C. B. Cohen, Robert Deissler, Patrick L. Donoughe, Marvin Goldstein, John Howell, John Livingood, George M. Low, F. K. Moore, Simon Ostrach, Eli Reshotko, Robert Siegel, and Maurice Tucker.

[42] Simon Ostrach, "Memoir on Buoyancy-Driven Convection," unpublished manuscript, 1989, p. 2.

[43] Ibid, p. 4.

[44] Interview with Simon Ostrach, 29 September 1987.

[45] Ostrach, "Memoir on Buoyancy-Driven Convection," p. 3.

[46] Interview, 29 September 1987.

[47] NACA TN 2863, 1952.

[48] In 1987 the National Academy of Engineering had 1285 members in 12 fields of engineering and 106 foreign associates. Ohio had 34 members; New York, 110; California, 328; and Maryland, 34. For Franklin Moore's papers, see NACA TR 1124, TR 1132, TN 2279, and TN 2521.

[49] Interview with Simon Ostrach, 29 September 1987.

[50] This is based on a statement made by Abe Silverstein to the author and Arthur L. Levine, "United States Aeronautical Research Policy, 1915–1958: A Study of the Major Policy Decisions of the National Advisory Committee for Aeronautics," unpublished Ph.D. dissertion, Columbia, 1963, p. 97.

[51] Transcript of interview with Abe Silverstein, 5 October 1984, p. 11.

[52] Eckert, *Introduction to the Transfer of Heat and Mass.*

CHAPTER SIX

OPERATIONS RESEARCH

Operations research fell at the applied end of the research spectrum. It concerned when to certify an airplane for take-off and landing. It was an opportunity to save lives. Even in an area so close to applications or development, the NACA shaped its research to illuminate general problems to benefit the entire industry. During World War II icing research was unquestionably "development," as distinct from fundamental research. The anti-icing hardware developed for military aircraft during the war was only a short-term solution to the icing problem. A fundamental understanding of what constitutes the icing cloud was necessary. In 1944 the NACA began a program to compile statistical data to define icing conditions, culminating in the 1950s in guidelines for the design of ice-protection systems, which became the basis for federal regulations in certifying these systems. As it evolved, icing research became a discipline that combined both theoretical and experimental approaches.

Icing on aircraft is caused by flight through an icing cloud consisting of small supercooled droplets that strike the aircraft surfaces and freeze into a porous white mass called rime ice. If larger supercooled droplets strike the aircraft, not all of the water freezes on impact. As water accumulates and enough heat is dissipated, the water freezes into a clear, hard mass called glaze ice, a much more serious problem because it is difficult to remove. Ice adds weight and impairs the aerodynamic efficiency of an airplane, often leading, in severe conditions, to a crash.[1] After the bombing of Pearl Harbor, military planners suggested that the most promising route for an invasion of Japan was across Alaska and the Aleutian Islands. Anticipating severe aircraft icing problems, the Army asked for a broad attack on many fronts. General Electric, the Massachusetts Institute of Technology (MIT), and all three NACA laboratories joined the effort to find ways to protect aircraft from this silent enemy.

In aircraft powered by piston engines during World War II, ice accumulated on the propellers and the plane's leading edges, blocked the air intakes of the engines, and choked the carburetor. Icing of windshields cut down pilots' visibility. Before the war aircraft manufacturers used a simple, inexpensive, mechanical method to remove ice. An inflatable rubber boot was fitted over the leading edges of the wings and tail. When ice began to build up, the boots were inflated and deflated to knock off the ice. However, the boots impaired the aerodynamic effectiveness of the aircraft's surfaces and increased drag. These clumsy and increasingly ineffective de-icing methods had to be replaced with a more aerodynamically efficient system of ice prevention. Heat to prevent ice build-up seemed to promise a more satisfactory method to conquer the icing problem.[2]

Much of the wartime research in icing by the NACA focused on the pioneering development of a thermal anti-icing system for military aircraft. Although the idea of diverting the heat from the engine's exhaust to the leading edges of the wings and tail was not new, prior to the war, aircraft manufacturers were unwilling to incur the additional production costs required by a thermal anti-icing system. Under Army auspices, engineers at Langley, led by Lewis A. Rodert, designed and installed a thermal system in the wings of a Lockheed 12 airplane, the NACA's first so-called "flying laboratory." Rodert continued this work at Ames. After flight testing the new system, in 1941 Rodert's group issued its first report demonstrating the feasibility of using exhaust-heated wings to protect against icing.[3]

During construction of the Altitude Wind Tunnel at Lewis Laboratory, an Icing Research Tunnel was added to the original plan to take advantage of its extensive and sophisticated refrigeration system. It was hoped that the new icing tunnel in Cleveland would be useful in assisting in the development of Rodert's thermal system. Proposed in 1942 and completed in spring 1944, the icing tunnel was not part of the original plan for the laboratory. However, it is one of the few facilities built during the war still used for its original function. Because the designers of the icing tunnel, Alfred Young and Charles Zelanko, thought that the icing problem would be solved within a short time, they proposed a tunnel suitable also for aerodynamic testing of engine components.

Young and Zelanko were aware that the design of an icing tunnel was far more complex than that of a simple wind tunnel. The need to simulate the atmospheric conditions of an icing cloud presented them with an extremely demanding engineering problem. In hindsight, it is apparent that neither the science of meteorology nor the state of engineering knowledge was adequate for the job at hand. As Zelanko later recalled, they knew how to design ordinary wind tunnels, but the problems of creating icing conditions were almost without precedent. "Logic, theory, and speculation were the only design tools that were available."[4] Only when the tunnel's spray system was replaced in the early 1950s could tunnel tests yield accurate icing data. Until then, flight research provided more reliable information on the phenomenon of icing.

Icing tunnels were not entirely unknown before the proposed Cleveland tunnel, but they were smaller and did not have the advantage of the extensive refrigeration system Carrier had created. However, Young and Zelanko studied the tunnel of the B. F. Goodrich Company (Akron, Ohio), which manufactured rubber pneumatic de-icing boots, and MIT's special icing wind tunnel. They proposed a tunnel with a maximum speed of about 400 miles per hour with a 7-foot x 10 foot test section, later scaled down to a 6-foot x 9-foot test section. To simulate icing conditions in the tunnel, air was cooled to −30° F by passing it over the fins of the heat exchanger. A spray system introduced an atomized stream of water into this refrigerated airstream. The unnaturally large size of the water droplets remained the problem that defied solution.[5]

As the tunnel began to take shape, Wilson H. Hunter took charge of the Icing Research Section. A 1930 graduate of Yale in mechanical engineering, Hunter brought firsthand experience in the design of rubber de-icers from the B. F. Goodrich Company. However, by June 1944, when Hunter supervised the tunnel's first test, the era of the mechanical de-icing had passed. The wind tunnel testing program focused on testing components of Rodert's thermal protection system. This work was unabashedly hardware development. More basic research would have to wait until the feverish activity of meeting wartime demands could yield to a more measured step.

The NACA made extensive use of a simple instrument to measure ice accumulation. It consisted of rotating metal cylinders of graduated diameters. By measuring the thickness of the ice buildup, the researcher could determine the mean size of the water droplets, distribution, and liquid water content in the icing cloud. The group at Ames grappled with the problem of defining the characteristics of the icing cloud using a statistical approach. What range of liquid water content, drop size, and temperature defined an icing encounter? The Ames project under Alun Jones was strengthened by the additional talent of William Lewis, a meteorologist on loan from the U.S. Weather Bureau. J. K. Hardy, on loan during the war from the British Royal Aircraft Establishment at Farnsborough, tackled the problems of heat transfer in a heated wing, a study that culminated in an important paper published in 1945, "An Analysis of the Dissipation of Heat in Conditions of Icing from a Section of the Wing of the C-46 Airplane."[6]

In 1946 Lewis Rodert took charge of the icing program at the Cleveland laboratory. In a March 1947 memo, Rodert stressed the importance of gathering statistical data on icing clouds. These data would allow the Civil Aeronautics Administration to craft regulations to certify new aircraft if they met guidelines in providing ice-protection equipment. Reliable data were needed because of the "general disagreement over what constitutes a safe design basis for the heated wing."[7] The Cleveland and Ames laboratories collaborated on this program.

Wilson Hunter, Head of the Icing Research Section, demonstrates the dangerous icing of the propellers of a P-39 after a wind tunnel test. General Arnold (left) and George Lewis (far left) listen attentively.

Harry S. Truman presents Lewis A. Rodert with the 1946 Collier Trophy for the wartime development of a thermal ice protection system.

By 1948 the program had logged a total of 249 icing encounters and had taken about 1000 measurements of liquid water content and droplet diameter. This was a collaborative flight research program carried out by the Air Force in the upper Mississippi Valley, by Ames in the West, and by Lewis Laboratory in the Great Lakes area. John H. Enders, an intrepid pilot from Cleveland's Flight Research program, flew the dangerous missions over Lake Erie, bringing back his Consolidated bomber encrusted with ice. In October the NACA group presented a tentative table of design conditions to the NACA Subcommittee on Icing Problems. This report defined the parameters for which icing protection was necessary for safe operation.[8] The statistical data in this NACA report became the basis for the design criteria for federal requirements for aircraft icing protection adopted by the Civil Aeronautics Administration in the mid-1950s. In reflecting on the success of this effort, William Lewis wrote in 1969, "Considering the fact that we had data from 167 encounters in layer clouds and 73 in cumulus, statistical extrapolation to a probability of 1/1000 was more than daring, it was down right foolhardy." Nevertheless, more recent research using a much larger data base confirmed the conclusions of the 1949 report.[9]

In 1949 Abe Silverstein asked Irving Pinkel to take over as the new associate chief of the Physics Division. Supervision of icing research fell among Pinkel's duties. It appeared that NACA work in icing had reached a natural point of termination. Ames closed down its program and transferred equipment and personnel, including William Lewis and D. B. Kline (also on loan from the Weather Bureau), to Cleveland. Silverstein thought that icing research was too close to development and should be phased out, but in Pinkel's view the icing group was "very able and much maligned." Previously, Pinkel had worked with the icing group as a member of the Wind Tunnels Analysis Panel to encourage a more analytical approach to the problems of icing. Born in Gloversville, N.Y., he graduated with honors from the University of Pennsylvania in 1935. Pinkel began his government service in Pittsburgh, Penn., as a physicist with the Bureau of Mines, where he worked on synthesizing liquid fuels from coal. In 1940 he joined his older brother Ben at Langley, where he focused on the nonstationary aerodynamic forces of airplane flutter. He transferred to Cleveland in 1942 to work on the hydraulics problems of engine lubricating systems. A member of Silverstein's Special Projects Panel after World War II, he contributed pioneering papers on lift and thrust developed by heat addition to the supersonic flow beneath an airplane wing.[10]

Pinkel listened attentively to his staff's arguments for the continuation of icing research. His engineer's sixth sense told him that terminating it was premature. "I saw that the people who were involved in it were, in fact, trying to create an engineering discipline out of it, which seemed the correct thing to do."[11] Instead of closing down the division, he broadened it.

But what did it mean to make an engineering discipline out of the work? The cut-and-try testing of components had characterized most of the NACA's prewar and wartime icing research. Postwar engineering demanded analytic skills. Testing without analysis as a guide was expensive and time consuming. The icing group at Lewis was composed of men with mechanical engineering degrees, the majority of whom took their first jobs with the NACA immediately after graduation. Women with a mathematical bent, but usually only high school graduates, assisted the men as computers and data takers. As a whole, the staff at Lewis lacked the analytic skills that basic engineering research demanded. After the war, a process of self-selection took place. As the manpower of the icing division was reduced, the engineers who remained began to form a corps,

A NACA pilot measures ice on a turbojet engine's inlet. Until 1950 flight into icing clouds provided more reliable data than tests in the Icing Research Tunnel.

113

which developed an attachment to icing as a discipline. They began to assimilate and integrate new knowledge from the fields of heat transfer and meteorology.

Like many of their colleagues in other areas, such as supersonic aerodynamics, they taught themselves what they needed to know. With ties to the National Research Council of Canada and the Mt. Washington Research Station and access to Soviet data, they were in the mainstream of world icing research.

Under Pinkel's direction, the icing group focused on extending the basic understanding of the icing cloud. They launched a new research program with the commercial airlines and the Air Force to gather statistical icing data from areas throughout the world. They developed a simplified pressure-type icing rate meter that could record the frequency and intensity of icing conditions automatically. The meter was installed in about 50 commercial and military aircraft that flew over the North Atlantic, the Continental United States, Alaska, the Pacific and parts of Asia. Over a period of five years, data were gathered for 1800 icing encounters. The icing meter was superior to the rotating multicylinder method, not only because it did not require the constant attention of research personnel, but, more important, because of the far greater number of encounters and range of conditions that it was now possible to record. The rotating multicylinder provided data for a small number of flights into deliberately sought, abnormally severe, conditions. Now routine flights into all degrees of severity could be monitored. In addition, weather reconnaissance information gathered over a two-year period by the Air Weather Service and the Strategic Air Command was made available to the icing group at Lewis. All these data were entered on IBM punch cards for analysis using one of the first IBM computers at Lewis.[12] In general, the data supported the findings of the laboratory's original study, adding, in particular, new knowledge about the vertical and horizontal extent of icing encounters. Because of difficulties in the calibration of the meter, the results were not entirely consistent for the icing rate and liquid water content.[13]

Another problem the icing research group tackled was the complex analysis of the path of a water droplet. As an aircraft moves through an icing cloud, only a small percentage of the supercooled droplets actually strike an aircraft and freeze. The majority of the droplets follow streamlines that move around the leading surfaces of the airplane. With the knowledge of the water content and droplet size (determined by the rotating multicylinder technique), it was possible to calculate the droplet trajectory. The rate of icing on a given surface or shape of a component could then be predicted.[14] The Lewis group extended the available data over a range of airfoil shapes and thicknesses through the use of a differential analyzer. Harry Mergler of the Instrument and Computing Division adapted this early computer designed at MIT by Vannevar Bush to meet the needs of icing research. Although calculating the trajectory of a droplet was still a laborious process, the differential analyzer reduced the time it took for a single calculation from weeks to about four days. Women who had formerly worked the problems on simple mechanical calculators made the transition to the gargantuan differential analyzer with comparative ease. Often they were given the distinction of having their names appear as co-authors of the reports of these studies, no doubt because their contribution went beyond the sheer drudgery of "number crunching." In addition to reducing the time for arduous calculations, the differential analyzer was a potential teacher of higher mathematics. The calculus unfolded mechanically through the gearing and shafts; the chart recorders taught the operators "to grasp the innate meaning of the differential equation." The machine trained them to think in the same logical steps that the machine ground through in making a calculation. Through the back door, women assigned to toil on this giant calculator gained access to the abstruse realm of partial differential equations—a realm in which not all engineers hired during World War II were comfortable.[15]

With new information now available on the phenomenon of the natural icing cloud, the tunnel engineering staff set about the redesign of the spray system for the icing tunnel, long recognized both within the NACA and by outside authorities as inadequate.[16] The droplet size was ten times larger than the statistical definition derived from actual icing encounters, and instrumentation for measuring the properties of the artificial icing cloud was lacking. Vernon Gray, known as "Mr. Icingologist," took this problem under his wing. He directed the efforts of Halbert Whitaker, a fluid systems engineer, to develop a system that would produce an atomized spray. Day after day, through trial and error, the team perfected the design, which consisted of a battery of approximately 80 spray nozzles mounted on six horizontal bars. The system produced an icing cloud of approximately 4 feet by 4 feet. To verify whether tests in the tunnel accurately reproduced actual flight conditions, the heat transfer data obtained by J. K. Hardy at Ames in his famous study of the heated wing were compared to tests on the same wing mounted in the icing tunnel. The data were in agreement.[17]

The spray system was a complex engineering achievement. It was now possible to run tests that were much closer to natural icing conditions. At this point the tunnel became a valuable research tool, and a group that included Dean Bowden, Thomas Gelder, Uwe von Glahn, Vernon Gray, and James P. Lewis inaugurated a new program to test cyclic de-icing systems. As the era of high-speed, high-altitude turbojet fighters and transports dawned in the early 1950s, it became clear that thermal anti-icing systems required an excessive amount of heat. Bleeding this heat from the engine severely impaired performance. In a cyclic system, ice is permitted to form on aircraft surfaces. This ice is melted and removed by aerodynamic forces at intervals by short, intense heating periods. The new program at Lewis Laboratory may have been stimulated by new research on intermittent heating by L. M. K. Boelter's heat transfer group at the University of California at Los Angeles.[18] The study of thermal cyclic de-icing systems required a level of sophistication in the field of heat transfer and aerodynamics unknown in the wartime era.[19]

Between 1949 and 1955 flight research also continued. In addition to checking the results of tests in the tunnel with the performance of the new systems during actual icing encounters, the flight research group evaluated the rotating multicyinder method for determining droplet size, distribution, and liquid water content with a view to understanding both the strengths of the technique and, more important, its limitations. This

It took a few days for women "computers" to mechanically calculate the trajectory of a water droplet across an airfoil on the gears and cams of the huge differential analyzer, acquired in 1949.

Vernon Gray investigates the new spray system, completed in 1950, for the Icing Research Tunnel.

was "normal engineering" in the sense that it involved no dramatic scientific or technical breakthroughs, but an extension and refinement of previous knowledge and practice. For example, using dimensionless parameters, Rinaldo J. Brun, William Lewis, Porter Perkins, and John Serafini produced a technical report that calculated the impingement rate of cloud droplets on the rotating multicylinder. The report shows a solid command of boundary layer theory, heat transfer, experimental physics, and instrumentation that sets it strikingly apart from the simple empiricism of the reports of the mid-1940s. The discipline had indeed been placed on a rational basis.[20]

Ironically, the steady improvement of the jet plane contributed to the phasing out of icing research at Lewis Laboratory in 1957. By the late 1950s, the turbojet engine had come into general use for commercial flights. In contrast to the more recent development of the turbofan engine, early turbojets were overdesigned. They were not affected by the "bleeding off" or diverting of compressor air, which was piped through the wings for icing protection. The aircraft manufacturers could tailor inexpensive icing protection systems to specific designs without compromising the performance of the airplane. Moreover, since turbojet engines provided greater power than the reciprocating engines they replaced, higher altitudes were possible. Aircraft could fly over the icing clouds rather than through them, leaving take-off and landing as the only potentially dangerous icing situations. However, as Irving Pinkel pointed out, "With new technology old ideas can get a breath of life again." Problems solved for one set of conditions recur as technology advances in other areas. When the more efficient turbofan engine revolutionized engine design in the mid-1960s there was less compressor bleed air available for ice protection. Production of helicopters and small general aviation aircraft increased in the late 1950s and 1960s. Because they fly at lower altitudes, these aircraft are much more sensitive to icing. Even though the Icing Research Tunnel at Lewis Laboratory was officially closed in 1957, a few tests of hardware under development by industry were permitted. In 1978, in response to increased industry demand, NASA officially reinstituted the tunnel testing program after the icing tunnel was renovated and its instrumentation updated. The tunnel now runs more tests than other wind tunnels of NASA.[21] However, the nature of the work has changed. Industry now contracts with NASA to run tests on hardware under development.

THE CRASH FIRE PROGRAM

In 1947, the Committee on Operating Problems, chaired by the charismatic executive of American Airlines, William Littlewood, debated the question of whether the NACA should enter a new area of aircraft safety—the control or prevention of fires after a airplane crash.[22] The Committee directed Lewis Laboratory to make a preliminary study of the crash fire problem. At the same time, it took steps to form a new Subcommittee on Aircraft Fire Prevention. The crash fire issue was of direct concern to the aircraft industry—to the aircraft manufacturers and to increasingly successful commercial airline operators like American, United, Trans World (TWA), and Pan American. They pushed for a greater involvement with the crash fire problem on the part of the NACA.

The previous year the problem of air crash fires received wide publicity. Of a surprisingly high total of 121 air carrier

Two instruments to measure icing rates during flight through an icing cloud are calibrated in the Icing Research Tunnel. The lower device is Langmuir's rotating multi-cylinder. The upper u-tube device is the NACA pressure-type icing meter used to gather statistics on the duration and severity of icing encounters in the early 1950s.

accidents during that year, 22, or 18 percent, involved fire. Of that number, 5 percent were attributed to fires in the air; the remaining 13 percent were due to fires following a crash.[23] A new generation of commercial passenger planes made by Martin, Douglas, Lockheed, and Convair made air travel more reliable and comfortable. Even more important, the volume of travelers increased; and air travel, once only for the wealthy elite, became affordable. Yet, from the industry point of view, the full development of commercial aviation was being held back by the public perception of its dangers.

Aircraft manufacturers tended to be more concerned with fires in the air because they were often caused by design flaws, but fires after a crash resulted in greater loss of life. Their causes, however, could not always be determined, and they were often blamed on pilot error or airline operating practices.[24] Thus, the operators of commercial airlines were especially concerned that the crash fire problem be studied systematically. The airplane of the late 1940s had become a complex system whose very design contained inherent fire hazards. The new commercial airliners traveled long distances without refueling. To achieve maximum seating density, large fuel tanks were placed in the wings. For stability and aerodynamic efficiency, designers favored mounting the engines at the center of the wings. This design, however, brought ignition sources and fuel into dangerous proximity. In a crash, if the wings broke apart, a spark from the engine or the hot gases from the engine's exhaust quickly ignited the fuel. In addition to the danger of the wing-engine configuration, there were numerous other potentially dangerous ignition sources: cabin heating and ventilation, pressurization systems, and hot gas de-icing equipment. Electrical systems required miles of wires, often packed together next to other lines carrying extremely flammable hydraulic fluids or lubricating oils.[25]

If less theoretical than high-speed aerodynamics or heat transfer, nevertheless the study of crash fires bore directly on the NACA's charter to find practical solutions to the problems of aviation. The crash fire problem excited the imaginations of a panel on "Reduction of Hazards Due to Aircraft Fires" set up at Lewis Laboratory. Chaired by Abe Silverstein, with Lewis Rodert serving as the coordinator of the fire research program with outside agencies, the panel consisted of fuels experts R. F. Selden, Louis C. Gibbon, and W. T. Olson, as well as Henry C. Barnett and Gerald J. Pesman.[26]

In their preliminary report, members of the panel recommended a research program that would tackle the crash fire problem from many points of view. The main focus of the program was the investigation of the origin and rate of propagation of fires in actual crashes. The systematic study of full-scale airplane crashes had previously been carried out by the U.S. Army Air Corps in a study of single-engine fighter aircraft between 1924 and 1928 and in England by W. G. Glendinning. However, there was no precedent for the scale and complexity of the research program envisioned by the NACA panel. Members of the panel argued that full-scale crash tests were justified because unknown scale effects made data from simulated crashes of models unreliable. They proposed basic research on the ignition characteristics of various inflammable liquids—fuels, hydraulic fluids, and lubricants—along with a study of fire-extinguishing agents. Factors involved in general layout would also be considered. Was the placement of engines on the tips of the wings, as far from the fuel tanks as possible, feasible? Could better fuel tanks be designed? What about developing a safety fuel that was less volatile than the gasoline-type fuels currently in use? Like the point of icing research, the ultimate aim of the crash fire program was to provide the federal government with reliable data to establish codes for the design of safer aircraft.[27]

This ambitious plan raised the hackles of the Civil Aeronautics Administration. In addition to gathering information on accidents, the CAA also conducted a limited research program that involved crash testing components at its Experimental Station in Indianapolis, Ind. With this program now regarded as inadequate, Harvey L. Hansberry of the Civil Aeronautics Administration objected that a similar full-scale program now under consideration had been proposed by the CAA in 1946 and turned down because of its excessive expense.[28] However, the NACA program had the strong backing of the Aircraft Industries Association, representing the manufacturers, and the Air Transport Association, representing the operators. In their view, the Civil Aeronautics Administration was partly responsible for the public perception of the dangers of air transportation and the financial losses due to recent crashes. Lewis Rodert pointed out after a visit to the West Coast aircraft industries, "The CAA is presently being blamed for the present situation because, in the opinion of many aircraft engineers, the CAA research has not been adequately broad nor penetrating and the airworthiness requirements relating to the fire hazard have not been realistic."[29]

TESTING AT THE RAVENNA ARSENAL

In 1949, when Irving Pinkel inherited the icing program, he also assumed leadership of Lewis's Crash Fire Program. His background in fuels made him a natural choice for leadership of the program. However, at first the work did not particularly appeal to him. He was told that the request to the NACA had come directly from President Truman.[30] The main players on the crash fire team were Dugald O. Black, Arthur Busch, Gerard J. Pesman, G. Merritt Preston, and Sol Weiss. They were backed by an intrepid group of pilots and technicians in the hangar who worked closely with William Wynne, Ernest Walker, and other members of the photographic branch.

The NACA obtained about 50 twin-engine cargo planes from the Air Force. These planes had been used in the Berlin airlift and were so service weary that they were flown to Cleveland with their doors open so that the pilot could jump, if necessary. The Army granted the NACA permission to use the grounds of one of its World War II arsenals in Ravenna, Ohio, as the site for the full-scale crash tests. John Everett designed and supervised the construction of a 2000-foot runway.

The crashes were carefully choreographed. They were to be survivable, assuming that a fire could be prevented. A plane was sent down the runway at take-off and landing speeds by remote control. It ran into a barrier that tore off the landing gear and damaged the propellers. The engine, however, had to remain attached to the main body of the aircraft. The plane then slid through a set of poles to rip open the wing tanks before sliding into an open field. The airplane was painted white and the fuel dyed red for ease of photography.

Each airplane carried various instruments to record temperatures, fire location, distribution of combustible mixtures, and times at which various failures occurred. These instruments converted the data into electric signals recorded on meters located in a fireproof, insulated box on the airplane. Seven additional motion-picture camera stands were located at various points near the runway. To correlate the exterior photographs with the data simultaneously photographed inside the box, a timing light on the top of the fuselage flashed at intervals of one second or less.[31]

The program's goal was to uncover the mechanism of the crash fire and the exact nature of the structural breakup of the airplane. What was the rate, pattern, and area over which the liquid fuel spread? Did it form into a spray? What, if anything, could be done to prevent it? One by one the old myths tumbled before the facts: the mistaken idea of pilots that turning off the ignition before a crash prevented fire; the belief that fuels with low volatility were safer than conventional gasoline.

By 1957 the group under Pinkel, now chief of the Fluid Systems Division, had extended their careful engineering analyses from piston engine aircraft to planes powered by turbojets. They received strong support from the airlines, particularly United, for work on a design for an

In the crash fire program at the Ravenna Arsenal, a service-weary cargo plane (C-82) was run down a launching track into a crash barrier. Engineers studied the crash fire to determine ignition sources.

inerting system, despite a projected weight penalty of 1200 pounds. Pratt & Whitney was less enthusiastic. Representatives objected that over 50 holes drilled into the engine case of the J-57 for a spray system might affect the engine's reliability.[32] The team designed an inerting system that could cool the hot exhaust system and cut off the fuel and electrical systems within this short interval. With the inerting system to prevent the ensuing crash fire, all but the most severe crashes were survivable.

However, the NACA had no political clout to force the airframe and engine manufacturers to install the new system. Despite the desire of some of the airline operators to purchase aircraft with crash fire protection, the manufacturers were under no obligation to provide this added equipment. The Civil Aeronautics Administration, possibly alienated by the NACA's strong showing in a field that it had previously dominated, did not take up the cause to force compliance through regulation. Unlike the icing criteria, which became the basis for federal design standards, for fire safety the NACA had to rely on persuasion, and the manufacturers were not ready to make the investment. Although the Crash Fire Program had provided convincing evidence that the inerting system could prevent crash fires, the added weight of the system forestalled acceptance. Even with a motion-picture film, convincingly narrated by David Brinkley, the NACA failed to entice the manufacturers to incur the added expense of the system.[33]

Although the aircraft manufacturers did not adopt the NACA inerting system in the mid-1950s, gradually designers incorporated safety features similar to those recommended by the NACA.[34] Fires following crashes became rare.

Concern with safety continued to shape operations research programs at Lewis Laboratory. From the Crash Fire Program, Pinkel and his group moved into the investigation of the crashworthiness of airline seats, restraining harnesses for passengers, design of seats to reduce impact forces, maximum seating density, and lightning hazards. In the late 1950s, when NASA's Mercury Program required engineers with experience in protecting human beings from the buffeting of crash landings, Lewis was ready with an experienced cadre of individuals.

Irving Pinkel receives the NACA Distinguished Service Award in June 1957 from James Doolittle, Chairman of the NACA, as Ray Sharp looks on.

CONTINUITY UNDER NASA

As the Mercury Program got under way at Langley, some of the members of Pinkel's division became the nucleus of the Flight Operations Division at Cape Canaveral, Fla. G. Merritt Preston, who had authored many of the reports on the Crash Fire Program, became the Division's first manager.[35] Other early members of the Space Task Force who transferred to Langley to work under Robert Gilruth were Elmer Buller, A. M. Busch, W. R. Dennis, M. J. Krasnican, Glynn S. Lunney, André J. Meyer, W. R. Meyer, W. J. Nesbitt, Gerard J. Pesman, Leonard Rabb, and Scott Simkinson. Simkinson, whose background at Lewis was in testing full-scale engines, perhaps exemplified what Lewis-trained individuals could contribute to the space program. He knew hardware and could "smell a problem a mile away."[36]

Other members of Pinkel's division contributed their expertise to the group at Lewis in charge of the Mercury capsule's instrumentation, automatic separation from the Atlas rocket, its stabilization and control systems, and its retrorockets for reentry into Earth's atmosphere. Their first assignment, the altitude control system for Big Joe (the test vehicle to precede manned flight), presented the first opportunity to apply their knowledge of aviation to flight beyond the atmosphere. Substituting a safer fuel, cold-gas nitrogen, for the hydrogen peroxide rocket thrusters used in the X-15, Harold Gold, Robert R. Miller, and H. Warren Plohr worked with Minneapolis-Honeywell to design a system that automatically moved the capsule into the desired alignment after separation from the Atlas booster.[37]

Testing this new control system required the engineering ingenuity of a score of Lewis engineers. David S. Gabriel conceived a gigantic tinker-toy-like simulator called MASTIF (Multiple Axis Space Test Inertia Facility), which could turn and tumble a 3000-pound space capsule on three axes inside three sets of gimbals. Louis L. Corpas executed the details of the design, and Frank Stenger developed the system of air jets to push it at 60 revolutions per minute. This "gimbal rig" was placed in Lewis's vacuum chamber, actually the old Altitude Wind Tunnel, converted by a team of engineers working under William Fleming to the new task of simulating atmospheric conditions up to 80,000 feet.[38]

In mid-1959, with engineering imaginations conditioned by issues involving human safety, James W. Useller, a mechanical engineer, and Joseph S. Algranti, a test pilot, saw the potential of the gimbal rig for astronaut training. They enlisted several local physiologists and ten test pilots (including several women) to test the effect of roll, pitch, and yaw on human physiology. In 1960, beginning with astronauts Gus Grissom and Alan Shepard, each Mercury astronaut submitted to a ride of a tolerable limit of 30 revolutions per minute. They learned how to activate the nitrogen jets that acted as brakes to bring them out of their dizzying spin while the external cages continued to whirl about them.[39]

The gimbal rig at Lewis was used to teach Mercury astronauts how to bring a capsule tumbling in space under control.

Because of the expertise developed over years of research on the crash fire problem, NASA looked to Lewis Laboratory for assistance in determining the cause of the Apollo fire in January 1967. Irving Pinkel joined the investigation panel and spent tension-filled days and nights at Cape Canaveral. The panel concluded that the fire did not originate in the pure oxygen atmosphere of the astronauts' suits, as people had first surmised, but was caused by a short circuit that began in the cabinet that housed the environmental control unit. Wires of the electrical system ran under the door to the cabinet. Every time the door was opened, it chafed on the wires placed next to a combustible nylon netting. In short, the capsule had been poorly designed by NASA's contractor, North American Aviation. The fire had been entirely preventable. However, there was also blame to be assigned to NASA. One author called the disaster "murder on pad 34," citing sloppy management practices and a hurried atmosphere that precluded high engineering standards and careful supervision of its contractors by NASA.[40]

In response to the tragedy, James Webb asked Irving Pinkel to create and head an internal agency called the Aerospace Safety Research and Data Institute to serve as a clearinghouse for safety information, primarily for NASA and its contractors. The role of the government as a clearinghouse for information was not a new idea to Pinkel. That was the NACA's forte in the days when NACA reports put the latest innovations in engine technology within the reach of industry's engine designers. Located at Lewis Laboratory, the institute's functions were to organize existing safety information, to find gaps, and to fill them with appropriate research. The information was computerized to facilitate access and quick responses to requests. Within four years the institute had fallen prey to the 1972 cuts in appropriations.

NOTES

[1] G. M. B. Dobson, *Exploring the Atmosphere* (Oxford: Clarendon Press, 1968), p. 84.

[2] George Gray, *Frontiers of Flight* (New York: Alfred A. Knopf, 1948), p. 307-329.

[3] Lewis A. Rodert, William H. McAvoy, Lawrence A. Clousing, "Preliminary Report on Flight Tests of an Airplane Having Exhaust-Heated Wings. NACA Wartime Report A-53, 1941. In 1946 President Truman presented the prestigious Collier Trophy to Rodert for his wartime thermal de-icing work.

[4] In 1987 the Icing Research Tunnel was designated an International Historic Mechanical Engineering Landmark by the American Society of Mechanical Engineers. Extensive documentation from National Archives Record Group 255 and NASA Lewis Records on the design and construction of the Icing Research Tunnel is available as part of the application submitted by William Olsen to the ASME. The quotation is from the booklet prepared for this occasion.

[5] Alfred W. Young and Charles N. Zelanko, "Memorandum for the Construction Administrator," National Archives, Record Group 255, Box 131. For a full description of the icing tunnel prior to 1986 refurbishing, see Uwe von Glahn, "The Icing Problem—Current Status of NACA Techniques and Research," NASA TM-81651, August 1981, appendix A. For accounts of NACA wartime icing research, see George Gray, *Frontiers of Flight*, p. 307-329; Edwin P. Hartman, *Adventures in Research*, NASA SP-4302 (Washington, D.C.: U.S. Government Printing Office, 1970), p. 69-77; Elizabeth Muenger, *Searching the Horizon: A History of Ames Research Center, 1940-1976*, NASA SP-4304 (Washington, D.C.: U.S. Government Printing Office, 1985), p. 19-22; James Hansen, *Engineer in Charge*, NASA SP-4305 (Washington, D.C.: U.S. Government Printing Office, 1987), p. 110-111. See also comments on current use by A. Richard Tobiason, "Overview of NASA's Programs," in *Meteorological and Environmental Inputs to Aviation Systems*, NASA Conference Publication 2388, 1983, p. 35.

[6] NACA Report 831 (1945). See discussion by Hartmann, *Adventures in Research*, p. 76. British studies indicated that for bombing missions the increased weight of icing protection systems meant that the bomb load would have to be reduced. See R. V. Jones, *The Wizard War: British Scientific Intelligence 1939-1945* (New York: Coward, McCann and Geoghegan, 1978), p. 387-388. The first report describing the rotating multicylinder method was Bernard Vonnegut, A.A.F. Tech. Report, No. 5519, 1946. *The Mount Washington Monthly Research Bulletin*, vol. II, no. 6, June 1946, published an anonymous description. See also Victor F. Clark, "Conditions for Run-Off and Blow-Off of Catch on Multicylinder Icing Meter." Harvard-Mt. Washington Icing Research Report 1946-7, *AF Tech. Rep.* 5676, p. 190-218. See also Irving Langmuir, "Super-Cooled Water Droplets in Rising Currents of Cold Saturated Air," Report No. RL-223 (1943-1944) in *The Collected Works of Irving Langmuir*, vol. 10 (New York: Pergamon Press, 1961), p. 199. Biographical information can be found in *Dictionary of Scientific Biography* (New York: Scribners, 1973), vol. 8, p. 22-25.

[7] Lewis Rodert to Chief of Research, 12 March 1947, NASA Lewis Records, 34/Icing. The Civil Aeronautics Authority and Air Safety Board were established by the Civil Aeronautics Act of 1938. In 1940 they were reorganized into the Civil Aeronautics Administration and the Civil Aeronautics Board. The Federal Aviation Administration was set up in 1958.

[8] Alun R. Jones and William Lewis, "Recommended Values of Meteorological Factors to Be Considered in the Design of Aircraft Ice-Prevention Equipment." NACA TN 1855, March 1949.

[9] William Lewis, "Review of Icing Criteria," p. 3. From *Aircraft Ice Protection*, Federal Aviation Administration, April 1969 (typescript). I am indebted to the late Dr. William Olsen for providing me with a copy of this paper. These data are now the basis of icing certification in Federal Aviation Regulation (FAR 25), Appendix C. The exact date for the adoption of these regulations by the Civil Aeronautics Administration is unclear. Copies of correspondence (courtesy of William Olsen) indicate that as late as 1956 the regulations, although proposed, had not yet become law. NACA data were used in "Engineering Summary of Airframe Icing Technical Data," Federal Aviation Administration ADS-4, 1963 (known throughout the world as the "Icing Bible"), and "Engineering Summary of Powerplant Icing Technical Data," FAA RD-77-76, 1977.

[10] Transcript of interview with Irving Pinkel by Walter T. Bonney, 22 July 1973, NASA History Office Archives, Washington, D.C., p. 13-14. Transcript of interview with author, Lewis Research Center, 30 January 1985, p. 19.

[11] Ibid.

[12] The results of the statistical survey are summarized in Porter J. Perkins, "Summary of Statistical Icing Cloud Data Measured Over the United States and North Atlantic, Pacific, and Arctic Oceans During Routine Aircraft Operations," NASA RM 1-19-59E, 1959. For an extremely helpful overview of NACA icing research see Uwe von Glahn, "The Icing Problem—Current Status of NACA Techniques and Research", reprinted in *Selected Bibliography of NACA-NASA Aircraft Icing Publications*, Lewis Research, August 1981, NASA TM-81651. I am not certain whether the IBM computer referred to in von Glahn's report is the IBM 601, a system with mechanical storage used between 1954 and 1956, or the IBM 604, the first electronic computer in use between 1955 and 1957.

[13] See William Lewis, "Review of Icing Criteria," p. 4. The meter is described in detail in Porter J. Perkins, Stuart McCullough, and Ralph D. Lewis, "A Simplified Instrument for Recording and Indicating Frequency and Intensity of Icing Conditions Encountered in Flight" *NACA Research Memorandum*, E51E16, 1951.

[14] Irving Langmuir and Katherine B. Blodgett, "A Mathematical Investigation of Water Droplet Trajectories," Technical Report No. 5418, Air Materiel Command, AAF, 19 February 1946.

[15] See, for example, Rinaldo J. Brun, Helen M. Gallagher, and Dorothea E. Vogt, "Impingement of Water Droplets on NACA 65A004 Airfoil at 8° Angle of Attack," NACA Technical Note 3155, 1954. For a description of how the differential analyzer worked, see Larry Owens, "Vannevar Bush and the Differential Analyzer: The Text and Context of an Early Computer." *Technology and Culture* 27:63–95. The quoted passage is on p. 85–86.

[16] See "Progress Report Submitted by Professor H. G. Houghton [MIT], for Meeting of Subcommittee on De-Icing Problems, April 9, 1947." National Archives, Record Group 255, 115.24.

[17] Thomas F. Gelder and James P. Lewis, "Comparison of Heat Transfer from Airfoil in Natural and Simulated Icing Conditions," NACA TN 2480, 1951. Hardy's original paper is cited in note 14. See also Uwe von Glahn, "The Icing Problem," note 5.

[18] See Myron Tribus, "Intermittent Heating for Aircraft Ice Protection," Ph.D. Dissertation, University of California at Los Angeles, 1950.

[19] See, for example, Vernon H. Gray and Dean T. Bowden, "Comparison of Several Methods of Cyclical De-Icing of a Gas-Heated Airfoil," NACA Research Memorandum E53C27, 1952.

[20] R. J. Brun, William Lewis, Porter Perkins, and John Serafini, "Impingement of Cloud Droplets on a Cylinder and Procedure for Measuring Liquid-Water Content and Droplet Sizes in Supercooled Clouds by Rotating Multicylinder Method," NACA Report 1215, 1955, p. 1–43.

[21] The first sign of the reawakened interest in icing research by the Federal Aviation Administration was the republication of old NACA data in "Engineering Summary of Airframe Icing Technical Data," FAA ADS-4, 1963; and "Engineering Summary of Powerplant Icing Technical Data," FAA RD-77-76.

[22] Minutes of Meeting of Subcommittee on Aircraft Fire Prevention, 3 February 1948. National Archives, Record Group 255, 115.35.

[23] "Preliminary Survey of Existing Data on Aircraft Fire Problem and a Suggested Research Program," 10 December 1947. National Archives, Record Group 255, 115.35.

[24] Minutes of the Meeting of Subcommittee on Aircraft Fire Prevention, 3 February 1948. National Archives, Record Group 255, 115.35.

[25] Allen W. Dallas, "Views of the ATA on the Aircraft Fire Problem." National Archives, Record Group 255, 115.35.

[26] Minutes of Meeting of Panel on "Reduction of Hazards due to Aircraft Fires," 31 October 1947. National Archives, Record Group 255, 115.32.

[27] Preliminary Survey, 10 December 1947. National Archives, Record Group 255, 115.35.

[28] Minutes of the NACA Subcommittee on Aircraft Fire Prevention, 3 February 1948. National Archives, Record Group 255, 115.32.

[29] Lewis A. Rodert to Director, "Visit of Mr. Lewis A. Rodert to West Coast Aircraft Industry in Regard to Fire Problem," 12 March 1948. National Archives, Record Group 255, 115.35.

[30] Transcript of interview with Irving Pinkel by V. Dawson, 30 January 1985, p. 13.

[31] Irving Pinkel, G. Merritt Preston, and Gerard J. Pesman, "Mechanism of Start and Development of Aircraft Crash Fires," NACA Technical Report 1133, 1953. Also typescript, unsigned and undated, by a member of the photographic branch, author's files.

[32] Irving Pinkel to Associate Director, "Visit of Airline and Airframe Personnel to NACA-Lewis on January 13, 1958." NASA Lewis Records, Box 297, 116.9.

[33] Film TF-26: G.M. Preston and I. I. Pinkel, "NACA Crash Fire Research," 1953. Cited in NACA Film Catalogue, Lewis Flight Propulsion Laboratory. Available at NASA Lewis Photo Laboratory.

[34] Correspondence from R. S. Sliff, Federal Aviation Administration, Larry H. Hewin, U.S. Army Air Mobility Research and Development Laboratory, Marc P. Dunnam, Air Force Aero Propulsion Laboratory (ASFC), and Franklin W. Kolk, American Airlines, to Irving Pinkel supports this conclusion.

[35] In May 1963 G. M. Preston received a medal for outstanding leadership in the Mercury Program. The roles of Scott Simkinson, Joe Bobik, and others at Cape Canaveral are discussed in Charles Murray and Catherine Cox, *Apollo: The Race to the Moon* (New York: Simon & Schuster, 1989).

[36] Murray and Cox, *Apollo*, p. 48.

[37] Loyd S. Swenson, Jr., James M. Grimwood, and Charles C. Alexander, *This New Ocean*, NASA SP-4201 (Washington, D.C.: U.S. Government Printing Office, 1966) p. 201.

[38] Ibid, p. 44.

[39] Ibid, p. 244–245.

[40] Eric Bergaust, *Murder on Pad 34* (New York: Putnam, 1968). See also Murray and Cox, *Apollo*, p. 189–205. Transcript of interview with Irving Pinkel by V. Dawson, 30 January 1985, p. 18.

CHAPTER SEVEN

PUSHING INNOVATION AND INDUSTRY RESISTANCE

In 1958, when the NACA became part of NASA, NASA became its own principal customer. It supervised contracts with industry to provide NASA with hardware for space exploration. During the NACA period Lewis Laboratory's relationship with industry was substantially different. The laboratory's role was to stimulate innovation in engine design. There was no legal mechanism to facilitate the transfer of technology generated through government research to industry. Exactly how the ideas in a NACA report took concrete form in the design of an engine could never be determined. It was part of the unwritten rules of this interaction that the government did not ask for credit or receive patents. No engine company liked to admit that innovation did not come from within its own laboratories or from the shop floor.

In the early post-World War II period, the engine industry was fearful that the NACA would interfere in the development of engine prototypes. In 1946 and 1947 the Industry Consulting Committee, composed of aircraft and engine manufacturers, criticized the laboratory's research plans for not being fundamental enough. Oscar Schey remarked that the manufacturers did not object to the NACA's research in principle, but there was no agreement over what exactly constituted fundamental research. Industry defined fundamental research as "anything that can be done with a pencil and slide rule and such facilities as the industry does not have."[1] If research were limited to the more theoretical aspects of the aircraft engine—problems solved with pencil and slide rule—the laboratory might be accused of duplicating the work of the universities.[2] The laboratory valued its intermediate position between industry and academia. The heart of its work was to prod industry to innovate, but it had to avoid being used by industry to clean up immediate development problems. At the same time, it could not allow its research to become so advanced that it was of no practical use. The balance was never easy.

Although testing engine prototypes could be construed as development, it seemed essential to the laboratory's mission. The laboratory could only promote innovation if it had a thorough knowledge of existing engines. Through testing in the Altitude Wind Tunnel and later in the "four burner" area, engineers learned the mysteries of all types and makes of gas turbine engines. The machine itself was a teacher, and expertise came, in Bruce Lundin's view, from "running engines." Lundin, who graduated from the University of California in 1942 with an engineering degree, reflected, "The reason you have the expertise is that you learn in the facilities. You don't get your expertise by a slide rule or running a computer... You get your expertise by working with real hardware and real conditions."[3]

The Industry Consulting Committee and members of the NACA Executive Committee at the Cleveland laboratory, September 26, 1945. Vannevar Bush is second from left.

Although testing isolated components like cylinders in the piston engine could provide data to predict engine performance, the jet engine as a dynamic system was far more complex. It required full-scale testing, in either a wind tunnel or a special propulsion systems laboratory. Although the jet engine's components—the compressor, combustor, and turbine—were also tested in special "rigs," some problems were apparent only when the entire system was "bolted together." On the importance of the systems approach, one engineer reflected:

> An engine constitutes a dynamic system and how it reacts and behaves to external and internal changes and disturbances is of vital significance to safe flight. For example, too rapid a throttle advance can cause a compressor to go into "stall" and trigger a "surge" in the engine system. This can result in physical damage and/or combustor flame-out. How and why such phenomena occur and developing analytical means to describe and predict such events from component data are legitimate research objectives. The theories that are developed can only be verified by running a variety of systems at full scale over a range of flight conditions.[4]

One of the goals of basic research in gas turbine engines was to isolate and define problems common to them all. This required knowledge of all types of existing engines. In the early post-World War II years, the engine companies had no choice but to allow the Cleveland laboratory to test their engines; neither the military nor the engine companies had adequate engine facilities. They had to rely on the NACA to test military engine prototypes. Through an understanding with the military services, after the completion of a particular company's test program, the laboratory kept the engine for an additional six months. The engine was completely disassembled by machine shop technicians so that the engineers could study its components and run tests. At the end of six months, Cleveland engineers knew the engine's strengths and weaknesses as well as, or better, than its original designers.

NACA engineers welcomed the increased interaction with industry brought about by this testing program. The new relationship with the engine industry had begun with the reform of the Power Plants Committee in 1940, when the engine companies won representation. Ben Pinkel, who represented the NACA on many of the subcommittees during the war and early postwar period, recalled this reform as a positive step in the creation of an effective relationship with industry. "We worked in the dark down at Langley. We did what we thought was good, but we weren't sure." There was no system for getting information about the kinds of problems industry needed solved. Contact between engine manufacturers and NACA engineers was limited to a yearly conference. "After each talk, we would ask them, 'Well, what are your problems?' The engine company people would not talk in front of an audience that contained its competitors." Although representatives of the airframe manufacturers made many follow-up visits to Langley to communicate their requirements confidentially, the engine manufacturers remained secretive. Power Plants engineers at Langley were never able to duplicate the productive working relationship between the NACA and the airframe industry. It took the new committee structure, created by George Mead, to foster the development of trust between the proprietary engine industry and government researchers. In Ben Pinkel's view, service on various NACA committees "allowed us to get an insight, a very intimate insight" into the problems of the engine companies and the military. Government and industry engineers formed strong working relationships. For the first time, when information or a piece of equipment was needed, a phone call could bring immediate results. "The idea of this personal contact, of knowing the people in the field," Pinkel recalled, "I don't know if everybody appreciated that, but it was great."[5]

Although the results of research were published by the NACA, industry engine designers had no obligation to use the knowledge made available to them. More than the availability of advanced research was necessary to encourage innovation, which was costly, and the potential benefit of a small change had to be weighed against problems that it might cause in other parts of the complex engine system. To become an instrument in the transfer of advanced engine technology to industry, Lewis Laboratory had to create a market for its expertise through the building of a network of personal contacts with the growing and highly competitive industry.

PROPRIETARY RIGHTS AND THE BRITISH NENE

Theodore von Kármán, often critical of the NACA, aptly called it "skeptical, conservative, and reticent."[6] von Kármán could speak with the relative freedom of the academician; he could never appreciate the constraints placed on the government researcher. The practice of restricting the flow of information from the NACA originated at Langley in the 1930s through the efforts of the NACA's fastidious Executive Secretary, John Victory. All correspondence was reviewed at the branch level and signed by the engineer-in-charge. Incoming mail went first to the engineer-in-charge, and phone calls were strictly monitored. Although national security considerations may have influenced the retention of these practices after World War II, it is most likely that they originated from the need to protect secret or proprietary information. Given the traditional near-phobic concern of the engine industry about proprietary matters, NACA engineers had to be extremely careful about what information they shared with the aeronautical community outside the laboratory. A loose tongue might reveal an innovation painstakingly developed by one company to its competitor.

This need for reticence, however, presented the NACA with a dilemma. The purpose of the laboratory was to encourage innovation and to stimulate competition among the engine companies by making information freely available to its entire constituency. Industry allowed publication of certain basic research, but new knowledge that could be used to make a profit was considered proprietary, the property of the company. Innovations made by industry scientists and engineers were either protected by patents or kept secret or proprietary to prevent competitors from reaping the fruits of the arduous and expensive development.[7] It became apparent that, to preserve its relationships with the engine industry, Lewis Laboratory had to be willing to protect the proprietary interests of individual companies by respecting limitations on the free publication of its research.

In the testing of full-scale engines, the Cleveland laboratory ran into the teeth of the proprietary rights issue. The laboratory existed to promote competition among the engine companies, not to become a competitor itself. The government was not supposed to participate directly in development; its role was to provide basic research to support the development of engines by private industry. In practice, as long as the laboratory had facilities superior to those of the engine companies, its work could legitimately shade off into development. Industry needed the NACA to test its engines and was willing to listen to suggestions for their improvement. However, since the engine companies were in the process of building their own facilities, this aspect of its work might be curtailed in the near future. Without early access to state of the art engines, the laboratory was in danger of losing its place on the cutting edge of propulsion research.

Carlton Kemper, Executive Engineer of Lewis Laboratory, expressed this dilemma in a memo to Headquarters, November 1, 1946: "It is realized that fundamental research can be conducted on obsolete and obsolescent models of a given aircraft powerplant, but interest is always at a low ebb unless results are presented for the latest aircraft-engine models."[8] He suggested that the laboratory should "cooperate wholeheartedly with these manufacturers" and that part of a successful relationship would depend on working out a mutually satisfactory policy on proprietary rights. Only this would ensure a continuing supply of engines in the development stage. General Electric, stung by the Army Air Forces award of the production contracts for the I-40 and the TG-180 engines to the Allison Company, was the first to voice its concerns to the NACA. The company admitted that Allison could produce engines more cheaply because of its government-owned factories. Nevertheless, General Electric was determined that in the future "engineering knowledge will not be turned over to a competitor at no cost, as was done in this case."[9] Kemper warned that General Electric's productive relationship with the laboratory was in jeopardy unless a satisfactory solution to the problem of proprietary rights could be found. Specifically, Kemper reported, General Electric did not object to the release of wind tunnel data as long as the laboratory refrained from discussing how improved efficiencies in the turbine or compressor, for example, were obtained. "Since the war is over and they are now in a highly competitive field, they request that the Committee refrain from releasing their engineering designs to their competitors."

Kemper revealed that General Electric's decision to stay in the aircraft engine business would mean "real competition" for Wright Aeronautical, Pratt & Whitney, and the Allison Division of General Motors. That was all to the good. The more players in the engine business, the more likely they were to feel pressure to innovate. In Kemper's view, General Electric had wisely decided to concentrate on development of new designs and would not invest in production facilities. Rather, it planned to subcontract with other companies for the manufacture of its new engines.

This strategy by General Electric had implications for the future research role of the laboratory. Kemper stressed that, with its new policy, General Electric would be all the more insistent that the laboratory concentrate on fundamental problems in jet engines, particularly the improvement of specific components.

> To maintain our position in the research field we must concentrate on the fundamental problems of the compressor and turbine, on the design of NACA combustion chambers that incorporate the fundamental information gained by the Committee on combustion, controls, metallurgy, operating cycles, and on methods of designing more efficient compressors and turbines. It is only by having better ideas than industry that we can maintain our outstanding position in the jet-engine field.[10]

Despite Kemper's warning, a collision course over the proprietary rights issue had already been set. The NACA came into conflict, not with General Electric, but with Pratt & Whitney, when the company took its first step in the new field of jet propulsion. An article in *Flight Magazine* in spring 1946 first called attention to the superiority of the British Nene to General Electric's I-40. From the same design in less time and with inferior facilities for testing, Rolls Royce had produced a superior engine. Development of the Nene, initially ten months behind that of the I-40, had continued after World War II.[11]

Exactly what precipitated the Navy's interest in the Nene is unclear, but it may be related to the problems that Westinghouse was encountering in the development of the 19XB and the 24C, its turbojet with an axial-flow compressor. Toward the end of 1946, the Navy Bureau of Aeronautics had obtained two Nene engines and tested them at the Navy's engine laboratory near Philadelphia, Penn. In a hurry to develop the Nene, the Navy invited Pratt & Whitney to tackle the job, betting on the company's solid engineering reputation to carry it off despite limited experience with turbojet engines.[12] Interservice rivalry may have played a role in this decision. With the Army Air Forces committed to the I-40, the Nene represented an opportunity to upstage the Navy's rival. However, satisfaction in having a superior engine was no doubt tempered by the sobering knowledge that Great Britain, as a goodwill gesture under a Labor Government, had allowed Rolls Royce to sell the license to the Nene to the Soviet Union in 1946.[13] A superior engine in the hands of a potential enemy made the production of the Nene a high national priority.

Prior to its purchase of the license to manufacture the Nene from Rolls Royce, Pratt & Whitney lacked experience in the new jet propulsion technology. The company realized that the new companies in the aircraft engine field—General Electric and Westinghouse—had the advantage of a head start. Pratt & Whitney's strategy was to leap frog over its competition, building on the solid engine expertise of the British. However, from a national security point of view, the setting up of Pratt & Whitney in the production of a foreign engine had a negative side. Would the superiority of the Nene, produced by a strong and experienced engine company, squeeze out the fledgling aircraft engine efforts of Westinghouse and General Electric?

The same recognition of the superiority of British gas turbine engines that made American companies eager to obtain licenses for their manufacture made Cleveland engineers anxious to test all types of British turbojet and turboprop engines. They needed experience. They knew the strengths and weaknesses of American prototypes and were in an ideal position to point out what made British engines superior. Testing the Nene seemed particularly desirable. In December 1946 Carlton Kemper wrote to the Washington office, "Such a study should be particularly valuable in that the Nene engine is reported to have higher thrust, lower specific weight, and lower fuel consumption than current American service engines."[14] Exactly why the NACA was unable to obtain the Nene directly from the Navy is unclear, but the NACA took the unusual step of purchasing an engine directly from the Taylor Turbine Corporation, which owned the American license prior to its sale to Pratt & Whitney.

The Army Air Forces stood behind the NACA's decision to test the Nene and to disseminate the results to all the companies that manufactured gas turbine engines. In the view of Colonel H. Z. Bogert, the Army Liaison Officer at the Cleveland laboratory, to limit the distribution of research results hindered the ability of the United States to compete with the British. With the Nene also in the hands of the Soviet Union, the issue went beyond protecting commercial rights to issues of national security. However, even within the Army, there was no consensus on the correct policy to follow. Should distribution be limited to the five companies already involved in turbojet engine development? The civilian engineers employed at Wright Field argued that the government did not have the right to violate the proprietary rights of individual companies, since the Army paid only about 15 percent of the expenses for research and development. Kemper, however, took Bogert's side and argued for a wide distribution of research results. He thought that "it was poor policy to spend large sums in operating the Altitude Wind Tunnel and then to make the pertinent information available to only five companies because of the proprietary information in the report."[15]

After Pratt & Whitney began negotiations in April 1947 to acquire manufacturing and sales rights to the Nene, it became concerned over what role the NACA would play in allowing competitors to share the results of the NACA study. In December, with the acquisition of the license from Taylor Turbine complete, Pratt & Whitney informed the NACA that they held exclusive rights to the Nene and Derwent series of turbojet engines. They were, as of that date, actively engaged in production for the Navy, and the engines were therefore "in the same competition category as other Pratt & Whitney Aircraft engines." They did not object to the testing of the engine, but requested that the results be kept entirely confidential.[16]

There was no question that, with a good jet engine, Pratt & Whitney would be able to compete very effectively against Westinghouse, General Electric, and Allison without the help of the NACA. Moreover, with a projected date of 1950 for the completion of its Wilgoos Turbine Laboratory in West Hartford, Conn., Pratt & Whitney would soon have facilities for testing comparable to those of the Cleveland laboratory. The debate over the Nene would have important implications for any future relationship that the laboratory might develop with Pratt & Whitney and the rest of the engine industry.

In May 1948 Cleveland engineers completed the preliminary report of the tests of the Nene in the laboratory's new Altitude Chamber, designed by Ben Pinkel. Located in the "four burner area" of the West Wing of the Engine Research Building, these "burner rigs" were the forerunners of the Propulsion Systems Laboratory completed in 1952. The NACA sent the report to Pratt & Whitney, Rolls Royce, and the military services. At the same time it expressed the desire to make the report available to other American manufacturers "who may need this research information to facilitate fulfillment of military contracts."[17]

Perhaps anticipating a problem with Pratt & Whitney over the distribution of the report, Hugh Dryden, Director of the NACA, brought up the general issue of reports involving specific

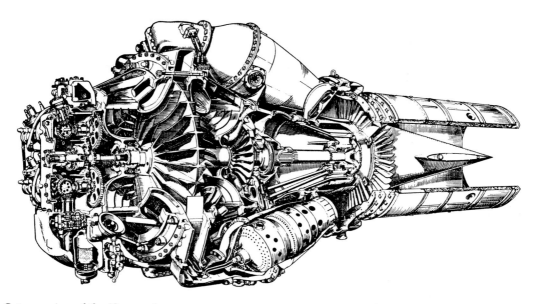

Cutaway view of the Nene engine.

engines in a meeting of the Power Plants Committee in May 1948. Dryden pointed out that the NACA did not want to undermine the "competitive free enterprise system," but "it was necessary to reconcile the interests of the military services, the engine manufacturer involved, and the engineering profession, which is interested in establishing a general body of knowledge on aircraft engine research."[18] Besides, Dryden pointed out, Pratt & Whitney had never objected to receiving reports summarizing the performance of the engines of its competitors, namely, Allison, General Electric, Packard, and Westinghouse.[19]

Pratt & Whitney's response was an unequivocal, if not unexpected, no. W. P. Gwinn, the General Manager of the company, responded, "From our point of view the information ceases to be confidential once it is given to competitive firms, either directly or indirectly. While an excellent report, in our judgment, it does not contain research information."[20] Research information, in Pratt & Whitney's view, should be more general. Pratt & Whitney objected to the report's careful record of data relating to performance and design characteristics.

Pratt & Whitney's commercial interest in the engine could not be protected. The Nene in the hands of the Soviet Union made it imperative that American engines surpass the standard it had set. Because of the Nene's challenge to the American jet engine community, it became known as the "Needle engine."[21] The role of the Cleveland laboratory was analogous. Its research became a prod or needle that kept industry from returning to its prewar path of extremely conservative (if profitable, in the short term) engine production.

The urgent need for a policy statement on the "release of information on specific engines" was brought up in December in the meeting of the Power Plants Committee, where it was debated at length. Dryden pointed out that "it would be uneconomical for the NACA Lewis Flight Propulsion Laboratory to construct engines for conducting research in comparison with obtaining engines built by the engine manufacturers." In general, specific engines were "supplied by the military services for research requested by them. In just one case the NACA purchased the engine." He warned that if the NACA were forced to provide its own engines with public funds, it would consider itself responsible to the industry as a whole. In other words, results of testing would be published freely, and proprietary rights would not be protected. With the present system, it was only after a certain time lapse that design improvements made by a particular company were disclosed to other manufacturers. While the total number of reports involved was relatively small, Dryden admitted that a policy that would provide a satisfactory definition of proprietary information was necessary.[22]

The question of why Lewis Laboratory had to test specific engines at all, although not actually raised, was pertinent. Why did the laboratory appear to go out of its way to engage in work so close to development? If the laboratory was doing fundamental research, why should it test the engine prototypes of a particular company? There were two reasons: first, the laboratory performed a service to the Air Force by testing aircraft engines prior to their purchase; second, in a field that was changing so rapidly, without experience with actual engines, Lewis engineers could not be sure that their work would be relevant to the engine problems that needed urgent solution. The development of the gas turbine engine was directly related to the security of the nation. Competition could not be protected if it meant that in the event of a war the United States might have to rely on inferior engines. As one of the military members of the Power Plants Committee stated during the debate over the Nene, "One problem from the Government point of view

Four burner area in the Engine Research Building.

was how desirable improvements which are known to the Government can be made in engines being purchased by the Government."[23]

The problem with an open market system at a time of heightened concern over national security was the conflict between national interest and what would be most beneficial to the individual companies. The NACA Power Plants Committee itself was a reflection in microcosm of this larger problem. As the minutes of the meeting in which these issues were discussed reported, "The Power Plants Committee is responsible to the nation as a whole, while the members of the committee from industry are responsible to the stockholders of their companies." Proprietary rights were necessary to preserve competition, but "the question is how much compromise there should be in the best interest of the country."[24]

The debate revealed that, in general, there appeared to be two classes of information whose release industry found objectionable. The first type involved defects and limitations of a particular engine that could be used to damage the reputation of a company. The second type could involve, for example, a superior component like a combustor. Pratt & Whitney's representative, Leonard S. Hobbs, observed, "A man is not improved by turning over to him what a good man did." With enough information a competitor could deduce what made the combustor superior and make similar improvements. The innovating company could lose the fruits of its investment in development. In response to Hobbs's objection, Massachusetts Institute of Technology (MIT) Professor Edward S. Taylor pointed out that improved performance "is an excellent stimulus to everyone else to obtain similar improvements." Edward P. Warner, former chief scientist at Langley, later professor at MIT and editor of *Aviation*, lent his prestige to the government side of the argument: "Everyone recognizes the desirability of releasing information that stimulates the other man to do as well."[25]

Although Lewis Laboratory won the privilege to distribute its report on the Nene because the engine was purchased prior to Pratt & Whitney's license, the policy hammered out in debates in the Power Plants Committee, the NACA Executive Committee, and the Industry Consulting Committee restricted a wide range of information from open dissemination. The policy approved in June 1949 stated that, to preserve a manufacturer's competitive position, technical information on models or components under active development would be withheld unless a specific agreement were reached with the manufacturer. Information on production models could only be furnished after review by the manufacturer. In addition, the manufacturer was to be furnished with the list of companies and individuals to whom the NACA intended to send information. Finally, any oral communication by the NACA before a report was issued was subject to review.

This strict policy on proprietary rights prevented free dissemination of knowledge gleaned at government expense. However, the NACA could not refuse to agree to it. Without a satisfactory relationship with industry, the Cleveland laboratory would lose its central position in the mainstream of jet engine development. The cardinal rule of the laboratory became discretion. When representatives of engine companies arrived to follow the tests on a particular engine built by their company, their movements on the laboratory grounds were strictly limited to prevent them from obtaining information about an engine of a competitor undergoing tests at the same time. The staff learned to choose their words carefully. They mastered the elaborate choreography of "who gets what information." This discreet behavior of NACA engineers contributed to the growing respect for the laboratory on the part of the engine companies. However, the NACA paid a price. Capitulation to the engine companies kept the NACA in the mainstream of engine development, but it limited the information the NACA could publish freely to the entire industry. Its role as a goad to promote innovation by stimulating competition was compromised.

The unfavorable outcome of the debate over proprietary rights reveals the vulnerability of the NACA as the tensions of the Cold War increased. Although military planners looked on the USSR as a possible enemy in the event of World War III as early as 1945, this threat did not seem immediate because of the perceived inferiority of Soviet technology.[26] The Nene design in Soviet hands began to change that perception. Oscar Schey, head of the Compressor and Turbine Division, pointed out in a 1948 memo that, in contrast to the engine situation in the late 1930s, when they had more than 20 years of experience in reciprocating engines, the engine community had barely four years of experience in jet technology. "As Dr. Lewis often pointed out at the beginning of World War II," he wrote, "we had to fight the war with the five engines that had already been developed and were in production." In 1948 the United States mass produced only one turbojet engine, the Allison J-33 (General Electric's I-40).[27] Knowledge of the limitations of the General Electric I-40 compared to the Nene heightened the concern of all knowledgeable engine experts. So great was the pressure to improve existing engines that Schey advocated an extension of the work week to 48 hours. When Congress passed the Unitary Wind Tunnel Plan Act the following year, the Air Force received funding for the Arnold Development Engineering Center in Tullahoma, Tenn. With extensive wind tunnels and other facilities for testing engines projected for Tullahoma, the facilities at the Cleveland laboratory would lose their unique value to the propulsion community. Moreover, the Act stipulated that the Unitary Plan tunnels built by the NACA were to be made available to industry for testing programs.[28] The Cold War threatened to push the laboratory back into development—its wartime role of mopping up for the engine companies.

WHY ARE BRITISH ENGINES SUPERIOR?

The focus on the Nene raised the question, why did the British produce superior engines when their facilities were markedly inferior to those of the United States? Not only did the United States have better facilities, but American engines were made of better alloys developed to withstand the higher temperatures of the combustor and turbine. A consensus emerged that the superiority of British engines was the result of meticulous engineering and closer cooperation between members of the propulsion community. For example, John Collins, Chief of the Engine Performance and Materials Division, believed that British superiority could be "attributed to a large extent to refinements in the details of the engine design and construction."[29] Dryden was more blunt. He observed after a trip to England at the height of the proprietary rights debate that the "lack of money for facilities has forced them to make the best use of their brains."[30] In addition, the British had been able to foster "a much closer collaboration between the engine companies in technical matters." Dryden called the attitude of Rolls Royce executives on the release of information, "in refreshing contrast to those of Pratt and Whitney, for example."[31]

Dryden's perceptions correctly reflected the more cooperative approach of British engine companies. The British Gas Collaboration Committee, established in November 1941 to spur the development of the turbojet, encouraged engineers to share information. Frank Whittle recalled that the committee "helped a lot to decide in what order things should be done." About ten groups involved in jet engine development met monthly, and, although the meetings were stuffy and formal, at the parties in the evenings, "we really found out what each other was doing."[32] The rationale for the Collaboration Committee was the belief that good ideas should be made available to whomever could use them. In Dryden's eyes, the difference in attitude on the part of British companies contributed to the continued superiority of British engines.

In the United States competition was regarded as the key to a healthy economy. The sharing of technical innovations was prohibited by American anti-trust laws.[33] As late as 1948, the general lack of coordination and communication among research laboratories and industry was noteworthy to P. F. Martinuzzi, an Italian gas turbine expert employed by the British. He remarked, on a trip sponsored by the American Society of Mechanical Engineers, that within the American industry "the general trend is to tackle the problems independently of past experience and of what competitors are doing." Available data were neglected by designers. The author had high regard for the research of the Cleveland laboratory, but it was hardly a clearinghouse for information. Companies engaged in development of jet engines did not pay much attention to what the NACA or any other laboratories were doing.[34]

To develop afterburners required full-scale engine testing. Here a system consisting of twin exhausts is tried on General Electric's I-40, 1949.

Despite the availability of NACA research, the engine companies resisted new ideas on the technological frontier. Hans von Ohain, then a research scientist at Wright Field, recalled that when they were invited to the Cleveland laboratory to hear the results of the laboratory's latest research, "it was almost a festival because they had such interesting and good things to say." The Air Force was "all ears," but the work at Lewis was so advanced that "industry fought it to the teeth."[35] This was particularly true in the compressor area, where fundamental work on the transonic compressor was eventually incorporated into the design of the turbofan. Von Ohain credits Silverstein with the vision to persevere with compressor research, despite the attitudes of the engine companies.

Gradually, the research of the Cleveland laboratory won respect and assisted in the transfer of new ideas from the realm of the research report to the design of an engine. In addition to published reports, technical transfer occurred through personal contacts between government engineers and scientists and their counterparts in industry. The most effective avenues for this exchange were special conferences to which selected individuals were invited. In addition, the laboratory held triennial inspections to show off its facilities and explain the latest research. Employees who were selected to give talks at various laboratory "stops" prepared their talks carefully. NACA engineers learned to be articulate, personable, and lucid in explaining complex material. Laboratory tradition also encouraged after-hours socializing with industry representatives. Gradually Lewis engineers became valued colleagues to their counterparts in industry. For the engine designer, being able to associate a report with a face and knowing the history of a particular piece of research through personal conversations created a general climate for acceptance.

A mutual desire to keep abreast of what the other was doing led to a series of official British and American contacts through the late 1940s and early 1950s. A series of British missions visited the Cleveland laboratory, and representatives from the laboratory went abroad. The Army organized one of the first American postwar tours, which came to be called by the British, "The American Gas Turbine Mission." Walter T. Olson represented the Cleveland laboratory on the nearly month-long tour in June 1947, visiting the major British engine manufacturers, as well as the British government laboratories, the National Gas Turbine Establishment at Whetstone, the National Physical Laboratories at Teddington, and the Royal Aircraft Establishment at Farnborough. The tour ended with visits to American engine companies to educate them concerning the latest British advances.

The mission drew no general conclusions about the reasons for continued British superiority. Nevertheless, an example cited by Olson showed the advantage of greater coordination and the sharing of information. The development of a "universal" combustor by the Lucas Company had led to its adoption by a number of British companies, thereby saving them the trouble of repeating work that had already been done. Olson wrote:

> The main advantage in combustion that England enjoys is that virtually all new gas turbine engines start off with a reasonably well developed combustor. In the United States the engines now under development have a variety of styles of combustor, many of them quite unproven. This is because in the United States there has been no one organization with the manpower, the money, and a clear mandate to develop a "universal" combustor for the industry, that is no counterpart of the Lucas Company.[36]

While the general superiority of British engineering, combined with a spirit of greater collaboration, could be seen in the Nene, British work on engines with axial-flow compressors, however, appeared to be behind that of General Electric's TG-180 and the various models of the Westinghouse "Yankee" engine (J34/24C). In compressor design, the strong emphasis by the NACA on the development of an axial compressor eventually allowed the United States to pull ahead of the British. Testing the Nene, in fact, contributed to the Cleveland laboratory's growing confidence that the Nene's centrifugal compressor had limitations that would soon be overcome by the more efficient axial design. Nevertheless, the British were also pushing the development of an engine with axial compressors. Rolls Royce's Avon engine was "without question the 'blue chip' project" because, Olson reported, many British aircraft companies with projects in the design stage planned to use the Avon engine.[37] The first major departure from the Whittle design, the Avon was used in the Canberra Bomber and other important British planes. It was selected for the De Haviland Comet, intended to be the world's first passenger jetliner.[38]

Clearly with the knowledge of the Cleveland laboratory's work on the axial compressor in mind, Olson noted, "It is quite generally appreciated among compressor research and design personnel that some theory for the effect of the boundary layers in compressors and cascades is urgently needed. Only trivial progress has been made on this problem to date."[39] Great Britain was at a disadvantage because it lacked altitude chambers to test full-scale engines and facilities to test components, such as compressors, at high speeds.[40] The National Gas Turbine Establishment was the only organization in Great Britain conducting large-scale cascade tests over a wide range of conditions, but Olson revealed, "The cascade results are inaccurate because of boundary layer effects in the cascade test rig itself."[41]

COMPRESSOR RESEARCH

Lewis Laboratory's Compressor and Turbine Division conducted research on both centrifugal and axial compressors. John Stanitz applied a relaxation solution to the problem of two-dimensional compressible flow in a centrifugal compressor with straight radial blades—an achievement that established him as an expert in centrifugal compressors.[42] However, the compressor staff always had greater enthusiasm for the axial compressor—a legacy of the NACA's first eight-stage axial compressor designed by Eastman Jacobs and Eugene Wasielewski in 1938 and tested in 1941. The smaller frontal area of the axial compressor made it more compact and better suited aerodynamically for flight than the more cumbersome centrifugal compressor. However, the greater aerodynamic complexity of the axial compressor presented enormous scientific and engineering challenges. An axial compressor had to be designed so that air moved smoothly across each of the rows of compressor blades. Research initiated in 1944 with the transfer from Langley of work on the Jacobs-Wasielewski eight-stage compressor laid the basis for the laboratory's future achievements in the compressor field. Jacobs and Wasielewski had approached compressor design by applying the theory for an isolated airfoil. This became the standard approach of American designers until the mid-1950s.[43]

Frank Whittle, for example, looked with bemused superiority at what he considered the Cleveland laboratory's misplaced emphasis on the axial compressor. On a visit to the laboratory in 1946, he asserted that the centrifugal compressor would continue to be preferred for its rugged dependability. In 1948 the abandonment of the centrifugal compressor by American designers was called a "pity" by the Italian expert P. F. Martinuzzi (at that time working for the British) "because it appears that the axial compressor types which have replaced the earlier centrifugals are not more reliable, are heavier and 'several times' more expensive." Martinuzzi speculated that American emphasis on the axial compressor might reflect "a desire to disclaim British influence."[44]

Between 1945 and 1950 the relative merits of the centrifugal versus the axial compressor were debated in Great Britain.[45] However, in the United States few engineering voices were raised in support of the centrifugal compressor. The main effort among American engineers focused in the early postwar period on developing the axial compressor. American industry designers came to rely on NACA-generated data based on the isolated airfoil approach. As Brian Nichelson pointed out in his recent Ph.D. dissertation:

> It made sense for the Americans to rely on the isolated airfoil method in light of the wealth of data available from the NACA on the performance of a large family of airfoil profiles. Whereas the Germans had rejected the isolated airfoil approach because it would have required a great deal of experimental data, the Americans already had such data available, courtesy of the NACA. It also made sense in another respect: Americans had long used a blade element design technique based on airfoil theory in designing propellers and single-stage fans and blowers. As a result, American designers not only felt comfortable using this type of design theory, they also began to view the time and energy spent in developing it as an investment. Thus the isolated airfoil approach became the main American axial compressor design theory during the 1940s.[46]

The isolated airfoil approach was not precise enough to give accurate predictions of compressor performance. The limitations of the isolated airfoil approach were first recognized by

British aerodynamicists A. A. Griffith, Hayne Constant, and A. R. Howell of the Royal Aircraft Establishment (RAE). Howell published his two landmark papers on cascade theory in 1945. However, American compressor designers, reluctant to abandon old approaches and habits, ignored the British cascade method until the mid-1950s. [47]

It is difficult to determine exactly what role members of the Lewis Compressor Division played in initially promoting the isolated airfoil approach and later coaxing the engine manufacturers to give it up. Industry designers never liked to admit they picked up useful information from NACA reports and conferences. From the early postwar years, members of the Compressor and Turbine Division had concentrated on developing a supersonic compressor based on the work initiated by Arnold Redding at Westinghouse and Arthur Kantrowitz at Langley during World War II. British cascade studies received increased attention as this work expanded. In the area of three-dimensional flows, the research of Frank Marble, Chung-Hua Wu, and Lincoln Wolfenstein built on Howell's work and that of German researchers Walter Traupel and Richard Meyer. Marble described the flow of an ideal incompressible fluid through an axial compressor. Wu and Wolfstein tackled the problem of a compressible fluid flowing across stages of an infinite number of blades.[48]

In 1952 efforts at Lewis Laboratory were directed by Robert O. Bullock to the development of a transonic compressor. Bullock headed a group that included William K. Ritter, William A. Benser, Harold B. Finger, John F. Klapproth, Melvin J. Hartmann, Arthur A. Medieros, Seymour Lieblein, and Irving A. Johnsen. Hartmann and others developed a flow model for estimating the shock losses that could be anticipated as the air flowed through the compressor. Seymour Lieblein developed the diffusion factor, D, now universally accepted as a measure of blade loading. Ten years of single- and multi-stage investigations culminated in the development of an experimental eight-stage axial-flow transonic compressor.[49]

To verify theories developed analytically, the compressor staff designed and built complicated facilities, called single- and multi-stage compressor test rigs. The data they provided were essential to industry designers. Without this verification of mathematical predictions, no engine company would have had the temerity to undertake the expensive development of a new compressor. Results, made available to the entire industry through NACA reports, became the "Compressor Bible" to members of the engine community. Eventually the Compressor Division prepared a manual that summarized the entire corpus of compressor knowledge. This manual, issued in 1956 as a three-volume NACA Confidential Research Memorandum edited by Irving Johnsen and Robert O. Bullock, marked the culmination of NACA compressor research.[50]

The NACA may have played a role in the development of compressors similar to that of the British Lucas Company for combustors. The laboratory concentrated on generic components for application in a variety of engines produced by different manufacturers. While

The Jacobs-Wasielewski eight-stage axial compressor perfected in the 1950s.

the Lucas company actually built combustors to sell, the NACA aimed to establish a body of knowledge on which designers could depend. NACA compressor work advanced the general state of the art through dissemination of information, thereby saving individual companies the cost and time of doing this research themselves. At the same time, by making knowledge freely available to the entire engine community, it discouraged one company from locking in a competitive advantage.

HOW VALUABLE ARE FACILITIES?

For the NACA, maintenance of elaborate research facilities cut into the time that could be devoted to actual research, and, at first, the British maintained their lead in the new field of jet propulsion. As Ben Pinkel recalled, a member of a British delegation once asked him, "When do you have time to brood?" However, in the long run these facilities paid off. In the absence of superior facilities, the British government funded basic research by the engine companies that was carried on independently of the development of specific engines.[51] Not only did the British differ in the way that research was funded, but also in styles of approach to the development of specific engines. The British used a cut-and-try approach that depended on building and testing successive models of a particular engine. As Ray Sharp observed on a lengthy trip to Europe in 1951:

> Instead of concentrating first upon acquiring the tools, the equipment, best suited for use in investigating powerplant problems and developing more powerful engines, the

One of the unique compressor rigs used to test axial compressors, 1948.

British spend great amounts of manpower and money to build large numbers of a new experimental model, each one slightly different from the other. They often come up with a very good end-product, but the cost is greater, I believe, than our system in which we first study the problems involved, using our equipment, and then go ahead and build only two or three of a new model.[52]

So respected was the resultant engineering from the British system that in 1953, when Westinghouse needed help with its foundering 24C turbojet engine, the company signed a mutual assistance agreement with Rolls Royce to share afterburner technology in order to benefit from British turbojet expertise. On a visit to the Cleveland laboratory after the signing of this agreement, the Rolls Royce representative confided that he had been "directed by Lord Hives to follow through on the collaboration between the two companies and see if Rolls Royce could 'make an engine company out of the bloody buggers.' "[53] However, while the British approach yielded short-term benefits, by the early 1950s British domination of the aircraft engine field had begun to slide.

The key to the postwar American approach to engine development was the involvement of government engineers. The Cleveland laboratory built the necessary facilities for testing complete engine systems, but its expertise went beyond full-scale testing to the study of individual components. NACA engineers developed theories to predict engine performance and verified these theories in special "rigs." The NACA tackled specialized areas of research, such as components, combustion and fuels, lubricants and seals, materials, and heat transfer. Through publication and interaction between industry and government engineers, the laboratory encouraged innovation while saving the engine companies some of the costs of development. Government research promoted innovation. A designer could not ignore a particular innovation if it was likely that his company's competitors were going to incorporate it into their latest engine prototypes.

The Korean War (1950–1953) marked a turning point in the development of the American turbojet industry, and the end of British dominance. Before the Korean War,

A Westinghouse axial-flow turbojet fitted with NACA variable area nozzle for afterburner studies in the Altitude Wind Tunnel, 1951.

more than half the aircraft engines produced in the United States were of the piston engine type. By the end of the war, the balance had shifted, primarily because of the reequipment of the Navy with jet planes.[54] During the war, Pratt & Whitney was the licensee for the production of the Rolls Royce Tay, or J48, the most powerful engine produced by either the United States or Great Britain. The Tay, however, was the last British engine to reflect the superiority of British engines. When Wright Aeronautical bought the license for the British Armstrong Siddeley Sapphire (designated the J-67 by the United States Air Force), a turbojet with an axial compressor, the company found that its thrust was too low for the aircraft it was intended to power. The failure of Wright's development of the Sapphire contributed to its demise.

Ironically, Pratt & Whitney, many years behind Westinghouse and General Electric in acquiring turbojet expertise, began to dominate the turbojet industry after its development of the JT3 (J57). The JT3 initially had better fuel economy and more than double the thrust of its competitors. The innovative design feature of Pratt & Whitney's engine was an axial compressor with a double shaft (also called a dual-rotor or two-spool), a feature that dramatically increased the efficiency of the compressor. This engine placed the company in the forefront of aircraft propulsion development.[55] General Electric's answer to Pratt & Whitney's JT3 was the J79 with an innovative compressor with variable stators.[56]

By the mid-1950s the American turbojet industry had matured and narrowed to two companies: Pratt & Whitney and General Electric. British aircraft engine companies found it increasingly difficult to compete against their American counterparts. Two tragic crashes of the Comet in 1954 left the De Haviland Company in an unfavorable competitive position. The crashes were caused by metal fatigue brought on by the cyclical pressurization of the cabin, not by the aircraft's Avon engines. Before the Comet regained its Certificate of Airworthiness, De Haviland had lost the commercial market to Boeing's 707 and the Douglas DC-8, powered by Pratt & Whitney's JT3.[57] The British had set the stage for the turbojet revolution, but they could not sustain their early lead.

The development of superior NACA facilities for testing engine prototypes played a role in American dominance in the engine field. This view is supported by remarks made by Rolls Royce representatives on a visit to Lewis Laboratory in 1955. They lamented that the company "has been 'led up the garden path' by the Labor and Conservative governments which have promised to provide full-scale test facilities for the British gas turbine industry since 1945."[58] Since these promised facilities still had not materialized, Rolls Royce planned to spend the equivalent of $15 million to build two small wind tunnels and two altitude test chambers. In addition, in 1955 the British made plans to

Pratt & Whitney's dual spool turbojet engine (JT3/P57) in the Altitude Wind Tunnel for nozzle studies as part of the NACA's aircraft noise suppression research, 1957.

build a large altitude test facility to test full-scale engines at the National Gas Turbine Establishment at Pyestock, with a second at Bedford. These facilities came too late to recoup the British lead. Rolls Royce continued to send its engines to Cleveland for testing. As late as 1956, records from the log of the Altitude Wind Tunnel indicate that the NACA tested the Rolls Royce Avon engine.

The Cold War justified the continued sharing of British engine technology with the United States—an exchange heavily weighted in favor of the United States. Lewis engineers developed an intimate knowledge of British engines they could share with Pratt & Whitney and General Electric. American engine companies received a financial boost from large defense contracts necessary because of the dominant role of the United States in the North Atlantic Treaty Organization (NATO). The early 1950s also marked a decline in the influence of Lewis Laboratory in the aircraft engine field. The military services and industry had begun to develop facilities comparable or superior to those of the laboratory. The era of the air-breathing engine research at Lewis seemed to be reaching a natural point of termination. It was time to reassess Lewis's future role in the nation's propulsion research.

NOTES

[1] Memo from Oscar Schey to the Washington office, "Survey of Fundamental Research of the NACA–Aircraft Industries Association Comments," 19 November 1946, NASA Lewis Records, 34/376. See also Minutes of the Industry Consulting Committee, 3 December 1947, Committees and Subcommittees, National Archives, Record Group 255.

[2] Memo for the Chief of Research from Eugene Manganiello, 25 February 1946, NASA Lewis Records, 34/624.

[3] Interview with Bruce Lundin, 15 July 1986. Also interview with Carl Schueller, 12 October 1984.

[4] Seymour C. Himmel, personal communication.

[5] Transcribed interview with Ben Pinkel, 3 August 1985, p. 17.

[6] Quoted by Walter A. McDougall, . . . the Heavens and the Earth (New York: Basic Books, 1985), p. 164.

[7] See George Wise, Willis R. Whitney, General Electric, and the Origins of U.S. Industrial Research (New York: Columbia University Press, 1985), p. 106.

[8] Memo from Carlton Kemper to NACA, 1 November 1946, NASA Lewis Records, 34/317.7.

[9] Memo from Carlton Kemper to Director of Research, "Visit to General Electric River Works, Lynn, Mass., with Colonel Bogert to Discuss Their Objections to the Method of Handling Proprietary Material in NACA Reports," 3 February 1947, NASA Lewis Records, 34/317.76.

[10] Ibid.

[11] Flight, 18 April 1946, p. 389–393. Note: Because at the time the Nene was developed, the British had no suitable airframe, the Rolls Royce Company built a scaled-down version, the Derwent series of engines, to power the Meteor, one of the few airplanes able to fly fast enough during World War II to shoot down the V-1. Development of the Nene was actually started ten months after the I-40, but, unlike General Electric, which stopped development at the end of the war, Rolls Royce engineers continued to perfect the Nene. See Robert Schlaifer, The Development of Aircraft Engines (Boston: Graduate School of Business Administration, Harvard University, 1950), p. 373 and 476.

[12] The Pratt & Whitney Aircraft Story (West Hartford: Pratt & Whitney Aircraft Division of United Aircraft Corporation, 1950), p. 168.

[13] Sir Stanley Hooker stated in Not Much of an Engineer (Shrewsbury, England: Airlife, 1984), p. 98, "With Sir Stafford Cripps at the Board of Trade, the left-wing British Government appeared perfectly happy to sell our latest engine to the Russians, and in September 1946 clinched a deal for 25 Nenes and 30 Derwents, the first few of which the team took back to the Soviet Union and copied exactly in double-quick time. They were produced in colossal numbers for the MiG-15 and -17, Il-28, Tu-14 and many other aircraft. These aircraft were also supplied to the Soviet satellite countries, and North Korea! Over 20 years later I saw VK-1s (Soviet Nenes) being overhauled in Romania." For a discussion of British labor policy, see also Keith Hayward, Government and British Civil Aerospace (Manchester: Manchester University Press, 1983), p. 12–27.

[14] Carlton Kemper to NACA, "Investigation of Rolls Royce Nene jet-propulsion engine," 9 December 1946, NASA Lewis Records, 34/623.

[15] Carlton Kemper, "Conference Called by Colonel Bogert at Wright Field, January 23, 1947, Regarding Proprietary Material in NACA Reports for the Army Air Forces," NASA Lewis Records, 34/317.7.

[16] W. P. Gwinn to NACA, 3 December 1947, Power Plants Committee, National Archives, Record Group 255, 4/112.05.

[17] Zelmar Barson and H. D. Wilsted, "Preliminary Results of Nene II Engine Altitude-Chamber Performance Investigation, I-Altitude Performance Using Standard 18.75-Inch-Diameter Jet Nozzle," NACA Research Memorandum E8E12, 25 May 1948. J. W. Crowley to L. S. Hobbs, 25 May 1948, National Archives, Record Group 255, 4/112.05.

[18] Power Plants Committee Minutes, 21 May 1948, National Archives, Record Group 255, 112.02, p. 9.

[19] Hugh L. Dryden to W. P. Gwinn, 2 August 1948, National Archives, Record Group 255, 4/112.05.

[20] W. P. Gwinn to J. W. Crowley, 9 July 1948, National Archives, Record Group 255, 4/112.05.

[21] *Pratt & Whitney Aircraft Story* (West Hartford: Pratt & Whitney Aircraft Division of United Aircraft Corporation, 1950), p. 168.

[22] Power Plants Committee Minutes, 10 December 1948, National Archives, Record Group 255, 112.02, p. 13.

[23] Power Plants Committee Minutes, 10 December 1948, National Archives, Record Group 255, 112.02, p. 11.

[24] Ibid.

[25] Ibid, p. 12.

[26] Michael S. Sherry, *Preparing for the Next War* (New Haven: Yale University Press, 1977), p. 169–219.

[27] Oscar Schey, "Memorandum for the Director," 11 March 1948, NASA Lewis Records, 34/376.

[28] Alex Roland, *Model Research*, vol. I, NASA SP-4103 (Washington, D.C.: U.S. Government Printing Office, 1985) p. 215–219.

[29] John Collins to Director of Aeronautical Research, 29 January 1947, NASA Lewis Records, 34/376.

[30] Minutes of the NACA Executive Committee, 9 September 1948, National Archives, Record Group 255, 14/112.05.

[31] Hugh L. Dryden to John Victory, 29 August 1948, NASA Lewis Records, 232/150.

[32] *An Encounter Between the Jet Engine Inventors*, History Office, Aeronautical Systems Division Air Force Systems Command, Wright-Patterson Air Force Base, Historical Publication, 1978, p. 97.

[33] Abe Silverstein's comment to the author, September 1986.

[34] P. F. Martinuzzi, "Gas Turbines in the United States," *Flight*, 7 October 1948, p. 439–441.

[35] Interview with Hans von Ohain by V. Dawson, 11 February 1985, National Air and Space Museum, Washington, D.C.

[36] Walter T. Olson to Executive Engineer, "Tour of Aircraft Gas Turbine Industry in England," 22 August 1947, NASA Lewis Records, 34/621.

[37] Ibid.

[38] See Michael Donne, *Leader of the Skies, Rolls-Royce: The First Seventy-five Years* (London: Frederick Muller Limited, 1981), p. 68; Keith Hayward, *Government and British Civil Aerospace: A Case Study in Post-War Technology Policy* (Manchester: Manchester University Press, 1983), p. 19–22.

[39] Walter T. Olson, "Tour of Aircraft Gas Turbine Industry in England," p. 5.

[40] Ibid, p. 87–88.

[41] Ibid, p. 4.

[42] See John D. Stanitz, "Two-Dimensional Compressible Flow in Conical Mixed-Flow Compressors," NACA TN 1744, 1948.

[43] Brian J. Nichelson, "Early Jet Engines and the Transition from Centrifugal to Axial Compressors: A Case Study in Technological Change," Ph.D. Dissertation, University of Minnesota, 1988, p. 115. John T. Sinnette, Jr., Oscar W. Schey, and J. Austin King, "Performance of NACA Eight-Stage Axial-Flow Compressor Designed on the Basis of Airfoil Theory," NACA TR 758, 1943. This report was first published as NACA Wartime Report E4H18 in August 1944. NACA TR 758 was actually published in 1945. John T. Sinnette, Jr., and William J. Voss, "Extension of Useful Operating Range of Axial-flow Compressors by Use of Adjustable Stator Blades," NACA TR 915, 1948. It seems likely that NACA data on the use of variable stator compressor blades contributed to the design (begun in 1951) of General Electric's enormously successful J79.

[44] P. F. Martinuzzi, "Gas Turbines in the United States," *Flight*, 7 October 1948, p. 439. Frank Whittle's comment was reported in an interview with the author by John Sanders, 6 April 1985. The Whittle visit is described in *Wing Tips*, 19 July 1946, NASA Lewis Technical Library.

[45] Brian Nichelson, "Early Jet Engines," p. 162–208.

[46] Ibid, p. 115–116.

[47] Ibid, p. 153. See also P. F. Martinuzzi, "Continental and American Gas-Turbine and Compressor Calculation Methods Compared." *Transactions of the American Society of Mechanical Engineers* 71:325-333. I am indebted to Captain Brian Nichelson for this reference and for his insight into the differing British and American approaches. Silverstein appears to have advocated the isolated airfoil approach as late as 1949 in the Twelfth Wright Brothers Lecture, "Research on Aircraft Propulsion Systems." *Journal of the Aeronautical Sciences* 16:197-226.

[48] Chung-Hua Wu and Lincoln Wolfenstein, "Application of Radial Equilibrium Condition to Axial-Flow Compressors and Turbines Design," NACA TN 1795, 1949.

[49] For a summary of this work, see Seymour Lieblein and Irving A. Johnsen, "Resume of Transonic-Compressor Research at NACA Lewis Laboratory." *Transactions of the ASME Journal of Engineering for Power*, offprint 60-WA-97, 1960.

[50] Members of the Compressor and Turbine Research Division, "Aerodynamic Design of Axial-Flow Compressors," vol. 1-3, NACA RM E56B03, E56B03a, E56B03b, 1956. A revised declassified edition was published as *Aerodynamic Design of Axial-Flow Compressors*, NASA SP-36, 1965. Reference to the "Compressor Bible" was made in an informal talk with the author by Marvin A. Stibich, Aero Propulsion Laboratory, Wright-Patterson Air Force Base, Dayton, Ohio. The division disbanded in 1957, when the laboratory shifted into nuclear and space-related projects. It was brought back to life in the late 1960s, when the laboratory returned to aeronautics work.

[51] Hugh L. Dryden to John Victory, 29 August 1948, NASA Lewis Records, 34/300.

[52] Interview with Sharp and J. J. Haggerty, *American Aviation Magazine*, December 1951, and E. R. Sharp biography file, NASA History Office, Washington, D.C.

[53] John H. Collins, Jr., "Visit of Messrs. L. Dawson of Rolls-Royce, Ltd. and R. P. Kroon, V. V. Schloesser, and M. Norton of Westinghouse Electric Corporation, on June 5, 1953," NASA Lewis Records, 232/150.

[54] Charles D. Bright, *The Jet Makers: The Aerospace Industry from 1945 to 1972* (Lawrence, Kansas: The Regents Press of Kansas, 1978), p. 15.

[55] In 1952 Pratt & Whitney received a Collier Trophy for the JT3, the first award for a power plant in 21 years. See booklet, "Presentation of 1972 Elmer A. Sperry Award to Leonard S. Hobbs and Perry W. Pratt," AIAA Ninth Annual Meeting, Courtesy of United Technology Archives, East Hartford, Conn. The dual-spool concept may originally have been British.

[56] Development of General Electric's J79, headed by Gerhard Neumann, began in 1951. It was flight tested in 1955. See *Seven Decades of Progress: A Heritage of Aircraft Turbine Technology* (Fallbrook, Calif.: Aero Publishers, 1979), p. 84–91.

[57] Keith Hayward, *Government and British Civil Aerospace: A Case Study in Post-War Technology Policy* (Manchester: Manchester University Press, 1983), explores some of these issues, although his discussion of the aircraft engine industry is limited.

[58] Carlton Kemper, "Visit of Personnel from Rolls Royce Ltd. England to Lewis on January 10 and 11, 1955," 19 January 1955, NASA Lewis Records, 232/150.

CHAPTER EIGHT

SEIZING THE SPACE INITIATIVE

There appears to be a strong parallel between the NACA's transition from aircraft piston engines to jet propulsion and the transition from air-breathing engines to rocket propulsion.[1] In both cases the NACA failed to anticipate the revolutionary change in the nation's propulsion requirements. However, the historical context in which these transitions occurred was different. The American propulsion community in the late 1930s ignored jet propulsion because they were caught up in the peacetime development of commercial engines. Just the opposite was true in the early 1950s. The same rocket intended to be lobbed at the Soviet Union could propel a satellite into orbit around Earth, but national security dictated the nation's propulsion priorities. Until 1955, when planning for the International Geophysical Year began, space was dismissed as science fiction. The military focused its energies during this period on missile development, and the NACA remained, willingly or unwillingly, on the sidelines. The launch of Sputnik by the Soviet Union in 1957 caught the nation, including the NACA, off guard.

Why the NACA stayed out of the mainstream of large rocket development may be as much a political question as a technical one. Hugh Dryden never went to Congress without a carefully conceived, down-to-earth program. He was all the more conservative when it came to asking Congress for funding outside of the NACA's specific aeronautics mandate. In the political climate of the early 1950s it was increasingly difficult to get the budget-minded Congress to support science and technology appropriations. The military requested and obtained funding for research folded into large budgets justified on national security grounds. This generous funding enabled the Air Force to build new research facilities at Wright Field and an array of the latest in wind tunnels at Arnold Engineering Center in Tullahoma, Tenn.

The Army, Navy, and Air Force found themselves with ample financial resources for missile development. Given the constraints on NACA funding prior to Sputnik, from the point of view of one NACA engineer the NACA "would have stood as much chance of injecting itself into space activities in any real way as an icicle in a rocket combustion chamber."[2] Yet the question remains. Could an earlier and more sustained attention to rocket research have positioned the NACA on the propulsion frontier before space missions captured the nation's imagination and forced Congress to open its pocketbook?

Between 1945 and the early 1950s research at Lewis Laboratory focused on improving the turbojet, a bulky, roaring, fuel-thirsty engine, to a quiet, dependable, commercially viable propulsion system. However, this program in support of existing technology did not preclude more advanced work. Beyond the duty to respond to specific requests from the military and industry, there was sufficient autonomy and flexibility within the program of research for projects to grow organically from within the laboratory. It was possible to allow work on less conventional projects in a few well-chosen areas. If a particular project won the attention of Abe Silverstein, it received support. Silverstein's "pet projects" may have had only a small percentage of the total budget of the laboratory, but he assigned some of his most talented staff to these projects and watched over their progress with an attentiveness that the more routine projects did not receive. The problem for the members of the rocket section was how to win the attention of Lewis's upper management. At first, they were frustrated by the lack of support for their work.

Since 1945, when the Cleveland laboratory established its rocket section, its small staff had continued to study rocket fuels despite the general attitude of headquarters and Lewis upper management against a strong NACA role in rocket development. The group's work was limited to the study of propellants, particularly high-energy fuels, thrust chambers of rocket engines, combustion, and cooling. By 1948, the rocket group had produced calculations on the performance of a number of propellants. Among liquid propellants worthy of experimental study, liquid hydrogen appeared to hold greatest promise because of its high specific impulse.[3] The rocket group became convinced that the potential of liquid hydrogen to produce greater thrust than conventional fuels could offset the disadvantages of its low density. However, the use of liquid hydrogen as a rocket fuel presented enormous technical problems. Liquid hydrogen is a cryogenic fuel, dangerous to handle and difficult to store. To verify predictions, laboratory facilities were needed. In addition, it was difficult to obtain an adequate supply of the fuel for experiments. The study of liquid hydrogen had to be passed over in favor of fuels like hydrazone and diborane to be used with oxidizers like hydrogen peroxide, chlorine trifluoride, liquid oxygen, nitrogen tetroxide, and liquid fluorine.[4]

When Abe Silverstein became Chief of Research, he allowed the rocket group more responsibility and visibility. In 1949 the rocket section became a branch within the Fuels and Combustion Research Division, headed by Ted Olson. John Sloop, head of the new branch, recalled, "It was moved up one level in the organizational hierarchy, named for what it was, and given more personnel."[5] However, in the early 1950s, rocket research remained a small fraction of the work of Olson's division, which focused on the combustion problems and fuels of turbojets and ramjets. Silverstein's interest was limited to encouraging the group to establish the criteria for propellant selection. Silverstein also became mildly interested in liquid hydrogen, perhaps in connection with nuclear rocket propulsion. A 1947 secret report by physicists at the Applied Physics Laboratory at The Johns Hopkins University had proposed hydrogen as the preferred propellant for a nuclear rocket.[6] Interest in hydrogen-fueled rockets thus dovetailed with the increasing emphasis on nuclear aircraft and rocket propulsion on the part of the Air Force. Liquid hydrogen also had possibilities as a fuel for high-altitude aircraft such as the U-2. Silverstein, however, did not lend any muscle to support requests for additional facilities. Without facilities, the experimental side of the research suffered.

Members of the rocket branch realized that, to change the attitude of Lewis management from polite tolerance to firm commitment, they had to do more than produce their quota of research papers. They became advocates for increased attention to rocket research to audiences both within and outside the laboratory. Although they were careful not to push the space applications too hard, other Lewis staff could not resist kidding them for becoming "Buck Rogers types." Sloop, for example, gave two lectures in 1949 as part of the Case extension course (ME 221) offered at Harding Junior High School. The first lecture tackled the general problems of rocket engines and performance, including regenerative cooling; the second, solid propellant rockets. Sloop's references reveal his command of the groundwork established by rocket pioneers Robert Goddard, Maurice Zucrow, Willy Ley, and Frank Malina. Sloop indicated that, beyond missile applications, step rockets could be used to escape Earth's gravity. He went so far as to suggest the establishment of a space station.[7] At local, regional, and national meetings of the Society of Automotive Engineers (SAE), Kiwanis Clubs, and American Legion Posts, Sloop and his staff hammered away at the same themes: the potential of rocket-powered missiles both as military weapons and as research tools to gather "basic scientific data about the upper atmosphere and interstellar space." They advocated "a vigorous, large-scale research and development program."[8]

In 1951, possibly in response to intelligence reports of Russian advances in rocketry, the NACA authorized a formal Subcommittee on Rocket Engines within the Power Plants Committee. That same year Lewis Laboratory received its first formal appropriation for rocket research. However, the number of personnel assigned to the rocket branch was still small, less than 3 percent. The experimental facilities consisted of four rocket test cells constructed during World War II and four larger test cells put up by an ad hoc laboratory construction group, paid for from laboratory operating funds. The laboratory still lacked adequate facilities for production, storage, and testing of liquid hydrogen rockets.[9]

Members of the rocket branch staff paid close attention to Army missile policy, which in 1952 was beginning to swing away from air-breathing propulsion systems. The rocket group began to plan a large rocket engine test complex for a remote location in the West, later scaled down to a single facility appropriate for a site at Lewis. In 1953 the laboratory acquired a hydrogen liquefier, but it had to wait until 1957 for the new high-energy rocket propellant test facility to be ready for operation.

In its quest for a large-scale rocket facility, the rocket group seems to have received greater encouragement from the new NACA rocket engine subcommittee than it did from either Dryden or Lewis management. John Sloop lamented:

> Ironically, it was the special subcommittee on rockets set up in 1951 and managed by NACA headquarters that was the most influential in prodding both headquarters and laboratory management into doing more research on rocket engines. The recommendations of the subcommittee, and particularly those of Chairman Maurice Zucrow, were crucial in getting the $2.5 million rocket propulsion laboratory for high-energy propellants, with construction beginning in 1953.[10]

Rocket Test Cell, 1952.

It is possible that the tarnished reputation of the NACA in the early 1950s made Dryden reluctant to push for an expanded role in the national program of rocket research. In 1951 the

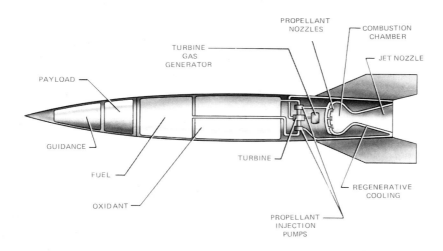

Diagram of a Liquid Propellant Rocket, 1953.

NACA was jolted by the arrest of William Perl. Perl, a brilliant theoretician, had worked at Langley before his transfer to Lewis. The previous year he had completed his Ph.D. under Theodor von Kármán. He was accused of perjury in connection with the sensational trial of Julius and Ethel Rosenberg. Perl had denied to a Grand Jury that he knew the Rosenbergs when, in fact, during his year as a graduate student at Columbia University, he had sublet an apartment rented to one of the alleged conspirators. The FBI suspected that Perl had communicated sensitive aerodynamic information, including national plans to develop a nuclear-powered airplane, to the Soviet Union through the Rosenbergs. These allegations were never proved. Perl was convicted of perjury and sentenced to five years in prison. Whether there is a connection between the Perl case and the NACA's funding difficulties after the Korean War is pure speculation. At the height of the nightmare of McCarthyism, it does not seem surprising that the NACA might have been considered a security risk.[11]

The NACA's woes were compounded in January 1952 when Albert Thomas, Chairman of the House Appropriations Subcommittee, demanded an investigation of the NACA by the General Accounting Office (GAO), the first such scrutiny the NACA had ever experienced. Thomas thought that the agency had too many civil service employees and possible duplication of research effort among the three laboratories. In September the GAO sent its auditors, followed by a visit from Congressman Thomas himself. One can imagine the trepidation with which laboratory management prepared for his visit. After an extensive tour, including stock rooms and new facilities, Mr. Thomas, it seems, went away favorably impressed.

At the Materials and Stresses Building he heard about the division's work in high-temperature materials and its progress in developing alloys and ceramal turbine blades. At the Propulsion Systems Laboratory still under construction, Sharp stressed the utility of NACA testing to support turbojet development. He reported to Dryden:

> He was impressed by the possibility of getting information on these engines before they went into production, and I think he realized for the first time the potentialities of this work since he commented that it was obvious that large savings could be made if the engines were proven before they were put into production. Over lunch Silverstein turned the discussion to the NACA's future research. He stressed "the need for more intensive research and development on the rocket engine in this country in a connection with the long-range missile." He let Thomas know that a request for new facilities for rocket development was part of the 1954 budget request.[12]

FROM MACH 4 TO INFINITY

In July 1955 President Dwight Eisenhower announced that the United States would participate in the International Geophysical Year (to begin in 1957). The United States planned to launch a satellite. The idea of space exploration now caught the imaginations of men higher up in the laboratory hierarchy—John Evvard, George Low, and Wolfgang Moeckel. Aware of the work in hypersonics at Langley and Ames, they thought that both space flight and propulsion problems related to aerodynamic heating should be explored.

Preparations for the International Geophysical Year sparked a new awareness and commitment within the scientific community to the peaceful development of space sciences. Possibly because of its scientific imprimatur and the fact that it was to be managed by a team of Americans, the relatively weak joint proposal by the Vanguard group at the Naval Research Laboratory and the National Academy of Sciences beat a proposal by the more experienced von Braun team.

Lewis Laboratory's preparations were more modest. To prepare the staff for the problems of flight beyond Earth's atmosphere, they began to consider what courses to offer the following year in the non-credit system that flourished under the direction of John Evvard. Because the course system served as a bellwether for new research initiatives and future reorganizations of the laboratory, Evvard carefully laid the groundwork through discussions with possible instructors. With considerable trepidation Evvard went to see Silverstein. In describing the proposed course, Evvard predicted that it could "change the thinking of the people who take the course," something that might not be desirable because of the dissatisfaction it could cause with more routine work.[13] They planned to call the course "From Mach 4 to Infinity." Without hesitation Silverstein gave Evvard his support. "From Mach 4 to Infinity" created a strong impression on those who took it in 1956. The second year it was offered, the course was enormously popular.

A respected group composed mainly of the laboratory's theoreticians—Melvin Gerstein, George Low, Roger Luidens, Stephen Maslen, and Harold Mirels—developed the part of the course that dealt with the concepts of hypersonic flight. Some basic research in heat transfer by Clarence B. Cohen, Eli Reshotko, and Ernst Eckert provided a useful starting point.[14] Wolfgang Moeckel began to explore the idea of possible flights to the planets using unconventional propulsion systems. As part of his lecture "Earth Satellites and Interplanetary Travel," Moeckel reviewed the literature on rocket propulsion. He recalled that he had first come across a description of

153

electric rocket propulsion in about 1949 in Hermann Oberth's 1929 book, *Wege zur Raumschiffahrt*. He was particularly intrigued by a chapter devoted to the electric rocket that suggested that, for space travel, rocket thrust could be produced by the flow of electrically charged particles.[15]

The chemical rocket was limited by the enormous amounts of propellant required to be carried into space for flight to distant planets. Although chemical rockets produced far greater thrust, they had to carry large quantities of fuel into space. Electric rockets got their power from a generator in space providing very small amounts of thrust over very long periods of time. This suggested to Oberth, as it had to Robert Goddard in 1906, that electric rockets might be useful for long-distance travel between planets. However, neither Oberth nor Goddard tackled the practical questions involved in the development of a power source. The electric rocket was consigned to the category of intriguing but impractical technical ideas.[16]

Moeckel's colleagues received his first lecture with considerable interest. Expanding these lectures later the same year, he came across two papers by Ernst Stuhlinger, who had worked on the V-2 at Peenemunde under Werner von Braun.[17] Moeckel may have heard about Stuhlinger's work at the semi-annual meeting of the American Rocket Society held in Cleveland in 1956 where Krafft Ehricke, also of the Peenemunde group, lectured on "The Solar-Powered Space Ship."[18]

Stuhlinger had become intrigued with the possibilities of electric propulsion as early as 1947 at the Army Camp at Fort Bliss when von Braun asked him to restudy Oberth's rocket work. Stuhlinger's first paper, published in 1954, tackled the question that Oberth had left unanswered: how to generate the necessary electric power in space. He suggested a solar turbogenerator that consisted of a system of mirrors and boilers. In his second paper, published in 1955, Stuhlinger took a more radical approach. He suggested a nuclear fission reactor as the power source. He reasoned that "a vehicle designed for a Mars mission would be lighter and somewhat faster if powered by a nuclear reactor than if it were powered by solar energy."[19]

Stuhlinger's papers impressed Moeckel because they were "much more concrete, comprehensive and realistic than previous work." Once Stuhlinger had suggested that electric propulsion was within the realm of technical feasibility, Moeckel set enthusiastically to work. "I immediately began a study of low-thrust trajectories, and the capabilities of such low-thrust systems for interplanetary travel."[20] If headquarters had been apprised of Moeckel's work, it might have been discouraged as "space-cadet" enthusiasm. Indeed, it has yet to find application in space exploration. However, like the analytic work done on liquid hydrogen before large experimental facilities were authorized, or the theoretical work on hypersonics, there was no need to inform Washington at this point. Moeckel received the strong support of his division chief, John Evvard, then head of the Supersonic Propulsion Division, who gave him the necessary freedom to think through his ideas.

Meanwhile, Walter Olson began to make a concerted effort to influence Dryden to take a more aggressive approach to NACA rocket research. In "A Suggested Policy and Course of Action for NACA with Regard to Rocket Engine Propulsion (1955)," Olson advocated "advancing the engine art" by experimental work on rocket engines of 250,000 to 1,000,000 pounds thrust. Although missile applications are clearly intended in the document's careful wording, Olson, almost apologetically, urged the NACA to also consider satellite flight "which still seems visionary to many minds now." Nuclear-powered aircraft, he suggested, might serve as launching pads for flight beyond the atmosphere. Rockets could also be used for auxiliary thrust to increase the speed of lumbering nuclear-powered aircraft.[21]

Although Dryden still demurred, Silverstein began to take a more active interest in the work of the rocket group on liquid hydrogen. The stimulus came unexpectedly from aeronautics. The Air Force, interested in liquid hydrogen to fuel turbojet engines for high-altitude reconnaissance aircraft, supported an experimental test program at Lewis Laboratory called Project Bee. Silverstein put Paul Ordin in charge of the project and made Donald Mulholland his assistant. This was exactly the kind of hands-on engineering project that Silverstein found most challenging. At last the work of the rocket branch in high-energy propellants had gained his full attention. He set up a room in the basement of the Administration Building directly below his office for the project so that he could personally direct it. The project staff modified a B-57B bomber equipped with two Curtiss Wright J-65 engines so that one engine could burn either jet fuel or hydrogen. After extensive ground testing of the hydrogen system, it was flight tested over Lake Erie. When the pilot switched the modified engine to hydrogen fuel, it worked perfectly. The program resolved the questions of insulation, structure, and pumping of liquid hydrogen in flight.

Project Bee validated the work of the rocket team, as well as proving the feasibility of liquid hydrogen as a fuel for aircraft. Through Project Bee, Lewis researchers received important practical experience in the handling and storage of liquid hydrogen that would later prove crucial when the laboratory took charge of the development of the Centaur rocket. Abe Silverstein, with Eldon Hall, wrote the final report: "Liquid Hydrogen as a Jet Fuel for High-Altitude Aircraft."[22] The laboratory set up an engine design group led by William D. Ritter to study liquid hydrogen turbojet engines for supersonic flight.[23]

In July 1956 Dryden at last began to reconsider his opposition to increased NACA participation in rocket research. He took the belated initiative to canvas the opinion of the NACA rocket subcommittee to determine the NACA's long-term research agenda. This conservative approach was typical of headquarters when entering a new area of research. Dryden's cautious *modus operandi* was to "solicit opinions and build a broad base of national support so that it would appear the agency was practically pushed into the new work."[24] For five years, Dryden had ignored both the rocket subcommittee's recommendations and pressure from Lewis Laboratory to allow more effort in rocket research. On the behalf of frustrated members of the NACA rocket subcommittee, Richard Canright (employed by Douglas Aircraft after leaving the Jet Propulsion Laboratory) wrote in July 1957:

> We have constantly spurred the NACA on to tests on a larger scale. We have urged them to become familiar with complete engines rather than work only on component R&D. We have tried to emphasize the importance of rocket technology to this country's defense effort and urged that the NACA devote a greater portion of its personnel and funding to this important field.[25]

On the eve of Sputnik, Dryden still hesitated to take up the recommendations of the rocket subcommittee, roll up his sleeves, and challenge a tight-fisted Congress for a larger NACA role in rocket development. Nevertheless, Lewis management was now solidly behind the work of the rocket group.

TRANSITION TO SPACE

Late in 1956 Abe Silverstein was ready to leave the problems of the turbojet engine to industry. Two new facilities under construction—the rocket engine test facility and the nuclear reactor at Plum Brook—required a rethinking of the laboratory's research program. Silverstein began to consider a major reorganization of the magnitude of the one that had accompanied the switch from the aircraft reciprocating engine to jet propulsion in 1945.

Silverstein selected some of the Compressor and Turbine Division's most versatile engineers and scientists to attend a "nuclear school." Eight additional engineers were plucked from other divisions of the laboratory and invited to drop their current projects and prepare for leadership in the anticipated reorganization by learning the principles of nuclear physics. They were taught by the small core of researchers at the laboratory who had been engaged in nuclear work for almost a decade and professors invited from Case Institute of Technology. In all, 24 engineers had no duties other than to attend the school for six months. The rationale for the nuclear school appears to have been to single out individuals with leadership qualities and teach them the fundamentals of new areas Silverstein believed would become the major focus of research in the future. Presumably, these individuals would be the division and branch chiefs after the reorganization. In January 1957 six engineers chose not to continue in the nuclear field. The remaining 18 were divided into three groups. Harold Finger headed a group to work on a nuclear rocket. In 1960 he would be selected by Silverstein to become project director of the joint Atomic Energy Commission-NASA nuclear projects at headquarters. Eldon Hall formed a group to study aircraft nuclear propulsion. He would also go to Washington with Silverstein after NASA was organized. Robert English focused the energies of his group on a design study for a nuclear space-power system. With the imagined goal of sending eight people to Mars, they proposed a nuclear reactor with the potential to act as the power source for an electric rocket under consideration by Moeckel's group.[26] Robert Graham, head of the Rocket Fluid Dynamics Section, took charge of planning the laboratory's first seminar on rocket propulsion to train additional staff in rocket technology.[27]

In March 1957 Silverstein's first act in shifting the laboratory's research priorities was to establish a research planning council. He abolished the Compressor and Turbine Division, long one of the premier divisions of the laboratory. Many of the aerodynamicists who had worked on the axial compressor were assigned to a new Fluid Systems Division to study the mechanics of flow within rocket systems. At the same time Silverstein created a Nuclear Reactor Division to direct new research connected with the reactor then under construction at Plum Brook.

A B-57 aircraft had one engine fueled with liquid hydrogen.

Meanwhile, the streams leading to space research were converging. In spring 1957, the staff began to plan for a fall conference on the evaluation of propulsion systems. Proponents of space-related research urged Silverstein to allow them to include sessions on space flight and space propulsion systems, as well as more conventional subjects, such as turbojets and ramjets. Never one to avoid considering unconventional technical concepts if there were a possibility they might ultimately prove feasible, Silverstein agreed to give them one afternoon session. With the imagination of many staff now sparked, research groups worked up sessions on liquid hydrogen, nuclear rockets, and space power systems. As Moeckel recalled, "The studies for this conference formed the foundation for the rapid expansion of our research in the fields of electric propulsion, power generation, and nuclear rockets." The paper submitted by Moeckel's group on "Satellite and Space Propulsion Systems" contained a distillation of the advanced thinking of the laboratory—flights to the Moon and Mars, with the focus on electric propulsion systems.[28]

As preparations for the propulsion conference moved into high gear in September 1957, Silverstein called a meeting of the Research Planning Council, whose members included Eugene Manganiello, John Evvard, Bruce Lundin, Walter Olson, Irving Pinkel, and Newell Sanders. He expressed the consensus of the group that "existing problems on the air-breathing turbojet engine were not of sufficient laboratory interest for the continuation of a large-scale program."[29] His proposal that rocket research be expanded, while proportionately reducing turbojet engine research, effectively marked Lewis Laboratory's transition to space research. However, as the November conference approached, Silverstein became increasingly nervous about possible criticism by Headquarters of the inclusion of a discussion on space propulsion. Would the laboratory be perceived as an amateur group of space-cadets? Not willing to eliminate the session entirely, he cut the panels from a full afternoon to several hours.

RESPONSE TO SPUTNIK

The tension between the foot-dragging of headquarters and the gathering momentum of the Cleveland laboratory toward space-related research mounted in September when representatives from headquarters visited the laboratory to evaluate its rehearsal for the finely orchestrated NACA Triennial Inspection. The theme of the inspection was to be a celebration of the tenth anniversary of the X-1, the first aircraft to fly faster than the speed of sound.[30] Unlike the anticipated more specialized propulsion conference directed toward a technical audience, NACA inspections were intended to convey its work in layman's terms to a group made up largely of politicians and industry executives. At one of the "stops," the rocket group proudly showed John Victory the new rocket laboratory from a small platform next to the huge new scrubber, part of the silencing and exhaust gas disposal system. During the prepared talk, Victory bristled when he heard references to space. Always on the lookout for anything that might offend potential Congressional sponsors, he ordered all references to space deleted from the presentations. As one member of the rocket group explained, "The climate in Washington in the fall of 1957 was very negative towards space." It was acceptable to mention the "slow-paced" Vanguard satellite managed by the Navy under the aegis of the International Geophysical Year, but "anything beyond it was considered 'space cadet' enthusiasm."[31] Nevertheless, Addison Rothrock, who was also in the headquarters contingent, was able to convince Victory to allow one of the first electric propulsion experiments—a rail accelerator—to be included in the presentations.

The intended celebration of ten years of supersonic flight caught the NACA looking backwards. On October 4 the question of whether to discuss space-related work was moot.

Between the rehearsal and the actual inspection, the Soviet Union launched Sputnik, the world's first artificial satellite. Suddenly Chuck Yeager's dramatic breaking of the sound barrier seemed like ancient history. Sputnik's flight beyond the atmosphere marked the dawn of the space age, a new era of discovery. However, to Americans, Sputnik also seemed ominous. Politically, the new satellite was a symbol of the rising technical competence of an enemy. In the context of the Cold War, Sputnik represented the Russian triumph in the first round of what immediately began to be perceived as a space race. Victory's earlier resistance to references to space put the conservative attitudes of headquarters in sharp relief. When the inspection began several days later, Lewis engineers proudly unveiled their work on chemical rockets and more visionary space propulsion systems.

The presentations on high-energy rocket propellants were the highlight of the inspection. Participants could admire a rocket engine capable of 20,000 pounds of thrust ready for experiments with liquid fuels when they visited the new rocket engine test facility.[32] Sputnik at last riveted the attention of the laboratory on work of the small contingent of "Buck Rogers types." They could describe with impunity an idea for a winged satellite, similar to the shuttle, lofted beyond the atmosphere by a multi-stage rocket booster. It was a day that vindicated their long commitment to rocket engines and fuels. They found themselves besieged by their colleagues in air-breathing propulsion for briefings on rocket fundamentals.

The most detailed consideration of Lewis Laboratory's work in space propulsion was reserved for the classified NACA-Industry Conference, held the following month. Once again, the rocket researchers held center stage. The presentation by John Sloop, A. S. Boksenbom, S. Gordon, R. W. Graham, P. M. Ordin, and A. O. Tischler discussed propulsion requirements for specific missions, including surface-to-surface missiles, Earth satellites, and Moon missions. They considered both circumnavigation of the Moon and an ambitious Moon landing, using an orbiting Earth satellite as a base, probably the first detailed discussion of a Moon landing in NACA literature. Frank E. Rom, Eldon W. Sams, and Robert E. Hyland's paper, "Nuclear Rockets," and the paper "Satellite and Space Propulsion Systems," by W. C. Moeckel, L. V. Baldwin, R. E. English, B. Lubarsky, and S. H. Maslen, were equally visionary.[33] John Sloop and his colleagues had at last found a receptive audience for their stubborn and lonely advocacy.

THE SPACE DEBATE

During the national soul searching that followed the Russian triumph in space, Lewis staff began to consider their role in the charged political and technical environment. Some engineers looked forward to abandoning air-breathing engines to tackle the problems of engines in zero gravity. For others, to exchange the familiar roar of the wind tunnel for the silence of the vacuum chamber seemed a travesty. Bruce Lundin recalled that half the laboratory was afraid of getting "sucked" into space and the other half was afraid of being left out. "And there was some concern among people, whose views I did not personally share at the time, that if we got into space we'd be into an operating mission agency and the good things that they were doing in research would be lost."[34]

Discussion of the NACA's role in space dragged on through meetings of the Lewis Research Planning Council and in informal debates in the cafeteria. This prompted the scholarly Walter Olson to draft a document in support of space flight research. He pointed out that space flight had important scientific and military applications. Space missions would benefit meteorology and astronomy by yielding new data on radiation, meteorites, gas composition, electromagnetic phenomena, and cosmic dust in space. Reconnaissance was an obvious military application. Olson also stressed the propaganda value of space exploration. It would not only be a means to demonstrate the technical superiority of the United States—the importance of having the "technological capability of massive retaliation"—but it would also keep *"both friend and potential foe convinced that such is the case."*[35] Olson listed 15 specific problem areas in which he thought the NACA could make immediate contributions to a new space initiative. Most would be collaborative efforts with other NACA centers or existing government agencies. They included space propulsion systems such as chemical rockets, nuclear rockets, and the study of ion, plasma, and photon jets; auxiliary power systems; and materials for space vehicles and exploration equipment. He advocated a new NACA laboratory to launch and manage a manned, orbiting, space platform. In his view this manned platform should be the main focus of NACA activities in space.

This plan was not bold enough for Bruce Lundin, although many of Olson's ideas were incorporated into Lundin's plan. Lundin thought that the NACA should aim at nothing less than leadership of an entirely new national space agency. At home on a quiet Sunday afternoon in early December, he produced a memo for Abe Silverstein that he called "Some Remarks on a Future Policy and Course of Action for the NACA." He argued against the collaborative approach, which he thought "weak and ineffective."[36] He advocated a "bold, imaginative, aggressive, and visionary" program. He warned that if the NACA focused on a specific project, like a manned space platform or placing a dye marker on the Moon, this might "dangerously limit our goals, restrict the range of our thinking, and give us nothing to grow on." Aeronautical research, not directly controlled by the military and directed to national goals, had been the traditional role of the NACA. In tones resonating with Cold War rhetoric, Lundin declared that space research was a matter of national survival:

The Rocket Engine Test Laboratory completed in 1957.

In our technological age, it will be the country that advances in science that will have the greatest impact on the emotions and imagination of men, that will command respect (or at least allegiance), and that will gradually assume world leadership. If Russia does this, eventually their way will be the way and we will have lost the struggle without knowing just when and how it occurred. The final victory in the struggle may well go to the country that offers mankind the greatest scientific achievements.[37]

The memo suggested that the NACA coordinate all American space-related research, both within the government and by industry. To have a successful space program, new knowledge had to be generated. Lundin took a shot at the "skeptical Congressmen and budget keepers." Even he, however, was not bold enough to suggest a development or a mission role for the new agency.[38] Silverstein shared Lundin's enthusiasm for a strong leadership role for the NACA in space research. He set up an informal committee to begin to formulate plans for an additional laboratory to be devoted to space flight research.

On December 18, Dryden called a meeting of the directors and associate directors of the laboratories to discuss the future role of the NACA. In preparation for this meeting, Silverstein honed Lundin's ideas into a memo called "Lewis Laboratory Opinion of a Future Policy and Course of Action for the NACA." At Headquarters, when Dryden called on Henry Reid and Floyd Thompson of Langley, they showed little enthusiasm for the idea of taking on a large role in a national space effort. Smith DeFrance of Ames emphatically opposed a NACA space initiative because he feared that the NACA would lose its identity.[39] Silverstein, last to speak, pulled the "Lewis Laboratory Opinion" from his briefcase. Not only did he argue for a central coordinating role for the NACA, but also he strongly advised that a new NACA space flight laboratory be authorized by Congress. Silverstein's strong advocacy swung the opinion of the meeting in favor of a new space agency. The ideas expressed in the "Lewis Laboratory Opinion" became the basis for NACA space policy, known as the "Dryden Plan."[40]

That evening, Dryden and James Doolittle, the Chairman of the NACA Main Committee, hosted the long-remembered "Young Turks Dinner" in the California Room of the Statler Hotel in Washington, D.C. The hosts intended to give the middle management of the three laboratories a chance to express their views on whether and how to redirect the goals of their venerable research organization. Silverstein selected Walter Olson, Eugene Manganiello, and Demarquis Wyatt to represent Lewis Laboratory. The sober Dryden gracefully accepted the barbs flung at him by some of his inebriated staff, who called him too cautious. He would encounter the same criticism after he testified in the House of Representatives that placing a man in a space capsule was like shooting a lady out of a cannon. John Stack of Langley Laboratory went so far as to call Dryden an "old fogey." The Young Turks of the three laboratories were enthusiastic about jumping into the space arena.[41]

Two days later the seven members of the Lewis Research Planning Council met to formalize the appointment of a special committee to plan the new space flight laboratory recommended in the "Lewis Opinion" document. The members of the committee were Howard Childs, Chairman, Edgar M. Cortright, Robert E. English, Edmund R. Johash, Bernard Lubarsky, Phillip N. Miller, and Isidore Warshawsky. William Mickelson served as secretary. They were given two months to produce the plan. On February 10, 1958, they submitted "A Program for Expansion of NACA Research in Space Flight Technology." Not surprisingly, given that it was conceived at Lewis Laboratory, the document defined the mission of the new laboratory in terms of launch vehicles—a stable of chemical, nuclear, and electric rockets. It would cost $380 million over a five-year period. The cost of expanding existing laboratories over five years would cost $55 million per year. Notably absent from this early planning document was a consideration of the mechanics of how missions would actually be carried out, and there was almost no mention of manned space flight. The document recommended that the NACA staff be increased from 8000 to 17,000 over a three-year period. It called for a budget increase from $80 million to $180 million.[42]

By NACA standards, this was a bold and visionary plan, but in hindsight it reveals the tenacious grip of the NACA's past practice. The new space laboratory would generate the knowledge, the technical know-how, necessary to make space flight missions possible. The development of the actual hardware to be sent into space and the operation of those missions would be left as it had in the past, to industry and to the military, respectively. There may not, however, have been a clear laboratory consensus on this last issue. Bruce Lundin later recalled that he "definitely thought that we should be responsible for the building and operation of launch vehicles and spacecraft just as we had always built and operated test models in our wind tunnels." In Lundin's view, the members of Silverstein's special committee represented the ideas of the group "that was afraid of getting 'sucked up' into space and who preferred the comfortable haven of their research beds."[43]

The significance of the February 10 document in the evolving plans for the new space agency is not entirely clear. In 1965, when he was interviewed by Mercury historians Lloyd Swenson, James Grimwood, and Charles Alexander, Dryden recalled what is unmistakably the February 10 document as "Lewis Labs' bid for a lot of propulsion—nuclear propulsion—all sorts of things and a launch site." Dryden criticized Lewis planners for neglecting manned space flight. He recalled his own past opposition, as well as the opposition of the von Braun group at Huntsville, Ala., to NACA participation in the "big rocket business."

> Now their principle problem was that Huntsville would have nothing to do with them, and they did get into the rocket business on a small scale, but I always resisted their building up big facilities for Thors, and that sort of thing. So this [the plans expressed in the February 10 document] represented a sort of culmination of many efforts of the propulsion laboratory to get into rocket propulsion on a big scale, just as they were in engine—jet engine—propulsion.[44]

Dryden claimed that the Lewis document had no status and never went further than his desk drawer. This is doubtful, since the document was later cited in the significant memo of March 5 from President Eisenhower as evidence of the NACA's competence to direct the new space agency.[45]

Initially it was not at all clear that the NACA would become the government agency around which the new National Aeronautics and Space Administration would be built. The external perceptions of the NACA after Sputnik, expressed both by the nation's scientific community and members of Congress, was that the NACA was too conservative to lead the exploration of space. Presumably, what made the NACA conservative in the eyes of the scientists was that it did applied research, an activity with a lower status than the work of the Navy's Vanguard group or university-based space science studies. To lawmakers, the NACA was a small agency without experience in the management of the huge budgets typical of defense contracts. The Cold War had accustomed Washington to think in terms of large-scale technology development. Firm centralized control of all three elements of the proposed space program—research, development, and operations—seemed required to calm the nation's fears of Soviet technical superiority. In the end, the NACA won the leadership of the new space agency, not because of its positive qualities as a research organization, but to avoid having the new agency become an instrument for the militarization of space and greater Cold War competition. Eisenhower favored building NASA around the NACA because he wanted a civilian agency to direct the conquest of space. "Such reasoning," according to historian Walter McDougall, "made elevation of the innocuous NACA an attractive answer to the question of what to do about outer space."[46]

There is no doubt that, as a small federal agency in the national security state of the 1950s, the NACA had taken a conservative approach to funding. Technically, however, the NACA could be quite daring. Dryden had encouraged the staff at all three laboratories to explore advanced technical concepts. National aeronautical policy had stipulated that fundamental research was the province of the NACA. Development was industry's prerogative. Operations belonged to the military.[47] During the so-called "lean years" between 1952 and 1957, the organizational structure of the NACA allowed its three laboratories—Langley, Ames, and Lewis—considerable autonomy. Many of the technical and scientific problems the laboratories tackled during these years belie the label of conservative. Obviously, each laboratory had to respond to the needs of the military and industry, but the NACA also prided itself on anticipating the technical needs of the nation by laying a base of knowledge on which to build future development.

Although it was understood that all NACA research would ultimately be applied to advance aircraft technology, projects whose immediate commercial applications were not clear always attracted considerable interest at the three NACA laboratories. Ames Laboratory's long and sustained interest in the problem of aerodynamic heating culminated in Harvey Allen's blunt body theory, later applied to the shape of the Mercury reentry capsule. In *Engineer in Charge* James Hansen describes the audacious reach of Langley's X-15 program to the edge of space.[48] The X-series of research aircraft, a joint program with the Air Force and the Navy, involved building aircraft prototypes. As applied research, the program came close to the line separating research from development, but it yielded valuable technical and scientific data.

Three examples of NACA research at Lewis Laboratory belie the label of conservative: high-energy rocket fuels, nuclear rocket propulsion, and electric rocket propulsion. Technically, two of the three areas of research—nuclear rocket propulsion and electric propulsion—have yet to find applications. They were too visionary rather than too conservative. The third, liquid hydrogen, contributed substantially to the ability of the United States to land human beings on the Moon. Because of the momentum that these space-related projects had developed prior to the launching of Sputnik in October 1957, the transition to space was not as dramatic as the transition from the piston engine to jet propulsion. Lewis was already primed for space. Sputnik took the lid off the pent-up desire for more funding and recognition for areas that were already receiving considerable emphasis. As *Business Week* reported, Lewis Laboratory "leaped over to space" because it had begun its jump well before Sputnik.[49] Nevertheless, in the context of the total research program, these efforts prior to Sputnik were small. Like the transition from the piston engine to jet propulsion, it was late. The NACA stayed too long in air-breathing engine technology. Silverstein missed the early opportunity to throw his full weight behind the efforts of the rocket group to develop high-energy rocket propellants.

FROM NACA TO NASA

On March 5, 1958, President Eisenhower announced his decision to organize the new space agency around the NACA. In his memo justifying the decision in favor of a civilian agency, he cited three documents to underscore the interest and competence of the NACA for leadership of the space program: the so-called "Dryden Plan," based on the ideas found in Silverstein's "Lewis Opinion," the February 10 plan for the new Space Flight Laboratory generated at Lewis, and the January 16 resolution of the Main Committee (drafted by the NACA's Special Committee on Space Technology, chaired by H. Guyford Stever). This resolution endorsed the role of the NACA as the national coordinator of space research.[50]

Between March and July, when the Space Act that authorized the National Aeronautics and Space Administration became law, a very different organization than the one envisioned by Lewis planners took shape. Although they had proposed a role for the NACA that they considered radical, because of the public furor raised in the wake of Sputnik, the new space agency could not be organized according to the old NACA model. After considerable debate within the Congress, the new agency was given extensive responsibility for development and operations (or missions), in addition to research.[51] Moreover, the NACA had to give up its flexible committee structure and the autonomy of its laboratories in favor of a more centralized management. Although it is often stated that the NACA became the nucleus for NASA, this is not entirely correct, because the NACA purpose and way of doing business was entirely transformed.

Once the NACA's mandate was clear, Dryden asked Silverstein to assist him in the creation of the new space agency. Silverstein turned down Dryden's first invitation to relocate to Washington, D.C., but when asked a second time in spring 1958, he complied. Among the leaders of the NACA, Silverstein was the best suited to take on the job of pulling together the diverse elements of the new space flight development programs. He had drive and organizational ability. For the first three years of the agency, Silverstein's Office of Space Flight Programs had full responsibility for the Mercury Program and NASA's unmanned satellite programs. Silverstein named the Apollo program, and his office also laid the early groundwork for the manned lunar landing. Because of Silverstein's technical competence, the force of his personality, and the quality of the staff he selected to serve under him, power at Headquarters was concentrated in his hands until Headquarters reorganized in mid-1961.[52]

When Dryden was passed over in favor of T. Keith Glennan as NASA's first administrator, Glennan took a leave of absence from the Presidency of Case Institute of Technology. Having served as a Commissioner of the Atomic Energy Commission from 1950 to 1952 and on the Board of the National Science Foundation, he had good Washington connections. Glennan wisely insisted that Dryden remain as NASA's Deputy Administrator. Both he and Dryden were sworn in by President Eisenhower on August 19, 1958. He was catapulted from a job managing an operating budget at Case of $6 to 7 million, to one of $615 million. Glennan approved the NACA plans for the Mercury Program with an enthusiastic "Let's get going and don't spare the horses!"[53]

Silverstein had assembled an impressive group of former Lewis staff in his Office of Space Flight Programs. He was used to fostering innovation in engines at Lewis Laboratory. At Headquarters, his innovations would be administrative. Nevertheless, Silverstein's people had a feel for the technology they supervised. Demarquis Wyatt, a former Assistant Chief in charge of Lewis's supersonic wind tunnels, knew how to keep day-to-day operations running smoothly. After a few weeks in Washington, Silverstein asked Wyatt to become his Technical Assistant in charge of budgets, personnel, and trouble shooting. Wyatt faced a significant problem in figuring out how to develop and manage a budget for the Mercury Program. Robert Gilruth, completely caught up in its technical demands, allowed financial details of payroll and contractor estimates to slide. Wyatt devised a financial control system for project management to streamline the unwieldy accounting system inherited from the NACA.

Silverstein selected Harold Finger, who had taken part in Lewis's "nuclear school," to become chief of NASA's nuclear programs. Francis C. Schwenk, also from Lewis, set to work under Finger to develop nuclear rocket concepts. Newell D. Sanders, who had first served under Silverstein in the Wind Tunnels and Flight Research Division, became Assistant Director for Advanced Technology. Edgar M. Cortright, Jr., and George Low, fraternity brothers at Rensselaer Polytechnic Institute, also took important positions in the fledgling agency. Both had come to Lewis Laboratory in 1949 with masters degrees in aeronautical engineering. Cortright, once Branch Chief for the 8-foot x 6-foot supersonic tunnel, had also taken part in the nuclear school. He had supervised some of the early planning to develop electric propulsion concepts. At Headquarters, Silverstein put Cortright in charge of Advanced Technology Programs in the Office of Space Flight. He headed NASA's meteorological satellite program, which included TIROS and Nimbus. Later he became Assistant Director for the Unmanned Lunar and Planetary Program.

George Low became Silverstein's deputy in charge of Manned Space Flight Programs. He shuttled tirelessly between Robert Gilruth at Langley and Silverstein to keep communications open and Mercury operations running smoothly. John Disher and Warren North, also spirited away from Lewis Laboratory, took key posts in Low's operation. They became early advocates of a lunar landing. In 1959, when Low served on NASA's Research Steering Committee on Manned Space Flight, chaired by Harry Goett, he pressed the committee to consider the Moon as a goal to follow after the Mercury program. By October 1960, Low had the green light from Silverstein to set in motion the first formal planning for a manned lunar program. Low's memo to Silverstein tersely stated, "It has become increasingly apparent that a preliminary program for manned lunar landings should be formulated. This is necessary in order to provide a proper justification for Apollo, and to place Apollo schedules and technical plans on a firmer foundation." Low advised the formation of a working group consisting of Oran Nicks, Eldon Hall, and John Disher. Silverstein's curt response, "O.K., Abe," hurriedly scrawled at the bottom of the memo, set in motion the careful technical planning that culminated nine years later in the "giant leap for mankind"— the historic lunar landing.[54]

Silverstein also took charge of the initial planning of Goddard Space Flight Center. Working with speed and informality, Silverstein chose the site for Goddard and suggested its name. He played a major role in negotiations with the Navy to bring the Vanguard team to Goddard. Silverstein stepped in to serve as acting director of the Space Flight Center until its mission within NASA was sorted out and he was able to prevail upon Harry Goett from Ames to become its new director.

Like the generation from Langley in the early 1940s who shaped the Cleveland laboratory, the team from Lewis imprinted the new NASA organization with NACA traditions as they attempted to modify old ways in response to the new goals of NASA. The pervasive NACA influence was not always appreciated by new NASA employees recruited from outside the NACA. At Goddard, where the core staff came from the Naval Research Laboratory, a disgruntled employee circulated cards embossed with the message "Help Stamp Out NACA Types." Although NACA influence at Headquarters gradually diminished, during the first four years of the fledgling agency, Silverstein was the "lynchpin in the whole effort."[55]

NACA's Special Committee on Space Technology, called the Stever Committee after its chairman, Guyford Stever, meets at Lewis, May 26, 1958. Left to right: Edward R. Sharp, Director of Lewis Laboratory; Colonel Norman C. Appold, U.S. Air Force, Assistant to the Deputy Commander for Weapons Systems, Air Research and Development Command; Abraham Hyatt, Research and Analysis Officer, Bureau of Aeronautics, Department of the Navy; Hendrik W. Bode, Director of Research-Physical Sciences, Bell Telephone Laboratories; W. Randolph Lovelace II, Lovelace Foundation for Medication Education and Research; S. K. Hoffman, General Manager, Rocketdyne Division, North American Aviation; Milton U. Clauser, Director, Aeronautical Research Laboratory, The Ramo-Wooldridge Corporation; H. Julian Allen, Chief, High-Speed Flight Research, NACA Ames; Robert R. Gilruth, Assistant Director, NACA Langley; J. R. Dempsey, Manager, Convair-Astronautics; Carl B. Palmer, Secretary to Committee, NACA Headquarters; H. Guyford Stever, Chairman, Associate Dean of Engineering, Massachusetts Institute of Technology; Hugh L. Dryden (ex officio), Director, NACA; Dale R. Corson, Department of Physics, Cornell University; Abe Silverstein, Associate Director, NACA Lewis; Wernher von Braun, Director, Development Operations Division, Army Ballistic Missile Agency.

One of Glennan's chief objectives was to supplement the core NACA personnel and facilities by acquiring the cream of the nation's science and engineering talent in satellite and rocket development. In his view, although the NACA staff was "composed of reasonably able people," they lacked "experience in the management of large affairs."[56] He met his first objective in December 1958, when the Army transferred to NASA its contract for the management of the Jet Propulsion Laboratory (JPL). After a faltering start, the JPL staff became NASA's experts in planetary and lunar probes.[57]

In Glennan's view, launch vehicles were the "limiting factor in the development of the nation's space program."[58] The Mercury astronauts were lofted into space by rockets with payload capacities well below those of Russian rockets. Glennan knew that the only way to trump the Russians in the space race was to acquire the large rocket expertise of the von Braun team at the Army Ballistic Missile Agency in Huntsville, Ala. The Army, however, resisted giving up its own plans for a manned space program. Threatened with termination of funds for the development of Huntsville's huge Saturn rocket, the Army at last capitulated in fall 1959.[59]

ENGINEERING, PLUMBING, AND PLAIN HOPE: SATURN V AND CENTAUR

The development of the Saturn rocket was a technical gamble because it went well beyond the existing rocket technology of both the United States and the Soviet Union. Glennan called it "one of the most amazing combinations of engineering, plumbing and plain hope that anyone could imagine."[60] NASA policy makers thought that it was the key to leap-frogging the Russians' early successes in space.[61] They were counting on a continuation of the strong ties with the American aerospace industry established by the missile program.

In December 1959 Silverstein assembled a committee to evaluate the proposed Saturn vehicle. The committee's specific charge was to decide on the configuration of the upper stages for Saturn, the vehicle that would power the astronauts to the Moon. Saturn had the potential to loft a heavy payload into space, but the configuration of its upper stages was a question with important implications. An upper stage fueled by liquid hydrogen could produce approximately 40 percent more payload per pound of lift-off weight than conventional propellants.

Silverstein's commitment to liquid hydrogen was a product of his experience with research on unconventional fuels at Lewis Laboratory. Project Bee had convinced Silverstein that hydrogen could be used safely. von Braun, however, did not share Silverstein's sanguine view of liquid

T. Keith Glennan, the new NASA Administrator, and Hugh L. Dryden (left), Deputy Administrator, are sworn in August 19, 1958, as President Eisenhower looks on.

Senior staff and secretaries ring down the curtain on the NACA, September 30, 1958, in Director Ray Sharp's office.

hydrogen. Fearing risks involved in the storage and handling of liquid hydrogen, von Braun urged the use of conventional kerosene-based fuels for the first two stages, with liquid hydrogen reserved only for the third stage. Actually, it is doubtful that von Braun thought that liquid hydrogen would ever prove itself. In Silverstein's view,

> The von Braun team was apparently willing to take on the difficulties of the 15 million-pound thrust-booster stage rather than the hazards which they contemplated in the use of hydrogen as a fuel. The Lewis team of NASA had pioneered in the use of hydrogen oxygen and had operated small rocket engines with hydrogen as a fuel for ten years prior to the time of the decision on Saturn. We had become very accustomed to its use and its safety.[62]

Silverstein came to the meeting of the Saturn Evaluation Committee armed with data from a NASA study on the feasibility of liquid hydrogen by Eldon Hall, Adelbert O. Tischler, and Abe Hyatt. He argued that conventional upper stages were too heavy for the required payload. For a week the NACA team and the von Braun group debated, until von Braun at last capitulated. The two upper stages of Saturn would use liquid hydrogen. "What led him to this final decision, I'll never know," Silverstein recalled, "but it was certainly the correct one... I believe that the decision to go with hydrogen-oxgyen in the upper stages of the Saturn V was the significant technical decision that enabled the United States to achieve the first manned lunar landing. The Russian effort to accomplish this mission without high-energy upper stages was doomed to failure."[63]

Commitment to liquid hydrogen among rocket pioneers had an impressive history. Konstantin Tsiolkovsky recommended it in ''Treatise on Space Travel'' in 1903. Hermann Oberth and Robert Goddard also discussed its potential. A group at Ohio State University tested a rocket using liquid hydrogen in 1945. By 1954, the rocket section at Lewis Laboratory had developed the nation's first regeneratively cooled liquid hydrogen-liquid fluorine rocket with 5000 pounds of thrust.[64]

Centaur originated in a proposal of Krafft Ehricke for using a liquid hydrogen upper stage for the Atlas missile developed by General Dynamics/Astronautics for the Air Force. Ehricke, once part of the Peenemünde group, had locked horns with von Braun over the practicality of liquid hydrogen in the face of the mind-boggling technical problems associated with using this unconventional fuel. The tragic explosion in the 1930s of the *Hindenberg* dirigible, lifted by gaseous hydrogen, had created an understandable prejudice against hydrogen in general. Rocket pioneers like von Braun had concrete reasons for doubting the feasibility of using liquid hydrogen as a fuel. Because hydrogen in its liquid state is cryogenic, it must be stored at very low temperatures. The temperature of liquid hydrogen at 1 atmosphere is –420° F. When it absorbs heat, it boils and expands rapidly. Tanks must be protected from all sources of heat, such as rocket engine exhaust, air friction during flight, and even radiant heat from the Sun. Because of liquid hydrogen's extreme cold and chemical reactivity with many metals, metal containers for hydrogen tend to become brittle and lose strength after exposure to hydrogen. Another serious drawback is that liquid hydrogen's low density requires light, but bulky, structures to contain the rocket's propellant. The von Braun group preferred heavy, solid structures—an approach Ehricke derisively compared to the conservative engineering of the Brooklyn Bridge. As John Sloop pointed out in *Liquid Hydrogen as a Propulsion Fuel*, ''This conservative design philosophy mitigated against the use of liquid hydrogen which, more than conventional fuels, depended upon very light structures to help offset the handicap of low density.''[65]

Ehricke, who had moved from Huntsville, Ala., to General Dynamics in San Diego, Calif., had tried to convince the Air Force to back his proposal for a liquid hydrogen upper stage on an Atlas intercontinental ballistic missile. The Air Force was not interested. In the post-Sputnik panic, Ehricke had more luck. He called on Silverstein in Washington in June 1958, during the transition from NACA to NASA. He wanted $15 million to initiate work at General Dynamics on a liquid hydrogen rocket. Silverstein shared Ehricke's enthusiasm for liquid hydrogen, but NASA had not yet received funding. He suggested that Ehricke present his proposal to the Advanced Research Projects Agency (ARPA).[66]

Shortly after NASA's formal creation in July 1958, Silverstein had set up a committee to define NASA's propulsion needs. By August this committee had concluded that, for launch vehicles requiring high-performance upper stages, the liquid hydrogen-liquid oxygen combination appeared to show the greatest promise. The consensus reached in this NASA committee coincided with ARPA's acceptance of Ehricke's proposal. Pratt & Whitney, already versed in liquid hydrogen as a fuel for a gas turbine engine through its work on the Suntan project for the Air Force, agreed to undertake the development of the Centaur engine. Pratt & Whitney personnel had developed a good working relationship with Lewis engineers on this project when they visited Lewis several times to study injector designs for the RL-10 engine. One of the important steps in the development of this hydrogen engine was the use of regenerative cooling, long an interest of Lewis rocket researchers. Experimental heat transfer studies, carried out by a group working under Robert Graham in the Cryogenic Heat Transfer Section, proved the feasibility of hydrogen as a coolant.[67]

Later, after Centaur management was transferred to Lewis Laboratory, Pratt & Whitney would work hand-in-hand with engineers at Lewis to complete the development of the RL-10 engine.

After the December 1959 meeting at which Silverstein had convinced von Braun that the upper stages of the Saturn rocket ought to be fueled with liquid hydrogen, the development of Centaur and Saturn V became inextricably intertwined. As an intermediate step NASA intended to use Centaur as the upper stage for an Atlas rocket to launch a probe to soft land on the Moon. No one was sure of the composition of the Moon's surface. Before astronauts could set foot there, NASA had to program this probe, named Surveyor, to land and photograph the Moon's surface. More important, the success of Centaur to launch Surveyor would prove the feasibility of using liquid hydrogen in Saturn's upper stages to power the astronauts to the Moon.

THE LUNAR DECISION AND NASA'S RESTRUCTURING

In May 1961 President John Kennedy announced the national goal of landing Americans on the Moon within a decade. Kennedy's commitment to a race with the Soviet Union transformed NASA. Its budget suddenly expanded from $1 billion in 1961 to a peak of $5.1 billion in 1964. The staff increased by a factor of ten, and Congress funded a new Manned Spaceflight Center in Houston, Tex. It was a bonanza for aerospace contractors and selected American universities, now able to develop new programs as a result of NASA's generous funding.

At Headquarters Silverstein had acted with the zest and informality necessary to get NASA off the ground. He had transformed an extremely capable and loyal team of engineers into effective NASA administrators. By 1961, Silverstein's Office of Space Flight Programs had become the operational hub of NASA. However, when James E. Webb became NASA Administrator in January 1961, he took steps to impose a more rational, hierarchical structure on Silverstein's seat-of-the-pants operation.

In June 1961 Webb set up a new Office of Programs under Demarquis Wyatt to report directly to Associate Administrator Robert Seamans. The creation of this office was designed to reduce the disproportionate concentration of power in Silverstein's Office of Space Flight Programs.[68] All the NASA centers would report directly to Seamans, a "frank recognition that the lunar landing decision had made manned spaceflight the dominant activity within the agency."[69] Webb invited Silverstein to head the Apollo Program under the new centralized regime, but Silverstein resisted the organizational changes, arguing for a semi-autonomous status of the Apollo Program. He would agree to head the Apollo Program only if the centers directly responsible for the success of the program—Goddard, Marshall, the new Manned Space Flight Center in Houston, and Cape Canaveral—were placed *directly* under his supervision. In Silverstein's view, having the directors of these centers report to both the Apollo Program Director and to Associate Administrator Seamans would divide authority and generate misunderstandings and disagreement.[70]

One of the reasons Webb decided on this new management structure could have been the well-known friction between Silverstein and von Braun. With strong technical backgrounds and equally strong opinions, each had operated within separate spheres of NASA. Initially, when the Army Ballistic Missile Agency became Marshall Space Flight Center in March 1960, it was placed under the newly created Launch Vehicles Programs. However, if Silverstein were to direct the Apollo Program under the decentralized, semi-autonomous structure he favored, von Braun would become his subordinate. With von Braun and Silverstein "at loggerheads," the situation would have been intolerable.[71] von Braun protested that he would not have his center run by a "colony of artists"—his characterization of the NACA engineers associated with Silverstein in the Office of Space Flight Programs.[72]

On a more fundamental level, the September 1961 reorganization of Headquarters was an effort to cut NASA loose from the old NACA practice of decentralized administration. During his years as Director of the NACA, Dryden had served merely to coordinate the activity of the NACA laboratories. The locus of power, the real decision making, took place in the three laboratories, which received suggestions, not orders. The laboratories told Headquarters what "made sense or didn't make sense."[73] Under the new regime, both technical and administrative decisions would originate from the top, in Washington.

Dryden urged Silverstein to take over the Apollo Program despite his misgivings. He reasoned that, once the management structure proved unworkable, it would be changed to the one Silverstein favored. To Silverstein this was a waste of time and money. Since he could not agree with the new policy, he felt he had no choice but to resign. With the helm of Lewis Laboratory unoccupied after the retirement of Ray Sharp the previous winter, Silverstein accepted the appointment. It was both an opportunity to return to research and a solution to his increasingly untenable position at Headquarters. Webb persuaded D. Brainerd Holmes from RCA, former manager of the Ballistic Missile Early Warning System, to head the Apollo Program.[74]

Abe Silverstein returned to Cleveland in November with the Mercury Program on the brink of success. Alan Shepherd's short flight beyond Earth's atmosphere had restored confidence in American technology. Now with a fellow Ohioan, John Glenn, scheduled to orbit Earth, Silverstein stepped out of the maelstrom of decision making at Headquarters to return to management and technical problems at the laboratory level.

NOTES

[1] See Arthur L. Levine, "United States Aeronautical Research Policy, 1915-1958: A Study of the Major Policy Decisions of the National Advisory Committee for Aeronautics." Ph.D. Dissertation, Columbia University, New York, N.Y., 1963.

[2] Ira H. Abbott, "A Review and Commentary of a Thesis by Arthur L. Levine Entitled, U.S. Aeronautical Research Policy 1915-1958: A Study of the Major Policy Decisions of the National Advisory Committee for Aeronautics' Dated 1963," HHN-35, 1964, NASA History Office, Washington, D.C., p. 197. Alex Roland has explored the conservatism of NACA Headquarters in *Model Research*, NASA SP-4103 (Washington, D.C.: U.S. Government Printing Office, 1985).

[3] R. O. Miller and P. M. Ordin, "Theoretical Performance of Rocket Propellants Containing Hydrogen, Nitrogen, and Oxygen," NACA RM E8A30, 1948, cited by John Sloop, *Liquid Hydrogen as a Propulsion Fuel, 1949-1959*, NASA SP-4404 (Washington, D.C.: U.S. Government Printing Office, 1978), p. 80.

[4] Sloop, *Liquid Hydrogen*, p. 75.

[5] Ibid.

[6] R. W. Bussard and R. D. DeLauer, *Fundamentals of Nuclear Flight* (New York: McGraw-Hill Book Co., 1965), p. 2.

[7] John Sloop, Lectures 8 and 9 for ME 221, "Aircraft Propulsion Principles." Case Institute of Technology, fall, 1949. In Lecture 9, "Solid Propellant Rockets," Sloop discussed the range and orbital and escape velocities for satellites, p. 12-16. Private papers courtesy of John Sloop.

[8] John Sloop, "Rocket Engines," American Legion Public Square Post, 12 June 1952, p. 6. Between 1948 and 1957 Sloop presented at least 15 papers at both professional and public meetings to urge rocket development for both missile and space applications. These papers, both published and unpublished, are available through Mr. Sloop, 8311 Melody Court, Bethesda, Md. 20034.

[9] Sloop, *Liquid Hydrogen*, p. 78.

[10] John Sloop, Comments on Manuscript History of the Lewis Research Center by Virginia Dawson, 5 September 1989.

[11] On William Perl, see Ronald Radosh and Joyce Milton, *The Rosenberg File: A Search for the Truth* (New York: Holt, Rinehart and Winston, 1983), p. 123-129, 202-207, and passim. I also consulted the Perl Files (65-59312) at the FBI Headquarters, J. Edgar Hoover Building, Washington, D.C. Although the files revealed nothing beyond the inconclusive evidence of Perl's guilt reported in Radosh and Milton, the interviews are interesting for their descriptions of the laboratory's work during that period. Much of the text of the files is still heavily censored.

[12] Memorandum for Director, NACA, from E. R. Sharp, "Visit of Congressman Albert Thomas and Mr. A. H. Skarin, Friday, Oct 3, 1952." NASA Lewis Records, 279/116.1-63.

[13] Interview with John Evvard, 14 June 1987.

[14] Notes from the Noncredit Graduate Study Course (1957), "Concepts of Hypersonic Flight," were obtained courtesy of George M. Prok, NASA Lewis Research Center.

[15] Moeckel to Stuhlinger, 2 June 1964, personal papers of Moeckel.

[16] Ernst Stuhlinger, *Ion Propulsion for Space Flight* (New York: McGraw-Hill Book Co., 1964), p. 6.

[17] Moeckel to Stuhlinger, ibid.

[18] K. A. Ehricke, "The Solar Powered Space Ship," ARS Paper No. 310-356.

[19] Stuhlinger, *Ion Propulsion for Space Flight*, p. 6.

[20] Moeckel to Stuhlinger, 2 June 1964, personal papers of Moeckel.

[21] Walter Olson, "A Suggested Policy and Course of Action for NACA with Regard to Rocket Engine Propulsion," 6 May 1955, p. 21-22 of "A Suggested Policy and Course of Action for NACA on Space Flight," 2 December 1957, part of communication to Eugene Emme from Walter Olson, 31 January 1972, Propulsion file, NASA History Office, Washington, D.C.

[22] See Abe Silverstein and Eldon W. Hall, "Liquid Hydrogen as a Jet Fuel for High-Altitude Aircraft," NACA RM E55 C28a, 15 April 1955. See also Sloop, *Liquid Hydrogen*, p. 102–107.

[23] Interview with Robert English by V. Dawson, 11 July 1986. William Ritter's group (including Merland Moseson, Robert Ziemer, and Wilfred Scull) transferred to Goddard Space Flight Center.

[24] Sloop, *Liquid Hydrogen*, p. 84.

[25] Quoted by Sloop, *Liquid Hydrogen*, p. 85.

[26] Interview with Robert English, 11 July 1986. Unfortunately, I was unable to find the curriculum of the nuclear school among what has survived of Lewis administrative records. Members of the Nuclear School were (list courtesy of Robert English):

From the Compressor and Turbine Division

Turbines: Hubert Allen, Art Hansen, Howard Herzig

Fundamental Turbines: R. Cavicchi, E. Davison, Robert English

Compressors: Dan Bernatowicz, Ted Fessler, Harry Finger, Sy Lieblein, Carl Schwenk

Turbine Cooling: Tony Diaguila, Pat Donoughe, Herman Ellerbrock, John Livingood, Henry Slone

From other divisions: Edgar Cortright, Tom Dallas, Irving Goodman, Eldon Hall, Jim Kramer, Herb Heppler, Bill Phillips, Lou Rosenblum

[27] Syllabus of Seminar on Rocket Propulsion, 28 February 1957; Memorandum for Personnel Taking Rocket Seminar and for Instructional Staff, 4 March 1957. Papers of John Sloop.

[28] Moeckel to Stuhlinger, 2 June 1964, personal papers of Moeckel. See Wolfgang Moeckel, L. V. Baldwin, Robert English, Bernard Lubarsky, and Steve Maslen, "Satellite and Space Propulsion Systems," NASA TN D-285, June 1960. Declassified paper presented at NACA Flight Propulsion Conference, 22 November 1957, previously published as NASA TMX 61622. Some of the Lewis work in the early 1960s is summarized in *Electric Propulsion for Spacecraft*, NASA SP-22, 1963.

[29] Research Planning Council (established 8 March 1957), 6 September 1957, NASA Lewis Records 298/117.

[30] "10 Years After X-1: Supersonic Anniversary Puts Flight Laboratory Here in Spotlight," *Cleveland Plain Dealer Magazine*, 6 October 1957.

[31] Sloop, *Liquid Hydrogen*, p. 90–91.

[32] Triennial Inspection, Lewis Laboratory, 7–9 October 1957. "High-Energy Rocket Propellants," personal papers courtesy of John Sloop.

[33] Papers of the NACA 1957 Flight Propulsion Conference were published in two parts. NASA TM-X-67368 (1971) contains six papers on air-breathing propulsion systems, three on rocket systems, including "Propellants," by E. A. Fletcher, H. W. Douglass, R. J. Priem, and G. Vasu; "Turbopumps for High-Energy Propellants," by Ambrose Ginsburg, Ward W. Wilcox, and David G. Evans; and "Performance and Missions," by J. L. Sloop, A. S. Boksenvom, S. Gordon, R. W. Graham, P. M. Ordin, and A. O. Tischler. The papers published as TM-X-61622 (1972) include the paper cited in note 28; Paul G. Johnson, James W. Miser, and Roger L. Smith, "Nuclear Logistic Carrier," and Frank E. Rom, Eldon W. Sams, and Robert E. Hyland, "Nuclear Rockets."

[34] Interview with Bruce Lundin by Eugene Emme, 5 June 1974. See discussion in Sloop, *Liquid Hydrogen*, p. 180.

[35] Walter Olson, "Suggested Policy and Course of Action for NACA on Space Flight," 2 December 1957, part of a communication to Eugene Emme from Walter Olson, 31 January 1972. Propulsion file, NASA History Office, Washington, D.C.

[36] A copy of the original memo, dated 9 December 1957, was obtained from Lundin, with Silverstein's handwritten comments. The typed Silverstein version called, "Lewis Laboratory Opinion of a Future Policy and Course of Action for the NACA," was found in NASA Lewis Records, 221/115.1-71,

[37] Ibid.

[38] Ibid.

[39] Sloop, *Liquid Hydrogen*, p. 180.

[40] "Minutes of December 20, 1957 Meeting of Committee on Space Flight Laboratory," personal papers of Isidore Warshawsky. From these minutes it appears that the "Lewis Laboratory Opinion" was the original document that, with modifications and input from the other two laboratories, became "A Staff Study of the NACA," dated 14 January 1958. This was further refined into a four-page document called "A National Research Program for Space Technology," referred to by later commentators as the "Dryden Plan."

[41] See Sloop, *Liquid Hydrogen*, p. 181; Hugh L. Dryden to Eugene Emme, "The NACA-NASA Transition," 8 September 1965, NASA History Office, Washington, D.C.

[42] Silverstein attended meetings on January 6 and 27 of the Lewis Special Committee on Space Flight Laboratory. From the personal papers of I. Warshawsky, I obtained the complete minutes of the meetings. The 10 February document is reproduced *in toto* by Alex Roland in *Model Research*, vol. 2, document 46, p. 732 ff. The final version, somewhat condensed and called "Summary of a Program for Expansion of NACA Research in Space Flight Technology," was found in NASA Lewis Records 295/117.71. From the 27 January 1958 minutes, it is clear that Langley and Ames offered similar proposals, but Headquarters decided to use the Lewis proposal for a brochure to be presented to the NACA Special Committee on Space Technology (Stever Committee). The final version is also attributed to Lewis senior staff by L. Swenson, Jr., et al., *This New Ocean*, NASA SP-4201 (Washington, D.C.: U.S. Government Printing Office, 1966), p. 76 and 533, note 7. This is presumably the earliest plan for Goddard, a laboratory completely different from the original Lewis conception.

[43] Letter from Bruce Lundin to V. Dawson, 27 May 1987.

[44] "Dryden Interview by Mercury Historians," 1 October 1965, Dryden file, Johnson Space Center Archives, Houston, Tex.

[45] Robert L. Rosholt, *An Administrative History of NASA, 1958#1963*, NASA SP-4101, (Washington, D.C.: U.S. Government Printing Office, 1966).

[46] Walter A. McDougall, *... the Heavens and the Earth: A Political History of the Space Age* (New York: Basic Books, 1985), p. 166. See also Homer E. Newell, *Beyond the Atmosphere*, NASA SP-4211 (Washington, D.C.: U.S. Government Printing Office, 1980) p. 90–91.

[47] For the postwar statement of "National Aeronautical Research Policy," approved 21 March 1946, see Alex Roland, *Model Research*, vol. 2, document 36, p. 693–695. For distinctions between fundamental (or basic), applied, and specific developmental research, see Ira Abbott, p. 5–6 and 186 (cited in note 2). Arthur L. Levine (cited in note 1) placed the so-called "fundamental or basic research" at about 10 percent of total NACA research.

[48] See James R. Hansen, *Engineer in Charge*, NASA SP-4305 (Washington, D.C.: U.S. Government Printing Office, 1987), p. 353–367.

[49] "How an Aircraft Lab Leaped Over to Space," *Business Week*, 4 June 1960, p. 98–102.

[50] Robert Rosholt, *An Administrative History of NASA*, p. 35. Although set up in November 1957, the Stever Committee did not actually meet until January 1958. It seems that by this time most of the NACA policy had been formulated, and the committee merely ratified already formulated NACA plans at that time.

[51] For the metamorphosis of the NACA into NASA, see especially Rosholt, *An Administrative History of NASA*, p. 37–70; Swenson, *This New Ocean*, p. 75–106.

[52] Rosholt, *An Administrative History of NASA*, p. 206–207. See also transcript of D. D. Wyatt interview with Eugene Emme, 21 June 1973, NASA History Office.

From Lewis Laboratory Silverstein selected Demarquis D. Wyatt, Assistant to the Director of Space Flight Development; Edgar M. Cortright, Chief, Advanced Technology Program; Harold B. Finger, Chief, Nuclear Engines Program; Eldon W. Hall, Chief, Analysis and Requirements Program; N. Philip Miller, Chief, Plant and Facilities Construction Program, Space Flight Program. Also George M. Low, Chief, Manned Space Flight Program; Warren J. North, Chief, Manned Satellite Program; Adelbert O. Tischler, Chief, Liquid Fuel Rocket Engines Program; Francis C. Schwenk, Nuclear Program (title unknown); Newell Sanders, Assistant Director, Advanced Technology Program; William Fleming, Chief, Project Review Division (chaired task group to prepare the "Fleming Report," the first study of the feasibility of manned flight to the Moon).

Of the approximately 40 members of the Space Task Group (which became Mercury Program), 10 were from Lewis Laboratory: Elmer Buller, A. M. Busch, W. R. Dennis, M. J. Krasnican, Glynn S. Lunney, André J. Meyer, W. R. Meyer, W. J. Nesbitt, Gerard J. Pesman, and Leonard Robb. Commuters to Langley from Lewis were John Disher and Kenneth Weston.

[53] Transcript of speech by Abe Silverstein, Kennedy Space Center Writers Conference, Cocoa Beach, Fla., 1-3 September 1977. NASA History Office.

[54] Memo from George Low to Abe Silverstein, 17 October 1960, Personal files of Abe Silverstein, also reproduced in Charles Murray and Catherine Cox, *Apollo: The Race to the Moon* (New York: Simon and Schuster, 1989), p. 57-58. Their discussion confirms John Logsdon's view that, by 1959, at least two years prior to Kennedy's dramatic announcement of the Apollo Program, policy committees within NASA had set a manned lunar landing as NASA's long-range goal. See John M. Logsdon, *The Decision to Go to the Moon:, Project Apollo and the National Interest* (Cambridge, Mass.: MIT Press, 1970), p. 56-57; see also discussion in Roger Bilstein, *Stages to Saturn: A Technological History of the Apollo/Saturn Launch Vehicles*, NASA SP-4206 (Washington, D.C.: U.S. Government Printing Office, 1980), p. 48-50. See also Richard J. Weber to Chief, Propulsion Systems Analysis Branch, "Visit of R. J. Weber to Headquarters on Feb. 17, 1960 for ABMA briefing on lunar projects," files of R. J. Weber, NASA Lewis Research Center.

[55] Wyatt interview with Emme, p. 99.

[56] T. Keith Glennan, "The First Years of the National Aeronautics and Space Administration," 1964, unpublished diary, vol. 1, p. 6-7. Eisenhower Library, Abilene, Kan.

[57] See Clayton R. Koppes, *The JPL and the American Space Program* (New Haven: Yale University Press, 1982). See also remarks of T. Keith Glennan, "The First Years," p. 17.

[58] T. Keith Glennan, "The First Years," vol. 1, p. 18. For a history of Project Mercury, see Swenson, *This New Ocean*.

[59] Herbert York, *Making Weapons, Talking Peace* (New York: Basic Books, 1987), p. 174-175.

[60] T. Keith Glennan, "The First Years," vol. 2, p. 15.

[61] Logsdon, *The Decision to Go to the Moon*, p. 117.

[62] Abe Silverstein, "How It All Began," Speech at Kennedy Space Center Writers Conference, Cocoa Beach, Fla., 1-3 September 1977, NASA History Office Archives, file marked Lewis Research Center.

[63] Abe Silverstein, "How It All Began." See also Sloop, *Liquid Hydrogen*, p. 232-235, and Logsdon, *The Decision to Go to the Moon*, p. 58. Members of the Saturn Evaluation Committee were Silverstein, Chairman; Abraham Hyatt, NASA; George P. Sutton, ARPA; T. C. Muse, ODDR&E; Norman C. Appold, U.S. Air Force; Wernher von Braun, ABMA; Eldon Hall, NASA, Secretary. For key documents, see "Report to the Administrator, NASA on Saturn Development Plan by Saturn Vehicle Team," 15 December 1959, NASA History Office, Silverstein biographical file.

[64] Sloop, *Liquid Hydrogen*, p. 91-93.

[65] Ibid, p. 208.

[66] Ibid, p. 191-197. Interview with Abe Silverstein by V. Dawson, 6 June 1987.

[67] Two classic papers on hydrogen heat transfer that grew out of the work with Pratt & Whitney are Robert C. Hendricks, Robert W. Graham, Yih-yun Hsu, and Robert Friedman, "Experimental Heat Transfer and Pressure Drop of Liquid Hydrogen Flowing Through a Heated Tube," NASA TN D-765, May 1961; "Experimental Heat Transfer Results for Cryogenic Hydrogen Flowing in Tubes at Subcritical and Supercritical Pressures to 800 psi Absolute," NASA TN D-3095, March 1966.

[68] Rosholt, *An Administrative History of NASA*, p. 206-207.

[69] Arnold S. Levine, *Managing NASA in the Apollo Era*, NASA SP-4102 (Washington, D.C.: U.S. Government Printing Office, 1982), p. 36.

[70] Interview with Abe Silverstein, 6 June 1987, not recorded.

[71] Transcript of D. D. Wyatt interview with Eugene Emme, p. 96.

[72] Interview with Bruce Lundin by V. Dawson, 28 May 1987.

73 Transcript of Wyatt interview with Emme, p. 68–70.

74 Silverstein interview with V. Dawson, 6 June 1987. Silverstein said that in November 1963 Webb asked him to head the proposed Manned Spacecraft Center in Houston, but he felt that Robert Gilruth had earned that. Charles Murray and Catherine Cox, *Apollo*, note p. 126, report that Silverstein opposed Gilruth's appointment. Dryden's prediction that the new management structure would ultimately be changed to the one Silverstein favored proved correct. The centers were later placed under program offices, instead of reporting to Associate Administrator Seamans. After Sharp retired in December 1960, Eugene Manganiello served as Acting Director until Silverstein returned.

CHAPTER NINE

THE APOLLO ERA: OPPORTUNITIES AND DASHED HOPES

Abe Silverstein returned to Lewis Laboratory optimistic that the success of the Apollo Program would be a major stepping stone in America's exploration of the cosmos. Trips to Mars and beyond would require new propulsion systems. Lewis Laboratory was poised to take the lead in NASA's program in electric propulsion. Silverstein also envisioned a major role for the laboratory in the proposed $1 billion program to develop nuclear rockets. If funded, Lewis would become the hub of NASA's nuclear propulsion program. NASA Administrator James E. Webb confirmed this commitment in a speech at a gala dinner at Cleveland's Auto and Aviation Museum hosted by the laboratory's loyal advocate, Frederick C. Crawford.[1] Yet the promise of 1961 did not become reality, and eight years later Silverstein would leave NASA bereft of his earlier sense of optimism for either Lewis or the space agency as a whole.

Four years in Washington had not changed Silverstein's physical appearance or his basic management philosophy. His compact build, slightly rounded shoulders, baggy suit, and carefully groomed jet-black hair seemed no different than the day he had arrived from Langley Field in 1943. Part of the Langley nucleus that had carried NACA traditions from Hampton, Va., only his title had changed. He was now Dr. Silverstein. In 1958 Case Institute of Technology had granted him an honorary engineering degree.

Silverstein had seen the facilities of the Cleveland laboratory rise from the flat fields that skirted the edge of Rocky River ravine. He had participated in the transition from the piston engine to jet propulsion and, as Chief of Research, had guided the laboratory through the thicket of turbojet propulsion problems from the late 1940s through the early 1950s. Silverstein liked to have a personal sense of the projects under his supervision. During his short trips across the parking lot to the Engine Research Building for unannounced visits, he could take in the metallic glow of the Altitude Wind Tunnel, a facility with its own distinguished but tortuous history. There Silverstein and his staff had generated key data to redesign piston engine baffles so that cylinders would not overheat. After World War II, they had constructed small supersonic tunnels tied into the Altitude Wind Tunnel's air intake and exhaust system to explore the aerodynamics of ramjets.[2]

The overhead pipes that connected the tunnel with the laboratory's central air system symbolized the network of human connections that breathed life into its complicated facilities. These facilities embodied the creativity of Lewis personnel. While Silverstein was away, the tunnel's cavernous space had been transformed into a vacuum chamber used to test the instrumentation for Big Joe. After the Atlas-D rocket had lofted Big Joe into space, NASA knew the Mercury capsule would be safe to carry humans.[3]

NASA Administrator James Webb envisioned Lewis as the hub of NASA's nuclear engine project. Left to right: Abe Silverstein, Frederick C. Crawford, T. Keith Glennan, James Webb. (Photograph Courtesy of Rebman Photo.)

Silverstein looked forward to working again at the laboratory level. He still had the rough edges of an engineer, more at ease with hardware than lobbying. At Headquarters, T. Keith Glennan had found Silverstein articulate, but stubborn. In Glennan's view the NACA management style had suited the NACA, but "hardly fits our needs today when we have so many relationships with industry and other elements of the government."[4] Silverstein could be gruff, tactless, and impatient with mediocrity, hardly the way to win friends in Washington. His engineering colleagues, however, recognized his leadership ability. In a *New York Times* interview, a NASA colleague called Silverstein a genius—"not in terms of invention and discovery but in his breadth of comprehension of technical matters and his remarkable facility for getting down to the fundamentals in any field he tackles."[5] With an intuitive feel for technical detail, he often became too involved when a project excited him.

Silverstein knew how to build effective engineering teams by carefully knitting together personalities and skills. He had a sure grasp of who moved best by being left alone and who had to be prodded to action. He could appreciate both ends of the research spectrum—not only the skill of the technicians in the machine shop, who could create a delicate instrument from an engineer's rough sketch, but also the analytic talent of the small group of research scientists at Lewis Laboratory.[6] During the NACA years, engineering applications had dominated the activity of the laboratory. Silverstein knew that NACA-trained NASA personnel were often looked down on by staff at the Jet Propulsion Laboratory (JPL) and Marshall Space Flight Center and by the Vanguard team at Goddard Space Flight Center because of the emphasis on applications of NACA's work.[7]

Glennan had not fully appreciated the NACA research tradition. The Space Act required that NASA supervise industry contractors and manage space missions. The former college president, a Republican, favored spending most of NASA's budget on contracts with the aerospace industry and universities.[8] He disapproved of the NACA policy of "farming out to industry only the repetitive and straight production items," saving the more challenging and creative projects for the staff.[9] Although the "proper balance" between in-house research and industry contracts remained unresolved, as long as Glennan set a deliberate pace for space flight development, the integrity and autonomy of the former NACA laboratories seemed secure. After President Kennedy's announcement of the goal of a lunar landing, however, the tight schedules of the Apollo Program threatened to compromise the independence of the former NACA laboratories to do basic research. Under Webb's new administration, their role was no longer clear.

WHITHER LEWIS LABORATORY?

Even before Silverstein returned to Cleveland, the laboratory had begun to struggle with the implications of the new NASA organizational structure. Like the other former NACA laboratories, Langley and Ames, it was now referred to as a research center to distinguish it from the new development- and mission-oriented centers within NASA. It was clear that the NACA research ideal needed modification. In a speech to the staff the preceding year, Acting Director Eugene Manganiello revealed his anxiety about how the work of the center fit into the larger NASA picture. He summarized the history of Lewis to get a clearer sense of current practice and future goals. He pointed out that the amount of research in rockets and nuclear propulsion had remained small until 1951, when these areas began to grow. In 1957 Lewis Research Center had dramatically reduced research on air-breathing engines. By 1960 work on chemical rockets was at 35 percent; nuclear propulsion, 20 percent; and electric propulsion and power generation, 14 percent. Air-breathing engine research was at a mere 7 percent, and was mainly in support of military projects such as the B-70 airplane. The remaining 24 percent included basic heat transfer, fluid mechanics, radiation physics, and instrument and computing research.[10]

Manganiello considered the primary mission of Lewis Research Center to lie in three research areas: advanced propulsion, including chemical, nuclear, and electric rockets; power generation; and materials. He thought that the center should, as in the past, maintain a mixture of basic research, applied research, and what he called "specific research" related to development problems, such as the restart capability of the Centaur engine, the Saturn base heating problem, and the B-70 inlet control problem.[11]

In the NACA era, Lewis workers had responsibility only for the "research end of the business." Industry had handled development and production, and the military had been responsible for operations. Now, however, the situation was different. Space exploration required national resources of a magnitude that precluded maintaining the distinctions between research, development, and operations. "Our place as a research center is not as unique and sharply delineated as it was in the past." NASA had the responsibility not only for research, but also for the development, procurement, and operation of space vehicles. Manganiello recognized that some former NACA staff thought that research and development should be kept separate. "The argument is that once the development camel's head is permitted in the tent it will inevitably take over completely and crowd research out of the shelter."[12]

Manganiello thought that the sharp distinction between research and development did not apply to current practice. *"Applied* research" and *"advanced* development" had become indistinguishable. The development centers—Marshall, JPL, and Goddard—did both. The research character of the former NACA laboratories, however, could be preserved if short-term development problems were avoided.

Eugene Manganiello, Acting Director after Sharp retired in 1960.

We at Lewis have no desire or intention to engage in the short-range activity or get into the problems of the construction of flight hardware. We are not particularly intrigued with the battle of the 'O' rings but we are, on the other hand, intensely interested in the advanced research and development end of the business, the nuclear rocket, electric propulsion and power generation, high-energy chemical rockets—their systems and components—where the scientific and engineering technology needs to be established before useful and reliable propulsion can be created .... We cannot afford to permit our basic research or our conceptual research into new and better ideas to become submerged or deemphasized so that we have nothing left to grow on.[13]

Manganiello did not mention Lewis Research Center's contributions to the Mercury program because exclusive focus on these types of projects—albeit necessary and valuable in terms of the space race against the Russians—would leave the laboratory without research capital for the future. A research laboratory was a place where unconventional new technology like nuclear, electric, and high-energy chemical rockets could be incubated. This advanced work had to be nurtured while some of the laboratory's efforts could be diverted to assist in trouble-shooting when NASA needed their particular expertise.

Abe Silverstein could appreciate the ideas in Manganiello's talk. For almost four years in Washington, he had tasted the drama and excitement of large development projects. However, he was also aware that the quickened tempo of the Apollo Program now threatened the balance between research and development within NASA as a whole. Dryden had favored preserving the research orientation of the former NACA laboratories. He had placed them under the Office of Advanced Research and Technology (OART) to protect them from the encroachments of the development and operations side of NASA. The integrity of research was a cornerstone of post-World War II technology planning. Vannevar Bush had regarded research, both basic and applied, as a government function. It was the nation's technical capital. In *Science, the Endless Frontier* he had warned, "Research will always suffer when put in competition with operations."[14] Manned space flight now gobbled up almost all of NASA's budget. Just as Webb's new management structure had eased many former NACA staff out of Headquarters, the camel of development and missions had begun to push Lewis Research Center, along with the other two research centers, Ames and Langley, out of the mainstream of NASA.

Silverstein's return rekindled the debate between staff committed to basic research and those who favored a vigorous involvement in development and operations. Should the laboratory give up its pretensions as a research center and join the quickened pace of NASA centers more closely identified with development? Most of the laboratory's work was done in-house. Silverstein felt that the strength of the laboratory lay in the organic, self-sufficient engineering environment it provided. This environment provided the conditions for the growth of individual engineering expertise and the freedom to cultivate areas of research beyond the secure arena of existing technology. Within NASA as a whole, however, the concept of in-house research was disappearing. NASA began to contract out support services, such as janitorial, grounds-keeping, and security. Eventually, support service contracting would include basic technology research. A windfall for the aerospace industry, this policy threatened the mission of the former NACA laboratories to perform basic and applied research. In 1961, 77 percent of NASA's employees were contractors. By 1964, contractors would command 92 percent of NASA's employment total.[15]

Silverstein had not decided what direction the laboratory should take when he returned to Lewis. Increased involvement with the development and mission side of NASA would mean that the laboratory would have to learn to deal with contractors. He also knew the danger of letting the camel of development into the research tent. How would he protect basic research? If Silverstein protected the research character of the laboratory by refusing to participate in large-scale development projects, he was aware that he needed more staff with graduate educations. Lewis's group of theoreticians was small. The majority of staff had degrees in mechanical engineering. When three members of the Applied Mechanics Group—Simon Ostrach, Stephen Maslen, and Harold Mirels—called on him to discuss the laboratory's future, Silverstein took heed. Ostrach recalled Silverstein's surprise at their audacity in proposing that he transform Lewis into a laboratory for basic research. "They sort of put us off in a corner and they thought that they should have bright guys around, but Abe was flabbergasted that we wanted to have something to say about the direction that the lab was going."[16]

At a meeting of division chiefs Silverstein presented the idea of the Applied Mechanics Group to model Lewis on AT&T's Bell Laboratories in Murray Hill, N.J. He wanted to hire only Ph.Ds. Although the general consensus was favorable, Bruce Lundin strongly opposed it. He had spent most of his career testing full-scale engines. To Lundin, Dryden's often repeated admonition that the NACA laboratories needed protection from the development and mission side of NASA had become a shibboleth. He argued that they were "really just a bunch of testing engineers." To transform the laboratory by adding a group of high-powered scientists would take ten years. Lundin thought that NASA needed the laboratory's technical competence. He suggested a compromise: divide the laboratory into two distinct parts, research and development. Silverstein, as director, could "provide the balance between the two and can protect the one from the other."[17] Lundin's plan seemed to offer the best of both worlds. With the backing of the other division chiefs, Silverstein reorganized the laboratory. He put Lundin in charge of development and John Evvard in charge of research.

The laboratory immediately began to experience the effect of strong Congressional support for the space program during the early Apollo years. Silverstein announced that Lewis Research Center would increase its payroll from $23.5 million to $28 million. He was authorized to hire 615 new staff, a major expansion of personnel. In addition, a large Developmental Engineering Building to house 1100 engineers was planned.

The location of this large office building outside the main gates reflected Silverstein's commitment to keep research physically separate and untarnished by the contracting side of NASA. Lundin's staff, many newly hired under NASA's more generous salaries, worked in the Developmental Engineering Building, with its separate cafeteria and security. They would learn the new realities of dealing with industry as a customer rather than a provider of technology. At first, the research side of the center was shielded from responsibilities connected with contracts. People who worked under Evvard still came through the Main Gate in the morning to work in their laboratories much as they had during the NACA era. However, even the research side of the laboratory began to be affected by the pressure of increased NASA-wide contracting.

TO THE MOON: DIRECT ASCENT OR RENDEZVOUS?

In November 1961, when Silverstein returned, it appeared that Lewis Laboratory would become an important center for nuclear rocket propulsion. With a nuclear stage proposed as the key to providing sufficient power to reach the Moon directly, Lewis Research Center was positioning itself to play a leading role in NASA. The Cleveland *Plain Dealer* reported that Lewis Research Center looked forward to "major participation in every manned space effort to follow the current Mercury Program and most future unmanned space exploits as well."[18] The Kennedy Administration was reluctant to approve costly expenditures for large technology development programs unless they could be justified in terms of specific applications.[19] The costs of the nuclear programs were astronomical, but tied to future missions beginning with Apollo; NASA counted on obtaining generous funding for nuclear rocket research.

The ambitious lunar mission called for a rocket that could provide enormous thrust, nothing less than von Braun's huge Saturn or an even larger rocket called Nova, first proposed by the Saturn Vehicle Evaluation Committee, chaired by Silverstein, in 1959. No consensus was ever reached on Nova's configuration, but one proposal considered a first stage powered by conventional fuel, a liquid hydrogen second stage, and nuclear upper stages.[20] The nuclear stages could give this behemoth the necessary thrust for direct ascent to the Moon, which involved a scenario reminiscent of the science fiction of Jules Verne. A rocket consisting of several stages would be fired directly at the Moon. It would need to brake against the Moon's gravity to land. For the return journey to Earth, a final stage would blast off from the Moon's surface. The first study of launch vehicle requirements for the lunar mission, chaired by William A. Fleming, formerly of Lewis, supported the direct ascent concept.[21] Projected costs and time for the development of a rocket of the required magnitude made some NASA planners question the feasibility of direct ascent.

Within NASA there were also strong partisans of a rendezvous method to reach the Moon in two stages via a space platform placed in orbit around Earth. von Braun and the Marshall group favored what came to be called the Earth-orbit rendezvous method. Two packages consisting of modules for the assembly of the platform and lunar vehicle could be launched separately by two

Saturn rockets to rendezvous in Earth orbit. The platform would then function as a launching pad to send the lunar vehicle to the Moon and back. The attraction of the Earth-orbit rendezvous method was that instead of a single large rocket, which existed only in the imagination of NASA's rocket designers, the plan depended on the smaller Saturn rocket already under development at Marshall Space Flight Center. By June 1961, after a NASA study chaired by Bruce Lundin, opinion began to shift in favor of the rendezvous concept, with Earth-orbit rendezvous the "clear preference" among members of the evaluation committee. Nova development, however, was still under serious consideration.[22]

A group at Langley Research Center favored a third approach—lunar-orbit rendezvous (LOR)—which at first seemed hopelessly complicated. It required three spacecraft: a command module occupied by the three astronauts, a service module for the propulsion and guidance systems, and a lunar excursion vehicle. These three vehicles would be fired into lunar orbit by a single expendable three-stage rocket. Once in lunar orbit, the astronauts would park the command and service modules in orbit. Two of the astronauts would don space suits and clamber into the excursion vehicle for their trip to the Moon's surface. Later they would rendezvous with the command module for the return trip to Earth, leaving the excursion vehicle behind. The advantages of this method were its lower fuel and weight requirements.

Silverstein favored direct ascent. He objected that the engineering required for the docking of two vehicles in space involved greater complexity and more risk to the astronauts should a component fail.[23] Although Silverstein returned to Lewis before NASA planners had hammered out the final decision, no doubt it came as a disappointment. Webb's announcement of the selection of the lunar-orbit rendezvous method in July 1962 ended all hopes for the development of Nova and took some of the urgency away from Lewis's nuclear rocket program. Nuclear power might be required for distant flights to Mars and beyond, but clearly, through the 1960s, NASA's energies would be directed to landing humans on the Moon.

Lewis staff wanted to salvage something from the lunar rendezvous decision. Because of the laboratory's expertise in propulsion, Lewis was the logical choice to design and monitor the development of the second vehicle, called the Lunar Excursion Module (LEM), needed to take the astronauts from the command module to the surface of the Moon. As early as December 1959, Lewis staff had set its sights on the development of a "lunar soft-landing vehicle." E. W. Conrad and Carl F. Schueller took up the idea at Headquarters with Cortright in 1959, long before NASA had decided on the details of the Apollo mission. Although no formal agreement was reached, Cortright gave them the go-ahead to begin to work up specifications. By 1960, the Analysis Branch of the Propulsion Systems Division was at work on two types of vehicles for manned lunar-landing missions. The first was a small-scale vehicle for lunar exploration to carry two or three astronauts, with a return capsule weight of about 10,000 pounds. A second larger vehicle to deliver 50,000 pounds of material to a large-scale lunar base was also designed. However, with Silverstein back at the helm of Lewis Research Center, this project had to be dropped. To develop the LEM would have required working with von Braun's group, in charge of the Saturn V. Although there may have been other considerations, in Bruce Lundin's opinion, Brainerd Holmes opposed creating this potentially abrasive situation. He was "not going to have Silverstein throw sand into his machine."[24]

THE TANGLED HISTORY OF NUCLEAR PROPULSION

The Lewis staff were old hands at dealing with the opportunities and disappointments associated with the development of nuclear propulsion. Interest at the laboratory in nuclear propulsion had developed steadily from the late 1940s under the leadership of Benjamin Pinkel and his branch chief, Eugene Manganiello. In 1948 a prestigious group at the Massachusetts Institute of Technology issued the secret Lexington Report, which concluded that development of nuclear rockets and ramjets presented nearly insuperable technical problems. Aircraft nuclear propulsion, however, was feasible, although development might take up to 15 years. To the American propulsion community, led by Colonel Donald Keirn and D. R. Shoults of General Electric (both prime players in the secret drama to import the Whittle engine), this was sweet music. They thought an engine powered by nuclear energy could create a propulsion "breakthrough" comparable to the turbojet.[25]

Silverstein envisioned increased cooperation with the Atomic Energy Commission and a strong role for the Cleveland laboratory in NEPA (Nuclear Energy Propulsion for Aircraft). In 1949 the laboratory acquired a cyclotron for basic research in materials.

Carving out a role for Lewis in aircraft nuclear propulsion proved an agonizingly slow process. Planning for a nuclear reactor began in 1954, and in 1955 Congress authorized its construction. After a survey of 16 locations in Ohio and Pennsylvania, Lewis leased 500 acres of land near Sandusky, Ohio, about 50 miles west of Cleveland. Originally known as the Plum Brook Ordnance Works, it had served as an explosives factory and storage area during World War II. In 1956 the Atomic Energy Commission Safeguard Committee approved the design for the reactor. At the time of the ground breaking for the new facility, aircraft nuclear propulsion appeared to be the propulsion frontier. Silverstein called it "the 'shining hope' for increasing the range of aircraft at high speeds and for increasing aircraft ranges to values unobtainable with conventional or special chemical fuels."[26] The laboratory hoped to contribute fundamental studies on the effects of radiation on materials. Only gradually did it become apparent that the nuclear airplane had become a technical dead end. Its detractors called it a shitepoke—an enormous skinny bird, hardly fit for eating or for flying. Development by Pratt & Whitney and General Electric over 15 years cost the nation $880 million, but as late as 1960, how it would benefit the nation's defense remained unclear. The weight of the shielding for the reactor, as well as a new awareness of environmental considerations, led to the national program's demise in 1961.[27]

Ironically, as interest in the nuclear airplane waned in the late 1950s, enthusiasm for a nuclear rocket waxed. In 1955 Robert W. Bussard of the Oak Ridge National Laboratory questioned the conclusions of the Lexington Report. He argued that the key to nuclear rocket development was temperature-resistant materials. His advocacy convinced the Air Force and the Atomic Energy Commission (AEC) to set up a joint program at Los Alamos Scientific Laboratory to develop Rover, a nuclear rocket intended to be launched from the ground.[28] Because hydrogen was the preferred propellant for nuclear rockets, the growing expertise of the Lewis staff in handling this fuel put them in high demand. They assisted in the design and testing of the KIWI series of experimental reactors, managed jointly by the AEC and NASA, at Jackass Flats, Nev.[29] Frank Rom, Chief of the Nuclear Propulsion Concepts Branch at Lewis, served as the laboratory's chief spokesman for its programs in materials, fuel element research, and hydrogen heat transfer.

The AEC, however, controlled the nuclear field through tough licensing requirements. It regarded NASA as an interloper in the nuclear field. T. Keith Glennan lamented that the Plum Brook reactor was "proposed and accepted at a time when the aircraft nuclear propulsion work was at its white hot heat."[30] Glennan stoutly defended the quality of the reactor's design, but whether Lewis could land a role in nuclear rocket development was in doubt. Senator Clinton B. Anderson of New Mexico was determined to see that funding went to the AEC's laboratory at Los Alamos. When NASA and the AEC set up a joint office called the Space Nuclear Propulsion Office (SNPO) in 1960, the two federal agencies began to enjoy a smoother relationship. The future of Lewis's programs in nuclear propulsion looked brighter. Harold Finger took charge of both the SNPO Office and NASA's Nuclear Systems Division.[31]

Despite the intensity of research on the part of NASA and AEC staff, the use of Rover in NASA's stable of launch vehicles was remote. Glennan asked the obvious question: "Just where one would launch such a beast with its ever present possibility of a catastrophic explosion resulting in the spreading of radioactive materials over the landscape is not clear."[32] In 1961 the Rover project was renamed NERVA (Nuclear Engine for Rocket Vehicle Applications).[33] After Congress authorized a major three-year $40 million building program for Plum Brook in the fall of 1962, Silverstein set up a design group to plan a $15 million facility for testing a nuclear rocket engine at Plum Brook. Although a nuclear upper stage for the Saturn launch vehicle seemed increasingly unlikely, the feasibility of a nuclear rocket for post-Apollo missions had to be demonstrated.

RETURN TRIP TO MARS

Lewis planners believed that landing on the Moon was only the first step in space exploration. NASA's next destination would be Mars or another planet. Chemical rockets like Saturn, or a nuclear rocket, could reach a near planet, but longer trips required different types of rocket systems. The advantage of an electric rocket was its low propellant consumption and continuous long-term operation. The group formed by Wolfgang Moeckel after the success of "From Mach 4 to Infinity" began studies of electric propulsion and space power systems that involved plasma physics and magnetogasdynamic and thermionic systems. They also investigated the possible applications of controlled nuclear fusion for space propulsion. The group explored the possibilities of using high-intensity, large-volume electromagnets with the lowest possible mass for power generation. In 1958 they initiated a small program on plasma heating to complement the studies of magnetic fields.[34]

Initially, the electric propulsion systems under investigation consisted of two major components, the electric power generator and the thrust generator. The electric power generator—either nuclear or solar—converted energy into electric power. The thrust generator used this power to accelerate the propellant out the back end in the form of thrust. The 1957 study of a nuclear turboelectric power plant indicated that sodium had the potential to make a good heat transfer fluid. By passing the fluid from the fission reactor through a neutron shield, a heat exchanger, and back to the reactor, the crew could be protected from radiation. The generator would provide a power output of 20,000 kilowatts, with 11,000 kilowatts of power in the form of thrust. A round trip to Mars would require a vehicle weighing 350,000 pounds. In addition to the structural weight of the vehicle, the eight-man crew would need 50,000 pounds of equipment and a 40,000-pound auxiliary rocket for landing part of the crew on Mars.[35] Admittedly fanciful, this power system was the basis of more sophisticated design studies and hardware development related to nuclear-turboelectric systems.

The enthusiasm and expertise of the group grew under the leadership of Howard Childs, William Mickelson, and Wolfgang Moeckel. Their work embodied Dryden's vision of advanced

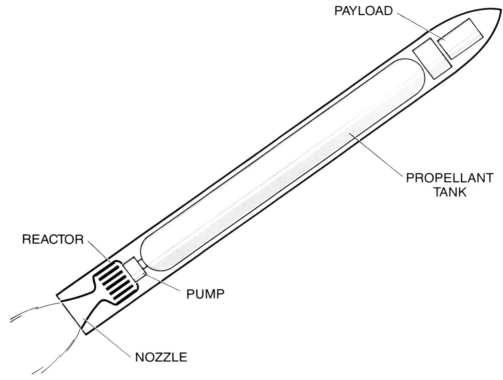

Nuclear Rocket.

technology research as distinguished from development. Moeckel explained in a talk at Headquarters in 1961:

> The approach taken by the Lewis Research Center in its electric propulsion program is to undertake studies of problems common to all systems. This approach is in contrast to that of development organizations, which must generally concentrate their effort on perfecting a particular system, based on current state-of-the-art. There are, of course, many areas of overlap, but in general the Lewis effort is directed toward obtaining the fund of knowledge and the new approaches required to design specific systems for various applications, rather than to design or produce those systems directly.[36]

The group worked with the AEC to develop the nuclear-turboelectric system, SNAP-8, intended to provide 35 kilowatts of on-board power in space. The first solar project, Sunflower, a joint effort with Thompson-Ramo-Wooldridge (TRW), yielded basic knowledge of dynamic solar power systems for spacecraft.

The generous budgets for construction of facilities during the Apollo era enabled the staff to build a large vacuum tank for electric propulsion studies. Because of Lewis's new facilities and the large number of staff involved, in 1961, shortly after Silverstein's return, NASA announced that Marshall Space Flight Center's electric propulsion program would be transferred to Lewis.

Water-filled quadrants surrounding the Plum Brook nuclear reactor, 1961.

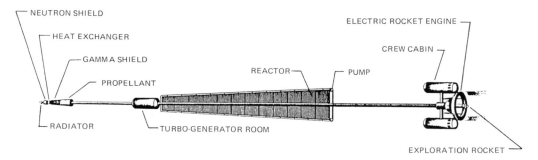

NEUTRON SHIELD

HEAT EXCHANGER

GAMMA SHIELD

PROPELLANT

RADIATOR

TURBO-GENERATOR ROOM

REACTOR

PUMP

ELECTRIC ROCKET ENGINE

CREW CABIN

EXPLORATION ROCKET

Diagram of electric space vehicle with nuclear power source for a round trip to Mars.

The laboratory environment supported the interplay between theory and hardware necessary to foster technical creativity. Technical support and relative freedom to pursue promising ideas regardless of immediate application allowed Harold R. Kaufman to design a more efficient and simpler electric rocket than Stuhlinger's earlier cesium thruster.[37] Kaufman was a member of the Mission Analysis Branch. He and a colleague, Wilbur Dobson, knew of Moeckel's interest in Stuhlinger's work but were not members of his division. Kaufman took a different approach. His invention, the electron-bombardment ion thruster, used mercury vapor as a propellant. The vapor flowed into an ionizer chamber; the mercury ions were then propelled toward a screen grid, which accelerated them to produce thrust.

In 1964 the SERT I (Space Electric Rocket Test) tested both Stuhlinger's cesium engine, built by Hughes Research Laboratories, and Kaufman's electron-bombardment thruster, designed and built at Lewis. Kaufman's approach proved superior. It also demonstrated that a stream of ions from a thruster in space could be neutralized to avoid the buildup of a space charge that would shut down the thruster. This established that ion thrusters could be made to work in space. The development of the ion-bombardment thruster culminated in 1970 in the successful launch of SERT II after ten years of painstaking development of Kaufman's design. SERT II, however, reached fruition at a time when the ability of NASA to support advanced technology was flagging.[38]

CENTAUR: ABE'S BABY

Centaur, the third program that came to prominence during the Apollo era, was a legacy of the laboratory's work on liquid hydrogen in the 1950s. Centaur was a development program urgently needed for the success of a lunar landing. It was originally funded through the Advanced Research Projects Agency (ARPA) and assigned to Marshall Space Flight Center after President Eisenhower insisted that all space programs without direct military applications be taken over by NASA. After NASA acquired the von Braun team, Centaur was designated the launch vehicle for Surveyor, the unmanned lunar lander program. It was managed under NASA's Office of Launch Vehicle Programs, clearly the development and operations side of NASA. Centaur came to Lewis by default. It was an unwanted step-child at a time when all the efforts of von Braun's rocket group were focused on the development of Saturn.

In September 1962 Edgar Cortright, then Deputy Director of the Office of Space Sciences at NASA Headquarters, remembered the keen interest in liquid hydrogen at Lewis. He asked Silverstein to come to Headquarters where he brandished a letter that his boss, Homer D. Newell, had received from Wernher von Braun. von Braun thought that NASA should cancel the Centaur Program. von Braun apparently was not yet convinced of the feasibility of liquid hydrogen as a fuel, despite his capitulation to Silverstein during the Saturn Evaluation Committee meetings in December 1959. He was also concerned about Centaur's structure. According to John Sloop:

> The von Braun team simply did not trust Karl Bossart's thin-wall, pressure-stabilized tanks first used by General Dynamics for Atlas and then for Centaur. Centaur had only a thin, common wall dividing the fuel and oxidant tanks, and at one time von Braun came to Washington to push a design change that separated the two tanks, a change that would delay the stage development. His request was denied by Robert Seamans. I believe that these structure concerns outweighed von Braun's concerns about using liquid hydrogen.[39]

von Braun recommended that the Saturn C-1/Agena D launch vehicle replace Centaur. The Jet Propulsion Laboratory (JPL), in charge of the Surveyor Program since 1960, concurred. von Braun convinced JPL that Centaur could not be developed in time to provide the necessary knowledge of the Moon's surface prior to the Apollo landing. In a letter to Newell, Brian Sparks, Deputy Director of JPL, cited "the deplorable situation in the current Centaur program" in support of cancellation. The development of a new rocket to use liquid hydrogen technology required too much time. To compete with the "doggedly determined effort of the Soviets," the existing technology of kerosene-based fuels had a greater chance of success. He wrote:

> The Office of Manned Space Flight has said that data from a soft-landed Surveyor in 1964 or 1965 would be an invaluable aid in Apollo design, and high-quality reconnaissance data from a lunar Orbiter in 1966 is desirable for Apollo flight planning. These objectives could be achieved on a C-1/Agena D but not on Centaur in this time scale.[40]

Problems with NASA's contractors, General Dynamics and Pratt & Whitney, plagued the development of Centaur. However, the supervision of these contractors by the von Braun team had also played a role in its recent failures on the launch pad. On May 8, 1962, 54 seconds after liftoff, the Centaur portion of an Atlas-Centaur launch vehicle had exploded. The investigation into this mishap revealed that an internal NASA report had predicted this failure: the insulation panels could not withstand the anticipated pressure loads. The accident investigators concluded that, although General Dynamics was responsible for the defective design, Marshall Space Flight Center's supervision had been neither prompt nor adequate. In addition, the investigation censured Marshall's supervision of Pratt & Whitney's development of the RL-10 liquid-hydrogen engine. Three explosions of engines on Pratt & Whitney's test stands at its Research and Development Center in Florida had resulted in both delay and $1.2 million worth of damage. The investigation concluded that these were preventable accidents. The company had failed to install standard safety devices that Marshall engineers, with extensive experience in the hazards of rocket engine development, should have insisted on.[41]

Cortright informed Silverstein that the relationship between Marshall and General Dynamics had reached an impasse. Both were aware that project management required a healthy give-and-take. Technical differences had created an adversarial relationship between General Dynamics and Marshall.[42] Marshall had accepted Centaur, but von Braun, never comfortable with liquid hydrogen or the Centaur tank design, did not assign his best engineers to the project.

In Silverstein's view, "They did not believe in Centaur because it was not really theirs. Centaur was not a program that they had initiated."[43]

In September 1962 the choice at Headquarters appeared to be either to drop the Centaur program entirely or find another NASA center willing to take over its management. When Edgar Cortright asked Silverstein if Lewis wanted the Centaur program, Silverstein needed no arm-twisting. He believed that liquid hydrogen would provide the key to a successful lunar landing. The transfer of launch-base operations from Kurt Debus's group to the Goddard Field Projects Branch at Cape Canaveral under Robert Gray completed the decoupling of Centaur from Marshall.

Harold R. Kaufman with his electron bombardment ion thruster.

When Silverstein announced to his division heads that NASA had assigned Centaur to Lewis, the response was lukewarm.[44] Although Lewis had tasted project management when NASA created the Nuclear Engines Project Office and the Sunflower program, these were slow-paced programs. The management of Centaur posed development problems that needed immediate solutions. In October, plane loads of boxes containing books, drawings, spare parts lists, unsatisfied change orders, and technical directions were sent to Lewis from Marshall. For men and women accustomed to working in a research environment consisting of blackboards, glistening hardware, and the roar of facilities, the silent mountain of government paper produced dismay. What did they know about the legal tangle of government contracts?[45]

Centaur forced its new project managers to leave the comfortable campus atmosphere of the research laboratory to deal directly with industry. Silverstein picked a technical team to tackle the Centaur Program that matched the Lewis administrative talent he had left in Washington. David J. Gabriel, a Lakewood native with a mechanical engineering degree from the University of Akron, shouldered the responsibility of project manager. Cary Nettles, Russel Dunbar, Ed Jonash, Jack Brun, and John Quitter, seasoned Lewis staff, formed the technical core of the project. Although Centaur fell within Bruce Lundin's administrative bailiwick, Silverstein himself was never far from what was going on in the Centaur project.

Silverstein called on Lewis's small law department to bring order out of chaos. Neil Hosenball, the laboratory's chief legal counsel, asked Len Perry, a vibrant attorney with boundless energy and unusual powers of persuasion, to assume responsibility for the contractual aspects of the Centaur Project. He hired Harlan Simon, an Ohio State Law School graduate in private practice, to assist him. They attended all the Centaur team's technical meetings with General

Pratt & Whitney's RL-10 hydrogen-oxygen engine is readied for testing, June 1963.

Dynamics to sort out the objectives of the program and where it had gone wrong. Simon recalled the intensity of Silverstein's involvement.

> It was Abe's baby, Abe's project. He made a promise not only to the world, but to himself. He selected the people. He is the one who chose the people for these various positions and he chose them, obviously, correctly. He was informed of every decision that was made of any significance. He participated in the decision making process. He argued with them. They argued with him. It was both dedication to the program and fear of Abe that made this program successful. You just didn't dare let him down. Otherwise, I don't know what would have happened. You almost felt as though you would have been disintegrated, if you ever let Dr. Abe down.[46]

The lawyers had a formidable challenge: to restructure the business arrangement with General Dynamics to permit flexibility and mutual trust. They had to devise a contract that, above all, would not slow down the pace of development.

The original contract with General Dynamics was a not a firm fixed-price contract, but a cost-plus-fixed-fee contract of rather loose construction. It was not geared to the development of new technology under the pressure of a tight deadline. Any technical change required not only ponderous paperwork, but worse, an increase in the costs of the vehicle even before the final design had been established. A liquid hydrogen rocket required a leap into the unknown. It was a leap constrained by a tight schedule.

Hosenball, Perry, and Simon devised two types of contracts to cover the requirements of technology development. The first was the "hardware contract," which took "all the knowns and entered into a contract which had very definite boundaries in dollars and time." To cover the unknowns—risks of development, support for unexpected failure—they devised a "management and engineering contract."[47] If a rocket exploded on the launch pad, another test could be done without waiting months for the necessary government paperwork to be completed. NASA could guarantee a profit to the company regardless of the outcome. This unconventional approach to government contracting could have left them open to criticism, but they were betting on success. The Centaur team worked at a frenzied pace, commuting to California to oversee work by General Dynamics and to Cape Canaveral to prepare for launches. Their labor was crowned with a string of successful launches, culminating in the flawless Surveyor mission in May 1966.

Centaur stage mated to Atlas booster at Plum Brook in the Dynamics Research Testing Stand, February 1964.

Silverstein's commitment to liquid hydrogen was vindicated, and a similar success with liquid hydrogen in the upper stages of the Saturn V proved von Braun's pessimistic view of this tricky fuel unjustified. He autographed a picture of the launch of Apollo 4, on November 9, 1967: "To Abe Silverstein whose pioneering work in liquid hydrogen technology paved the way to today's success."[48]

What explains the intensity of this commitment? Why was the Centaur program so successful? This extraordinary combination of energy, teamwork, and leadership cannot be explained simply as the result of the ample funding that NACA received during the Apollo era. Nor can the achievement of the Centaur program be dismissed as an attempt by Lewis staff to demonstrate that they could succeed where Marshall had failed. Rather, the explanation for the achievement of the Centaur program lies within Lewis's institutional fabric. Unlike Marshall, Lewis was a research laboratory. The NACA research tradition had fostered the commitment to liquid hydrogen through the 1950s as Lewis researchers gained expertise in the problems of this complicated and dangerous technology. Silverstein epitomized the breed of technical leader that Arthur Squires has described as a "maestro of technology"—someone who is thoroughly familiar with the technology, who knows his staff well enough to put together the right team for a specific task, and who protects them from the aggravations of unnecessary bureaucracy.[49] He inspired by example. His staff stayed through the night to untangle a technical problem because Silverstein did the same.

Beyond Silverstein were the extensive resources of a research laboratory. Lewis researchers faced a variety of problems in making liquid hydrogen usable as a rocket fuel. A research group in materials headed by Merv Ault studied the degrading effects of liquid hydrogen on various metals. Other Lewis staff examined how liquid hydrogen would behave in a weightless environment. They investigated pumps, turbines, and other components of the rocket engine. Testing in the 85-foot drop tower, and later in the zero gravity facility, provided data useful in modifying designs. Centaur staff had Lewis expertise in heat transfer to call on, as well as an extremely skilled group of technicians to build whatever part might be necessary to tease a recalcitrant rocket engine to life.

At the same time that Lewis inherited Centaur from Marshall, it acquired management of the Agena project. Agena was an upper-stage booster rocket usually coupled with a Thor or an Atlas rocket to launch spacecraft for NASA's planetary program. Unlike Centaur, Agena did not have the constant attention of Silverstein. Seymour C. Himmel took charge as project manager, flanked by his deputies C. C. Conger and E. F. Baehr. Technical branches were headed by E. H. Davidson, M. Weston, and H. W. Plohr. They were all "NACA types" who had been at Lewis since the 1940s. They had never worked on launch vehicles before, but their NACA backgrounds gave them the flexibility, management skills, and technical expertise they needed to organize the staff (supplemented with former military contractors for intercontinental ballistic missile programs) and to build relationships with contractors, the Air Force, and centers like Goddard and JPL in charge of the spacecraft. Thirteen months after taking over the Agena project, the team launched its first two spacecraft, Echo II and Ranger VI. Between 1962 and 1968, when Silverstein assigned the Agena's payloads to the Centaur rocket, they launched 28 missions, including several Rangers, Mariner Mars '64 and Mariner Venus '67. The spacecraft launched by Agena sent back some of the first pictures of Mars and Venus.[50]

The Centaur and Agena Programs were the glamour programs of the laboratory. Jobs in launch vehicles had visibility, mobility, and drama. The NACA-trained researcher looked on the

Photograph of launch of Apollo 4 with Wernher von Braun's message "To Dr. Abe Silverstein whose pioneering work in liquid hydrogen technology paved the way to today's success."

swashbuckling young engineering graduate recruited for project management with a mixture of pride and envy. Although research had more ample funding during the Apollo era than ever before, basic research lost status. The preparation of a research report, once the most respected activity of the laboratory, no longer stimulated the same intense commitment. The roar of a rocket at liftoff had supplanted the polite applause of engineering peers elicited by a well-presented paper. Some NACA-trained researchers like Harry W. Mergler, Simon Ostrach, Eli Reshotko, and Arthur Hansen drifted off to positions in academia. Basic work in materials, heat transfer, and tribology, the science of fuels and lubricants, quietly continued.

CASE INSTITUTE OF TECHNOLOGY AND THE NASA BANDWAGON

If the transformation of the NACA into NASA was a mixed blessing for former NACA laboratories like Lewis Research Center, universities stood to benefit from the sudden availability of large NASA grants. The NACA sponsored some university research through the 1940s and 1950s, but the amount of university grants had remained small because NACA laboratories preferred to do their research in-house.

The possibility of ample government funding infused Case Institute of Technology with new enthusiasm for aerospace engineering and a greater interest in cultivating connections with Lewis Research Center. Both Glennan, who returned to Case's presidency at the close of the Eisenhower Administration, and his successor, James Webb, supported strong NASA-university connections. In addition to specific NASA-sponsored research, NASA's charter stipulated that one of the agency's goals was to promote science education.

The first Case Institute of Technology proposal for an Interdisciplinary Materials Research Program in July 1960 described how its Cleveland location benefited Lewis Research Center. Case Institute's faculty had provided NASA with necessary additional training in materials in a recent in-house graduate course offered at Lewis. However, the former strains in the Case-NACA relationship may have influenced the proposal's rejection in favor of Rensselaer Polytechnic Institute.[51]

When Glennan returned to the presidency of Case Institute, he carefully laid the groundwork for an improvement in relations. In October 1962, he personally paid a call on Hugh Dryden and handed him a summary of the proposals awaiting action by NASA evaluators. In a memo to John Hrones, Vice President for Academic Affairs, Glennan revealed that the Case faculty thought it had been treated unfairly by NASA in the past: "I think that Dr. Dryden has protected the integrity of that memorandum which was rather critical of actions taken by one or more individuals in the NASA organization in the review of our proposals."[52] Case faculty claimed that its proposals were still being turned down for reasons that had more to do with personalities than technical quality in 1963, but by October 1964 the situation had improved dramatically. Case was doing quite well. Its acceptance rate for the previous 12 months had reached 100 percent.[53]

In 1963 Case caught a whiff of NASA's plans for a high-tech facility. It strongly backed the city of Parma's bid for the site for a NASA Electronics Center. Not surprisingly, given the strong ties of the Kennedy Administration to Massachusetts, the city lost out to Cambridge.[54] However, realistically, the Cleveland area had neither a cadre of Ph.D.s trained in electrical engineering nor strong industry support. Politics precluded two NASA facilities in the same city. Nevertheless, Webb saw a role for Case Institute of Technology in the government, industry, university partnership he envisioned. He hoped that Case would assist NASA in ferreting out Cleveland area industries that could use NASA-generated technology. He believed that space technology, turned to profits by industry, would mean a stronger American economy.

However, it was one thing to formulate a policy, another to implement it. With the exception of TRW and Eaton Industries, there was little high-tech industry in Cleveland that could benefit from aerospace technology. Cleveland's economy, beginning to founder, depended on heavy industries like steel. It was increasingly clear that the role that Lewis had played in stimulating innovation among the engine companies during the NACA years would be difficult to recast for the utilization of space technology, despite the good intentions of Case and the Lewis Technology Utilization Program. A conference sponsored by Lewis to discuss new technology available to the electric power industry as a consequence of the space program created interest but no real commitment to innovation. Lewis would discover in work with the automobile industry in the 1970s the difficulties of pushing innovation on a reluctant industry.[55]

Although Case's involvement in the technology utilization program was minimal, it had better success with an ambitious proposal for a Space Engineering Research Laboratory, submitted in January 1965. The proposal for $2,580,000 in construction funds emphasized Case's strong programs in space-related disciplines: digital systems engineering; control of complex systems; bio and medical engineering; engineering synthesis; fluid, thermal, and aerospace sciences mechanics; and plasma dynamics. It proposed concentrating some of these programs in one building. The proposal indicated that the relationship with Lewis was beginning to flourish, with new staff recruited from Lewis and over 100 Lewis staff currently in advanced degree programs, 17 of whom were Ph.D. candidates. When the new NASA laboratory was dedicated in 1969, it was appropriately named the Glennan Space Engineering Building to honor Glennan's dedication to Case, NASA, and the AEC.[56]

In 1966 NASA turned renewed attention to aeronautical research, neglected after Sputnik. At Lewis, although the major effort remained in space-related activities, several new projects were initiated. The return to aeronautics among NACA-trained staff meant a return to the intriguing problems of compressors and turbines. The phenomenal growth of air travel had caused airport congestion, overcrowding, noise, and chemical pollution. The development of quieter engines, as well as aircraft that could take off and land on short runways, offered the promise of new technical challenges. Lewis also took part in plans for a supersonic transport airplane to compete with the Concorde under development by the British and the French. However, after a hiatus of nine years, could the staff return to a position at the cutting edge of aircraft propulsion technology? Lewis's facilities for propulsion research were no longer unique. Not only had the aircraft engine industries developed their own facilities, but the Air Force now had its state-of-the-art wind tunnels at the Arnold Engineering Development Center in Tullahoma, Tenn.

Lewis had eliminated work on air-breathing engines when it shifted into space propulsion. Researchers at Ames and Langley never abandoned their work in aeronautics and did few space-related projects in the 1960s. Lewis's space work, particularly its management of Centaur and Agena, had swelled its budget in the 1960s, although a large portion of these funds went to contractors. In 1964 Lewis received $299.9 million for research and development, compared to $78.1 million and $40.3 million, respectively, for Langley and Ames. For construction of facilities, most of which were at Plum Brook, Lewis received $26.5 million, compared to $9.0 million for Langley and $11.9 million for Ames. In 1965 Lewis's research and development budget continued to rise. It received a peak of $323.2 million, compared to $106.6 for Langley and $54.2 for Ames. Funding for construction of facilities again gave Lewis a substantial budget in 1965: $18.6 million for Lewis, $7.2 for Langley, $13.6 for Ames.[57] However, the handwriting was on the wall. The

Vietnam War and the War on Poverty cut into NASA's budget. In 1966, as the Agena project was being phased down, Lewis's research and development budget declined by $73.3 million. The next year, it dropped by another $87.2 million as NASA experienced its first major cuts. The Hough riots in downtown Cleveland revealed the bitter incongruity of the expensive space race and the problems of the inner city. Staff cuts began to bite into the morale of the laboratory.

In 1969, when Apollo 11 astronaut Neil Armstrong stepped onto the pocked surface of the Moon, Lewis Research Center took special pride in the fulfillment of Kennedy's promise to land Americans on the Moon within a decade. Armstrong had started his career in Cleveland as a NACA test pilot. Lewis engineers had helped solve some of the problems of Saturn V's huge F-1 engines, and tests in the Altitude Wind Tunnel's vacuum chamber had helped to pave the way for the safe separation of the Apollo capsule from its boosters.[58] The Ranger spacecraft, the Lunar Orbiter, and Surveyor—launched by Agena and Centaur—had also contributed to the success of Apollo, but the flight of Apollo across the Sun had cast a long shadow. The nation's inability to deal with its social problems seemed to make a mockery of ambitious plans for space exploration.

For Silverstein 1969 marked not only the achievement of a manned lunar landing, but also 40 years of government service. Silverstein's technical leadership had shaped NASA's early years, but Headquarters was now in hands more attuned to the political winds than to charting a post-Apollo course to the planets. In his dealings with Headquarters, Silverstein became like a cactus with thorns.[59] True to the NACA ideal of cultivating expertise from within the laboratory, he fought NASA's increasing commitment to outside contracting at the expense of research. By 1969 all three former NACA laboratories—Lewis, Langley, and Ames—were outside NASA's mainstream. With the exception of the laboratory's management of unmanned launch vehicles, which included Titan and Atlas in addition to Centaur, Lewis received its funding through the Office of Aeronautics and Space Technology (OAST, formerly OART). OAST commanded a mere 5 percent of NASA's budget. With manned missions dominating the agency, the camel had forced its research occupants nearly out of the tent. The research centers were looked down on by other parts of NASA as "hobby shops."[60] Asked to chair a study for the expansion of Hopkins International Airport into Lake Erie, Silverstein chose to retire. It was the end of an era.

Abe Silverstein, Director of Lewis Laboratory from 1961 to 1969.

NOTES

[1] *Cleveland Plain Dealer*, 13 December 1961.

[2] Abe Silverstein and George F. Kinghorn, "Improved Baffle Designs for Air-Cooled Engine Cylinders," August 1943, issued as NACA WR L-767. Abe Silverstein, "Internal Aerodynamics of Ramjets," material presented at the NACA Conference on Supersonic Aerodynamics at AAL on 4 June 1946, NACA 1946/1 1475-9.

[3] " 'Big Joe', Lewis' Part in the Project Mercury Story," *Orbit*, 22 May 1959. Lloyd S. Swenson, Jr., James M. Grimwood, and Charles C. Alexander, *This New Ocean: A History of Project Mercury*, NASA SP-4201 (Washington, D.C.: U.S. Government Printing Office, 1966), p. 201 and 244-245.

[4] T. Keith Glennan, "The First Years of the National Aeronautics and Space Administration," 1964, unpublished diary, Eisenhower Library, Abilene, Kan., p. 84.

[5] *New York Times*, 12 March 1960. Silverstein biography file, NASA History Office, Washington, D.C.

[6] Interview with Simon Ostrach, 29 September 1987.

[7] See, for example, the description of the NACA by Homer Newell, *Beyond the Atmosphere*, NASA SP-4211 (Washington, D.C.: U.S. Government Printing Office, 1980), p. 90-91.

[8] T. Keith Glennan, "The First Years," vol. 1, p. 7.

[9] Ibid.

[10] E. J. Manganiello, "The Changing Trends in Our Activities," address to staff, 4 November 1960. RG 255 73A32, 116/1-52, Federal Archives and Record Center, Chicago, IL.

[11] Ibid.

[12] Ibid.

[13] Ibid.

[14] Quoted in Arthur L. Levine, "United States Aeronautical Research Policy 1915-1958: A Study of the Major Policy Decisions of the National Advisory Committee for Aeronautics," Ph.D. Dissertation, Columbia University, 1963, p. 90.

[15] *United States Civilian Space Programs, 1958-1978*, Report Prepared for the Subcommittee on Space Science and Applications, Serial D, Volume I, January 1981, p. 72.

[16] Interview with Simon Ostrach, 29 September 1987.

[17] Interview with Bruce Lundin, 28 May 1987.

[18] *Cleveland Plain Dealer*, 13 December 1961.

[19] See Daniel S. Greenberg, *The Politics of Pure Science* (New York: The New American Library, 1967), p. 258-259.

[20] Courtney G. Brooks, James M. Grimwood, and Lloyd S. Swenson, Jr., *Chariots for Apollo: A History of Manned Lunar Spacecraft*, NASA SP-4205 (Washington, D.C.: U.S. Government Printing Office, 1975), p. 46-47. See discussion in Roger E. Bilstein, *Stages to Saturn*, NASA SP-4206 (Washington, D.C.: U.S. Government Printing Office, 1980), p. 60-68.

[21] Brooks, Grimwood, and Swenson, *Chariots for Apollo*, p. 34.

[22] "Survey of Various Vehicle Systems for the Manned Lunar Landing Mission," Bruce Lundin, Chairman, 10 June 1961. NASA History Office, Washington, D.C.

[23] Interview with Abe Silverstein by V. Dawson, 6 June 1987.

[24] Interview with Bruce Lundin, 28 May 1987. On a lunar excursion vehicle, see Carl F. Schueller to Associate Director, "Visit to NASA Headquarters on November 23, 1959 by Mssrs. E. W. Conrad and C. F. Schueller." See also Richard J. Weber to Chief, Propulsion Aerodynamics Division, "Lunar Mission Studies by Analysis Branch, Propulsion Systems Division," 9 June 1960, personal files of R. J. Weber.

[25] See discussion by Arthur M. Squires, *The Tender Ship: Governmental Management of Technological Change* (Boston: Birkhauser, 1986), p. 94-102. The classic study of nuclear propulsion in all its facets, both scientific and technical, was published in the open press by two British scientists, L. R. Shepherd and

A. V. Cleaver, in the *Journal of the British Interplanetary Society* (Sept.–Nov. 1948 and Jan.–March 1949). Thereafter, technical interest in nuclear-powered rockets languished because of the enormous technical problems they seemed to pose.

[26] NACA Press Release, 26 September 1956, NASA Lewis Records.

[27] See "Remarks of Melvin Price," Congressional Record Appendix, 26 August 1960.

[28] See R. W. Bussard and R. D. DeLauer, *Fundamentals of Nuclear Flight* (New York: McGraw Hill, 1965), p. 1-4.

[29] For background see R. E. Schreiber, "Kiwi Tests Pave Way to Rover." *Nucleonics*, vol. 19, No. 4, April 1961, 11.77–79.

[30] Glennan, "The First Years," p. 165.

[31] See Harold B. Finger, "Space Nuclear Propulsion Mid-Decade," *Astronautics & Aeronautics*, January 1965. The Plum Brook reactor went critical in 1961 and reached full capacity in 1963. The reactor was shut down on 30 June 1973. By the 1970s Plum Brook had a staff of 635 civil servants and 132 support service contractors.

[32] Glennan, "The First Years," p. 71.

[33] For background on NERVA, see W. H. Esselman, "The NERVA Nuclear Rocket Reactor Program," *Westinghouse Engineer*, May 1965, vol. 25, p. 66–75. See also William R. Corless, *Nuclear Propulsion for Space* (U.S. Atomic Energy Commission, 1967). See also James Arthur Dewar, "Project Rover: A Study of the Nuclear Rocket Development Program, 1953–1963," Ph.D. Dissertation, Kansas State University, Manhattan, Kansas, 1974, to be published by Smithsonian Institution Press.

[34] W. E. Moeckel, "Status of Electric Propulsion Systems for Space Missions," Cryogenic Engineering Conference, Boulder, Col., 23–25 August 1960, RG 255 73A32 116/1-52, Federal Archives and Record Center, Chicago, IL.

[35] R. E. English, H. O. Slone, D. T. Bernatowicz, E. H. Davison, and S. Lieblein, "A 20,000 Kilowatt Nuclear Turboelectric Power Supply for Manned Space Vehicles," NASA RM 2-20-59E, March 1959.

[36] W. E. Moeckel, "Lewis Research Center Electric Propulsion Program," NASA Headquarters Presentation, 5 June 1961, RG 255 73A32 116/1-52, Federal Archives and Record Center, Chicago, IL.

[37] H. R. Kaufman, "Origin of Electron-Bombardment Ion Thruster," *J. Spacecraft*, 18:289–292.

[38] "SERT II—A First for Lewis," *Lewis News*, 16 January 1970.

[39] John Sloop, "Comments by John L. Sloop on Manuscript History of the Lewis Research Center by Virginia Dawson," 5 September 1989. NASA History Office, Washington, D.C.

[40] Brian Sparks to Homer Newell, 21 September 1962, Atlas-Centaur Launch Vehicle file, NASA History Office.

[41] "Review of the Atlas-Centaur Launch Vehicle Development Program," Report to the Committee on Science and Astronautics, House of Representatives, March 1963, Atlas-Centaur Launch Vehicle file, NASA History Office.

[42] See also files of Office of the Deputy Director 0100, Centaur Program, NASA Lewis Archives, Box 9.

[43] Interview with Harlan Simon, 20 March 1985.

[44] Interview with Bruce Lundin, 28 May 1987.

[45] Interview with Harlan Simon, 20 March 1985.

[46] Ibid.

[47] Ibid.

[48] Photo from personal files of Abe Silverstein.

[49] Arthur M. Squires discusses "maestros of technology" in *The Tender Ship*, p. 13–46. See also Abe Silverstein and Eldon W. Hall, "Liquid Hydrogen as a Jet Fuel for High-Altitude Aircraft," NACA RM E55 C28a, 15 April 1955.

[50] For greater detail on the Agena project, its management and significance, see Seymour Himmel, "Commentary" [on manuscript by V. Dawson], 28 August 1989.

[51] "A Proposal to the National Aeronautics and Space Administration for Support of Materials Research and Departmental Facilities at Case Institute of Technology," 8 April 1960. Case Central File 19 DC: 27: Asso. and Orgs. Gov. Gps. & Ind. Orgs., Case Western Reserve Archives.

[52] T. Keith Glennan to Dr. John Hrones, "NASA Support for Research Proposals," 8 October 1962, Case Central File 19 DC 27:2, Case Western Reserve Archives. Glennan also protected the integrity of the memo. It was not to be found in the Case archives.

[53] R. H. Thomas to Dr. T. Keith Glennan, "Visit by Dr. T. L. K. Small," 1 October 1964; and R. H. Thomas to J. A. Hrones, "NASA Visitor-Sid Roth," Case Central File 19 DC 27, Case Western Reserve Archives.

[54] "Conference on Proposed Electronics Center," 19 November 1963, Case Central File 19 DC 27:2, Case Western Reserve Archives. Also Abe Silverstein to Francis B. Smith, Area Survey Committee, 6 December 1963, NASA Lewis Records, 0100/9.

[55] See *Selected Technology for the Electric Power Industry,* a conference held at Lewis Research Center, Cleveland, Ohio, 11–12 September 1968, NASA SP-5057, 1968.

[56] "Proposal to the National Aeronautics and Space Administration for Case Laboratory for Space Engineering Research," 27 January 1965, Case Central File 19 DC 27: 1, Case Western Reserve Archives.

[57] *NASA Historical Data Book,* NASA SP-4102 (Washington, D.C.: U.S. Government Printing Office, 1988), vol. 1, p. 166 and 168.

[58] "Apollo Mans Moon," *Lewis News,* 18 July 1969.

[59] Interview with Robert E. English by V. Dawson, 11 July 1986.

[60] Ibid.

CHAPTER TEN

DOWN TO EARTH PROBLEMS

Nothing in Bruce Lundin's background prepared him to preside over the most difficult period in the history of Lewis Research Center. The 1970s were a time of trouble for NASA. Space no longer riveted the nation's attention, and NASA, unlike the NACA, now depended on the whims of public opinion to garner the votes of Congress. Lewis Research Center, increasingly vulnerable to staff reductions required by NASA's budget cuts, barely escaped closing. Research programs were expendable from the point of view of Headquarters, and projects carried out under the Office of Aeronautics and Space Technology (OAST) were the easiest to cut.

By 1971 Lewis had lost 700 civil service positions, but even larger cuts would be announced in 1972, one of the darkest years in the center's history. In that year NASA slated the Plum Brook Station for closing. The following year NASA terminated 400 staff in the areas of space nuclear power and propulsion systems. An additional 318 people, primarily in space research, received notices; at the same time at least 100 long-time employees chose retirement.[1] Many upper-level staff chose to retire rather than witness the dismantling of an institution they had worked to create. They were among the cream of the NACA-trained civil servants. In summing up the careers of the many staff who left during this period, a writer for the *Lewis News* found it impossible to describe "the moments of jubilation and the moments of heartache, day-by-day dedication, hard work, and loyalty of these and other employees that have made Lewis what it is and contributed mightily to making the United States what it is today." The *Lewis News*, still a staff newspaper, not a slick management organ, captured the ethos of the laboratory by quoting America's longshoreman philosopher Eric Hoffer's definition of patriotism: "To be honest is not to allow anything shoddy to escape your hands."[2]

Lundin was unabashedly from the development side of the laboratory, and with the Space Shuttle the single most important project in NASA, development was what NASA administrators wanted. Except for 18 months at Headquarters in the Office of Advanced Research and Technology, Lundin had spent the 26 years of his career at Lewis. In the early postwar period he had worked on afterburners and thrust augmentation. From 1952 until 1957, as Chief of the Engine Research Division, he directed testing of full-scale turbojet and ramjet engines. Lundin moved where the dominant activity of the laboratory had always been—amidst the roar of propulsion systems under test. For him, to build something, test it to the breaking point, and measure it expressed the ruling spirit of Lewis.

Under Lundin, project management of launch vehicles had established an impressive record. Lewis was in charge of medium-class launch vehicles, Atlas-Centaur and Titan-Centaur, part of the highly visible mission side of NASA. These programs were not affected by the cuts of the early 1970s. Between 1970 and 1980, Lewis took charge of a total of 39 launches. Eighteen had scientific goals. Space probes carrying cameras photographed the planets Mercury, Venus, Mars, Jupiter, Saturn, and Uranus. Two Viking missions, launched aboard a Titan-Centaur, soft landed on Mars. Nineteen launches put communications satellites in orbit around Earth.[3]

Bruce Lundin, Director of Lewis Laboratory from 1969 to 1977.

The decision to develop the enormously expensive Space Shuttle, a reusable space transport plane, squeezed the budgets of all the other programs. NASA staked its future on this single development project, the first step toward an ambitious manned space station.[4] Lewis's research programs in the 1960s had helped lay the technology base of the proposed shuttle's main engine. It would use liquid hydrogen, no longer considered an unconventional, dangerous fuel. The design of many of the main engine's components depended on Lewis research: pumps, seals, and bearings, fuel injectors, cooled baffle elements to control pressure waves, and heat transfer data to determine the proper wall thickness for combustion chambers. The main engine's unique coaxial injector element, developed and patented by Lewis engineer Samuel Stein, allowed its combustor to achieve 99 percent efficiency, a new record in rocket combustion. Despite its engine expertise, Lewis Research Center had only a limited role in shuttle development.[5] Why Lewis did not play a more significant part in the shuttle is a matter for speculation. Abe Silverstein had never given up the NACA's tradition of autonomy. He did not willingly take orders from Headquarters, and his attitude did not win friends for Lewis. Lundin followed in Silverstein's footsteps. He is reputed to have opposed the shuttle decision on technical grounds.

Lundin's relationship with Headquarters became increasingly acrimonious as he was forced to cut civil service positions and replace them with contractors. Janitorial and grounds maintenance, security, and clerical workers were the first to see their jobs turned over to contractors. Then technical services, jobs connected with running research facilities like wind tunnels and constructing experimental hardware were contracted out. This was much more serious because it compromised the ability of the laboratory to do research. Drafting, library services, and other support services followed.

Contracting fragmented the laboratory. The ideal of government service seemed compromised by the unwelcome introduction of new staff, which civil servants, rightly or wrongly, thought did not share the same high standards. The government made no long-term commitment to these new arrivals. Contractors had no job security. Although they often received higher salaries than their civil service counterparts, they were an expendable underclass. Civil service employees were advised by the law office to avoid any taint of direct supervision of these contractors. Knowledge, once shared freely among laboratory workers, became the prerogative of the civil servant. Contractors kept in ignorance were less threat to a civil service job. As support services personnel increased, contractors and civil servants had to learn to work side by side. Nevertheless, the existence of two distinct classes of employees with different values and aspirations changed the working atmosphere of Lewis.

Once the entire laboratory had functioned like a symphony. The director set the tempo. Although the engineers had played the themes, to make music, each section had contributed. Now there was a cacophony of themes. Not every employee followed the same conductor. Compounding the division between civil servants and contractors were new relationships with Headquarters. NASA projects were often split up among several NASA centers and directed by a project director in Washington. The director was no longer the conductor, but a concert master who had little influence over the orchestra's program. Through their management of launch vehicles, smaller programs in electric propulsion, and the nuclear rocket engine, former NACA personnel had learned effective project management. NASA had developed strict rules in dealing with contractors like General Dynamics and Lockheed. They supervised end-product contracts, which, unlike support services contracts, did not involve personnel actually working at Lewis. End-product contractors came to Lewis only to consult and negotiate contracts. They were not the same threat to civil service jobs, and cordial relationships developed. To uphold the government's interest, to maintain the highest safety standards, and to prevent the delivery of shoddy hardware, NASA's relationship with contractors, however, had to be carefully defined. Contractors were to be kept at arm's length. They could not share offices with civil servants. Lewis staff learned a new choreography in their relationship with industry. Now that they had power to make decisions affecting millions of dollars, they had to be careful to avoid any appearance of conflict of interest.

Given the unhealthy prognosis for a significant involvement in NASA's manned space programs, Lundin directed the laboratory's programs more strongly into aeronautics. Work expanded on the Quiet Engine Program, started under Silverstein. They would return to work on full-scale engines, this time not at the behest of the military, but in response to requests from the Federal Aviation Administration (FAA) and the Department of Transportation. The FAA asked Lewis to design and build a demonstration engine. The engine would combine state-of-the-art turbofan technology with special acoustic materials to reduce noise. The goal of the program was to develop a 22,000-pound-thrust engine that would be 15 to 20 decibels quieter than the current commercial jet transports.

Noise suppression research at Lewis was not new. The NACA Subcommittee on Noise had supported jet nozzle studies to make engines quieter as part of operations research at Lewis in 1957. However, in the NACA era cooperation with the engine manufacturers never went so far as a demonstration engine. While Lewis had been out of the air-breathing engine business in the early 1960s, the engine companies had introduced the turbofan, a more efficient engine, since not all of the air to produce thrust travelled through the compressor. Now Lundin hoped that Lewis's competence in air-breathing engines could be used to advance turbofan design. General Electric received a hefty government contract of $20 million to build three different fan designs and to mate them to an engine core. Lewis took charge of the test program to measure fan noise.

Although the formal contractual relationship with General Electric was new, Lewis was used to dealing with the company. The space initiative had interrupted their relationship, but both were willing to adjust to new contractual obligations mandated by the government.[6] Lewis also cooperated with General Electric on a demonstration program, the QCSEE (Quiet, Clean, STOL [short take-off and landing aircraft], Experimental Engine). The new demonstration engine was for an experimental transport plane that would be able to take off and land on short runways, a solution to the congestion of the nation's airports.

In another approach to the problem of a quieter engine for commercial transport planes, in 1973 Lewis, Pratt & Whitney, Boeing, and Douglas Aircraft negotiated a cost-sharing, no-fee contract for the test phase of what was called a refan program. The object of the program was to modify existing technology rather than redesign an entirely new engine. A single-stage fan was substituted for the two-stage fan of Pratt & Whitney's JT8D engine. The two airframe manufacturers agreed to install acoustical material in the nacelles, or pods within which the engines are housed, to muffle the noise of the engine. It was a simpler, less expensive, approach to the problem.[7]

The strong return to research in air-breathing engine systems included work on helicopters, widely used in the Vietnam War. Lundin agreed to a joint research program in low-speed aviation with the U.S. Army Material Command. This was the first time that civilian Army employees were integrated into the Lewis workforce. Although the program involved only a handful of engineers, this arrangement broke new ground in the relationship between the military and NASA. In the past, the Air Force Liaison Office had requested test programs carried out in NACA's wind tunnels, but the NACA had valued its independence. NASA of the 1970s did not have that luxury. The Army established an Air Mobility Research and Development Laboratory on Lewis grounds. Its research program is secret.

LEWIS TURNS EARTHWARD

The search for a new research agenda coincided with the national environmental concerns of the early 1970s. Louis Rosenblum and J. Stuart Fordyce formed the NASA Volunteer Air Conservation Committee to respond to the down-to-earth problem of air quality in the city of Cleveland. In the early 1970s, before the closing of many steel plants, the location of Cleveland industry downtown in an area called The Flats produced heavy air and water pollution. In 1969 an oil slick on the Cuyahoga River, which snakes through the industrial heart of downtown Cleveland, caught fire. The burning surface of the river caused the spectacular conflagration of several wooden bridges. National media attention brought the city shame and increased commitment to clean up the air, the river, and Lake Erie.

Local concern for the environment coincided with a new national awareness of the fragility of our life-sustaining globe. The probes of the solar system lofted by Atlas-Centaur and Atlas-Agena shattered illusions about life in outer space. The unmanned missions of Viking, Surveyor, and Mariner gave scientists a more precise understanding of the atmospheres and extreme surface temperatures of the planets and the Moon. Photographs of the stark, lifeless outlines of the Moon, Mars, Mercury, and Venus made scientists aware that they shared Earth's interminable geologic history. Life was unlikely to appear in the solar system for millions of years.[8] Popular arguments for extraterrestrial life were now balanced by the sobering thought that the biosphere might be unique after all. Earth's atmosphere had limits. It was a fragile membrane, wrote the essayist Lewis Thomas. ''The color photographs of the earth are more amazing than anything outside: we live inside a blue chamber, a bubble of air blown by ourselves. The other sky beyond, absolutely black and appalling, is wide-open country, irresistible for exploration."[9]

In December 1970 several scientists and engineers at Lewis began to look into the availability of graduate courses related to environmental problems. They found that within the center there was sufficient expertise to begin to plan a course similar to Evvard's "From Mach 4 to Infinity." Robert Hibbard, a scientist in Lewis's Advanced Research Institute, took charge of coordinating this informal graduate seminar. It drew an unexpected response of 100 students. The course covered topics such as "Pollution and Legislation," taught by Kenneth Coffin, "Combustion Fundamentals" by Sanford Gordon and Frank Belles, and "Fossil Fuels" by Robert Hibbard. Other lectures by Albert Evans, Helmut Butze, Charles Blankenship, Marvin Warshay, Frank Zeleznik, and Phillip Meng covered various potentially cleaner engine configurations. Gas turbines, steam cars, and electric cars caught the imaginations of Harold Rolik, William Strack, and Stuart Fordyce. Lester Nichols, Reese Roth, and Robert Rohal explored fission and fossil-fueled electric generating stations. These topics, which covered pollution caused by automobiles, airplanes, and nuclear and electric power generation, were the seeds from which an entirely new effort would grow.[10]

The following year, as grass roots support from within the laboratory strengthened, Lewis formed an Environmental Research Office to develop sensing techniques to identify and monitor trace elements and compounds in the city of Cleveland's air. Lundin worked out an agreement with Mayor Carl B. Stokes to lend technical assistance to the city's Division of Air Pollution Control. From 20 monitoring stations, the city would provide 50 samples a week for the laboratory to analyze. The goal was to develop inexpensive methods to pinpoint the source of a particular pollutant.[11] To identify trace elements in the air, the Plum Brook reactor staff got into the act. They developed a technique called neutron activation analysis to detect mercury, arsenic, cadmium, and nickel from substances in air samples. The center also initiated a project, funded through the Environmental Protection Agency (EPA), to study how treated wastes contributed to the pollution of Lake Erie, at that time choked with algae. A NASA program, directed from the Manned Space Flight Center in Houston, Tex., used RB-57F aircraft carrying remote-sensing instruments to photograph the effects of strip mining, crop diseases, and ice formation on the Great Lakes. In 1971 Lewis Research Center assisted in keeping track of the spread of corn blight over the mid-western states.[12]

In 1972 Lewis staff began to monitor samples from eight new meteorological stations in the city of Cleveland to study the effect of weather, particularly winds, on pollution levels. The stations were set up in Cleveland area schools, with students, supervised by a science teacher, taking the readings. A solar-powered remote control station located in the five-mile crib in Lake Erie tracked Lake Erie's effect on weather to show how pollution was spread in the Cuyahoga River Valley.

In 1970, to focus on pollution from automobiles, Lewis set up the Automotive Systems Office funded through the EPA. They hoped to develop a gas-turbine automobile engine based on the potentially cleaner and more economical Brayton cycle. Could a car powered by a gas turbine get good performance, fuel economy, and meet or surpass the 1976 Federal Emission Standards? Pushed by the rising voices of the environmentalists, the American automobile industry seemed poised to make the transition from the piston engine to the gas turbine. Lewis staff developed a type of thermal reactor to burn up carbon monoxide and hydrocarbons left from incomplete combustion. Members of the Materials and Structures Division tackled the problem of developing low-cost materials, such as ceramics, to withstand the high temperatures and corrosion produced during the combustion process.[13] In the mid-1970s they would add the Stirling engine and electric-powered cars to their automotive expertise.

THE ENERGY CRISIS

Staff cuts and the new commitment to the environment coincided with the growing awareness of the country's dependence on fossil fuels. Among the Lewis staff, Robert Graham saw a potential opportunity for Lewis to develop technology for new approaches to energy production. Graham argued in a memo to Bruce Lundin in October 1970 that Lewis had a unique capability to undertake energy research. "I know of no other major laboratory that incorporates the pertinent capabilities in thermodynamics, fluid mechanics, heat transfer, materials, chemistry, nuclear physics, plasma physics and cryo-physics under one organization."[14] He asked Lundin to consider a long-range program to examine various power-producing systems. Graham suggested that a special projects panel be formed to awaken interest in ground-based energy systems.

Robert English independently reached the same conclusion after reading Alvin Weinberg's *Reflections on Big Science*. Weinberg, then the director of the Oak Ridge National Laboratories, argued that government laboratories had an obligation to the country at a time of crisis. To face the energy crisis the country needed the task or mission orientation of government laboratories, not the "remote, pure and fragmented" approach of university science.[15] English thought Lewis should "step forward" to offer its propulsion expertise. New work in ground-based energy systems, in English's view, would also help solve Lewis's own crisis, brought about by the 1972 staff cuts.[16] A graduate of the University of Minnesota, English had been at Lewis since 1944. In thinking over the laboratory's past, he concluded that the essence of Lewis Laboratory was energy conversion. The skills and traditions that Lewis personnel had perfected as they advanced the turbojet were themselves a national resource. The same understanding of fluid dynamics, heat transfer, combustion, materials, turbine design, bearings and rotor dynamics, lubrication and seals, turbine cooling, and controls formed the basis of their work in rockets and space power systems. As chief of the Space Power System Division, English had contributed to the technology of the Brayton-cycle systems—designed to be used with either a solar or nuclear power source to heat the working fluid, a mixture of helium and xenon gases. In August 1972 this conversion system had completed more than 3200 hours of testing in Plum Brook's Space Power Facility. Now this work, conceived in 1957 and tested as early as 1966, was about to be shut down. English did not think that this experience should be lost. Brayton-cycle technology, developed as a closed system for continuous unattended operation in space, could be adapted for mass transportation needs. Buses and trains with revolutionary new engines would be cleaner and more energy efficient.

Lundin began to work with the U.S. Department of Transportation and the EPA. Since coal was cheaper than oil, it seemed feasible to investigate ways to make coal burning cleaner and more efficient. Knowledge of the potassium Rankine system in space power generation could be applied to improve coal-fired electric power generation. The Rankine system had the potential to wring more energy from coal through a topping cycle.

The Arab oil embargo of 1973 brought home what should have come as no surprise. The dependence of the industrialized West on oil made the United States strategically vulnerable. In the decade after World War II many technical writers raised the spectre of dwindling oil reserves and their effect on both economic development and military preparedness. In 1952 Eugene Ayres and Charles Scarlott, for example, had predicted an energy crisis in the 1970s in their book, *Energy Sources: The Wealth of the World*. Others also tried to awaken the nation to the need to conserve precious energy resources. Only after the aggravation of the long lines to purchase gasoline in 1973 did the Nixon administration fully appreciate the urgency of the energy situation. Nixon asked Dixy Lee Ray of the Atomic Energy Commission to chair a task force to define the problems and offer solutions. Ray set up 15 panels. English chaired the panel on energy conversion. Martin U. Gutstein, Harvey Schwartz, and George Seikel from Lewis also served on this panel. Lewis representatives on the Solar Energy Panel included Ronald Thomas, Gerald Barna, Daniel T. Bernatowitz, Patrick Finnegan, George Kaplan, Warren Rayle, and Joseph M. Savino. George Siekel served on the Fusion Energy Panel, and Thaddeus S. Mroz and Lloyd Shure on the Advanced Transportation Systems Panel.[17]

Wind, because it is driven by the Sun, was among the alternative energy sources considered by the Solar Energy Panel. The Lewis representatives on this panel were beginning to develop a unique expertise in wind turbine technology. In 1970, Cruz Matos, Secretary of the Interior of Puerto Rico, formally requested Lewis Laboratory to design a wind turbine to generate electricity for the Island of Culebra. Although no one knew if the wind turbine would actually be built, interest in wind as a substitute for fossil fuels began to grow. Louis Divone of the National Science Foundation, upon hearing of the Lewis design, decided to authorize the funds to construct and operate an experimental 100-kilowatt wind turbine at Plum Brook. At average wind speeds of 18 miles per hour, the system was expected to generate 180,000 kilowatt hours per year in the form of 440-volt, 3-phase, 60-cycle alternating current output. Later the wind turbine was upgraded to produce 200 kilowatts of electricity. In 1973 the National Science Foundation (NSF) and NASA sponsored a joint workshop on wind power that brought together all existing information on previous wind power development, including a full-scale wind turbine experiment carried out in 1940 by Palmer Putnam and the S. Morgan Smith Company at Grandpa's Knob, Vt. A paper by Ronald L. Thomas and Joseph M. Savino, "Status of Wind-Energy Conversion," presented at a symposium sponsored by the NSF in 1973, summarized the point to which work at Lewis had progressed.[18] In 1974 Lewis received $1.5 million for its wind energy program from NSF and the Energy Research and Development Administration (ERDA). A total of 13 experimental wind turbines, funded under ERDA and its successor, the Department of Energy (DOE), were put in operation between 1975 and 1979. The most impressive of these was a 3.2-megawatt Mod-5B wind turbine generator on the island of Oahu, Hawaii, now in commercial use.

Drawing on experience in developing solar cells for space power systems, Lewis also initiated programs to develop electric systems in remote areas of the country that could not be effectively serviced by the electric power industry. The village of the Papago Tribe at Schuchuli, Ariz. (about 120 miles from Tuscon) was chosen as the site for the world's first solar-powered village. A Lewis team, headed by Louis Rosenblum, designed and installed the system, which consisted of a solar cell array field of 192 photovoltaic power modules. Excess electrical energy, stored in a bank of lead acid batteries, provided power for lights and appliances in the evenings.[19]

Lundin could not win the full cooperation of the electric power industry. The new solar technology threatened the power industry. It proved easier to develop the technology than to achieve the hoped-for technology transfer. A memo from the Chief of Industrial Programs to Bruce Lundin made the situation clear:

Although entirely peripheral to the Lewis program of large-scale experiments (which relates directly to utility generation of bulk power), it is well to recognize that the overall solar program is viewed with reservation by much of the utility industry. This is because solar power devices used by their customers will reduce utility energy sales but will not reduce utility need for total generating capacity. The combination would add to their financial problems.[20]

Lundin and his staff discovered the difficulties of developing new relationships with industry. Industry's wary attitudes were similar to the initial reluctance of the aircraft engine industry. For many years Lewis had carefully cultivated its good relations with General Electric and Pratt & Whitney. The delicate interplay between the military, the NACA, and industry was missing in this ground-based energy venture. NASA had the capability to provide hardware based on the most advanced technical concepts, but it was powerless to get industry to accept the new technology.

The year 1974 brought new disappointment. The center's program in communications satellites, growing out of the revolutionary "depressed collector" traveling wave tube invented in 1971 by Henry Kosmahl of the Space Technology Division, was cancelled. This traveling wave tube dramatically increased the efficiency and reliability of satellite transmissions while it reduced costs.[21]

Despite emphatic denial by NASA Deputy Administrator George Low, rumors circulated that Lewis Research Center would sever what was now a very tenuous connection with NASA and become part of ERDA, where the major part of its research programs were concentrated.[22] Smarting from the devastating cuts in staff, Lewis professional staff unionized. Rather than affiliate with the existing union—the American Federation of Government Employees (AFGE) Local 2182, organized in 1962 at Lewis—they created the Engineers and Scientists Association in December 1974 under the leadership of Lyle Wright. They joined the International Federation of Professional and Technical Engineers.

Toward the end of Lundin's tenure as director, Congress authorized a NASA research and technology program in 1976 to find ways to conserve aircraft fuel. As a result of the Arab oil embargo, between 1973 and 1975 the cost of aircraft fuel tripled. Compared to the 1950s, it had gone up 1000 percent. Fuel costs were now an important factor in keeping the U.S. airline industries profitable. Under NASA's Aircraft Energy Efficiency (ACEE) program, Lewis took responsibility for two projects: the Energy Efficient Engine (EEE), or E^3, and in 1978, the Advanced Turboprop Program (ATP). Through the E^3 program, Lewis managed contracts with General Electric and Pratt & Whitney to develop new designs to improve the efficiency of their engines. Both companies were eager for the financial and technical assistance that NASA could provide. Now threatend by Japanese and European engine makers, only through continued innovation could they keep their dominance of the world engine market.[23]

The Advanced Turboprop Program was far more daring and innovative. A team of Lewis engineers had begun to cooperate with Hamilton-Standard, a division of United Technologies, as early as 1973. Under a program called Reducing the Energy Consumption of Commercial Air Transportation (RECAT), they began work on the design for a prop-fan, an aircraft powered by a propeller and gas turbine engine. Turboprops had fallen into disfavor after 1955 because they were slower and noisier than turbojets. In addition, they have complex gear boxes, making them difficult to maintain. However, with the potential to reduce fuel consumption by 20 percent, it

100-kilowatt wind turbine at Plum Brook.

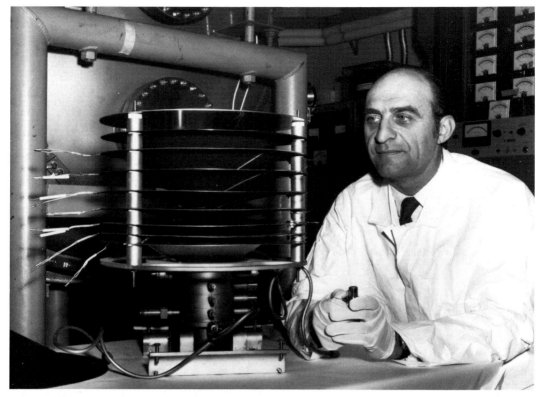

Henry Kosmahl's traveling wave tube made satellite transmissions cheaper and more reliable. In 1987 the center won an Emmy Award for contributions to television technology.

seemed worth trying to resurrect the concept, despite formidable technical problems. Engine and propeller acoustics, propeller efficiency and structures, and the problem of gearing to connect the engine with the propeller were among the many areas of research continued at Lewis through the 1970s.[24]

THE OUTSIDER: DIRECTOR JOHN F. McCARTHY, JR.

Lundin's skills were technical rather than administrative. He never learned to craft relationships in Headquarters to win concessions for Lewis. In his wrangling over the issue of contracting and his determination to find work for the laboratory outside NASA, Bruce Lundin isolated Lewis from NASA and failed to solve the question of the laboratory's future. The creation of the Department of Energy in 1977 brought new insecurity. DOE planned to manage its contracts from Washington, D.C., calling on Lewis only for expert advice. That would hardly guarantee the continuity of jobs at Lewis, which would depend on the year-to-year whim of the new agency. At the same time NASA Headquarters imposed a 350-man limit on Lewis's involvement in energy programs. This was perhaps the final blow for Lundin. He retired in 1977.

The post of director remained vacant, fueling speculation that Lewis would soon be closed. However, when NASA announced in late 1978 that John F. McCarthy, Jr., director of the Center

Testing the advanced turboprop. A team from Lewis won the Robert J. Collier Trophy for an outstanding contribution to aeronautics in 1987 for research begun in response to the energy crisis.

for Space Research at the Massachusetts Institute of Technology, had accepted the post, it seemed a good omen. McCarthy had distinguished academic credentials and strong connections with the aerospace industry. Headquarters probably counted on McCarthy to take orders from Washington and to bring Lewis back into NASA's fold.

McCarthy was the first leader of Lewis Research Center who was free of the NACA traditions that had given Lewis its character. No one at Lewis had ever met him. His first speech as center director did little to win the allegiance of the staff, particularly its upper management. He noted that one of the first things that needed work was Lewis's image. Lewis was perceived as a laboratory "searching for an image and a mission." He tactlessly reminded the staff of the embarrassment caused by the recent declaration of Cleveland's bankruptcy. Like the city of Cleveland, McCarthy declared, the laboratory was "supposed to have a severe case of hardening of the arteries." However, McCarthy also noted some of Lewis's positive qualities. He was impressed with "the expertise of the people, the caliber of the work, the facilities, and the fine workmanship." He also made it clear that Lewis had a poor record in the hiring of minorities and women—something that he planned to change. With respect to the issue of the balance between in-house expertise and contracting out support services, McCarthy was more sympathetic to the Lewis point of view than many employees expected. He was concerned with keeping at least a minimum of in-house expertise:

> As all of you know, we have tremendous pressure from Headquarters and the administration to contract work out. But the kind of work we do requires that we have a minimum level of capability in order to monitor contracts to do the kinds of expert work that we do. . . . When the thing becomes routine, boring, and mediocre, farm it out. If it is something that we cannot do on the outside, we should be able to do it in-house. And that balance will have to be looked at and monitored constantly.[25]

McCarthy thought the center needed to work more aggressively to promote itself both outside and within NASA. Sharp had reached out to the community beyond Lewis during his years as director. Silverstein and Lundin, more at home with technical problems, had failed to maintain these important connections, all the more important in the political agency that NASA had become.

In aeronautics, McCarthy set reduction of the center's reliance on full-scale testing as a goal, one of the recommendations of a study by the National Research Council in 1977. With the country's premier test facilities now managed by the Air Force, Lewis's future contributions to engine development would depend on basic research in components, accompanied by increased expertise in computing.[26]

McCarthy's appointment coincided with the funding of $6.14 million for the construction of a new Research Analysis Center to consolidate existing computer equipment and to acquire additional capacity. He reported that the center was perceived by Headquarters as weak in computational mechanics and "testing for the sake of testing without doing the analytical work required to justify that test."[27] Computing had grown steadily from 1949, when Lewis acquired the clumsy mechanical differential analyzer. In 1955 the first electronic system, the IBM 607, followed by the Sperry Rand Univac 1103, was used to process experimental data. The Central Automatic Digital Data Encoder (CADDE) was the first centralized computer system and the first to record data on magnetic tape. In 1966 Lewis acquired the IBM 650/653. Much of this previous computing capability was used to record the results of testing. McCarthy emphasized the potential of computer analysis prior to any kind of experimental work. The computer could eliminate much of the costly testing on which the laboratory had depended in the past.[28]

McCarthy fought hard to reverse the fortunes of Lewis. Much of his time was spent in Washington, D.C., rather than at the center, a change from the personal day-to-day involvement in Lewis management by past directors. Upper management resented these frequent absences. Nevertheless, McCarthy laid the groundwork for strong connections with the Ohio Congressional Delegation and never turned down an opportunity to speak at both local and national functions. Through McCarthy's advocacy, Congresswoman Mary Rose Oakar came to play an increasingly strong role in promoting the interests of the center. For example, McCarthy spoke at public hearings of the Subcommittee on Compensation and Employee Benefits Committee conducted by Oakar at the Cleveland Federal Building in July 1981. He described the reduction in staff over the previous ten years from 4200 in 1971 to 2690 by the end of 1981, a reduction of 1510 positions. McCarthy pointed out that Lewis had a high attrition rate because of a pay ceiling for federal workers and changes in the government retirement system that actually penalized senior people who did not choose to retire. "These individuals could not afford the economic penalty associated with not retiring, even though many would have preferred to stay on at Lewis. Many of these individuals have accepted positions in private industry at considerably higher salaries."[29] Of 1200 scientists and engineers, less than 6 percent were under the age of 30. It was difficult to attract young scientific and engineering talent because of the instability of Lewis programs.

The greatest blow to McCarthy's efforts to chart a new course for Lewis came with the publication of a study funded by the conservative Heritage Foundation. Prepared for newly elected President Ronald Reagan, the *Agenda for Progress* focused on ways to cut government spending. It included a short paragraph on aeronautical research and technology. The report called this research unnecessary because the aircraft and engine industries were mature enough to do their own research and development. It recommended that all civil aeronautics programs funded by NASA be abolished. With the 1983 aeronautics budget to be cut in half, it looked as though this time Lewis would not be spared.[30]

The adversities of the 1970s had toughened the Lewis staff. They were ready to take Lewis's future into their own hands. Mervin Ault organized the "Save the Center Committee" to work with members of the Ohio Delegation to Congress. Senator John Glenn, the former Mercury astronaut who had received some of his Mercury training at Lewis, and indomitable Congresswoman Mary Rose Oakar needed no convincing. They joined Howard Metzenbaum, Donald J. Pease, and Louis Stokes to pressure Congress to keep the center open.

McCarthy chose this inopportune moment to resign. However, he left in place a group of ten division chiefs, chaired by William "Red" Robbins and Joseph Sivo, charged with the first strategic planning for Lewis. They had the 1982 Strategic Plan ready the first day that Andrew J. Stofan returned to Lewis from Headquarters to take over as director. Stofan had the charisma and confidence of a former manager of the Titan-Centaur launch vehicle. He had directed the Launch Vehicles Program from 1974 until called to Headquarters as Deputy Associate Administrator for the Office of Space Sciences in 1978. The Office of Space Sciences was a locus of power within NASA. It put Stofan in a position to move Lewis away from its dependence on the weak and underfunded Office of Aeronautics and Space Technology (OAST) into the mainstream of NASA.

The Lewis planners recommended that Stofan go after five major programs: the power system for the space station, the advanced turboprop program, refurbishing of the Altitude Wind Tunnel for an expanded icing test program, the Advanced Communications Technology Satellite

(ACTS), and the Shuttle-Centaur Program. Of the five programs, the space power system was the most controversial among the members of the group.

Management of major projects like Shuttle-Centaur and the power system for the space station was new to Lewis. Although staff in the launch vehicles programs had managed large projects like Agena and Centaur, they had never dealt with the Manned Space Flight Program, with its strong political connections. Stofan saw that these large programs were the key to Lewis's future viability in NASA. He had the personal skills of persuasion that his predecessors had lacked. He landed four of the five programs. In Red Robbins's view, "it was a damn miracle."[31]

Energy research was gradually phased out. Stofan exorcised the NACA research ghosts that still haunted some of the facilities. He called past management autocratic and instituted "participative management" to heal some of the rifts between managers and staff caused by the prolonged trauma of the 1970s. After the Space Shuttle Challenger disaster in January 1986, Stofan reluctantly agreed to return to Headquarters to head the space station project. The present Director, John M. Klineberg, sees Lewis as less a research laboratory and more a conduit for ideas, technology, and funds to the private sector. In his view, Lewis's future rests with the large projects. With the center employing 2700 civil servants and 1200 support-service contractors, a return to the days when the laboratory functioned as a self-sufficient unit is unthinkable.

Lewis Research Center has come full circle. It is no longer a research laboratory where the majority of work is done in-house. It is now firmly established in NASA's mainstream: the development and missions side of NASA. The power system for the proposed space station is its key component. NASA administrators estimate that over the next ten years the country will spend $1.6 billion on the development of this system. Lewis staff will manage this development through contracts with industry, principally Rocketdyne and its subcontractors, Ford Aerospace, Lockheed, and General Dynamics. Case Institute, now part of Case Western Reserve University, is among the many universities that provide research to support the space station and other programs through contracts with NASA.[32]

The plans for the space station represent the fulfillment of T. Keith Glennan's vision for NASA. NASA has become a conduit for the nation's tax dollars to industry and the universities. Hugh Dryden's concept of a government research laboratory to provide technical capital for the nation's future in the form of ideas and innovations is no longer viable. The NACA research tradition, nurtured after World War II and brought to full flower from the late 1940s to the early 1960s at Lewis, now has but a small corner of the camel's tent. Lewis Research Center's struggle to keep a measure of autonomy was an effort to preserve the independence and creativity of its technical people. Although never free of Cold War pressure to improve existing engines, Lewis Laboratory kept its independence. While it served both the military and industry after World War II, it remained an autonomous institution. The success of liquid hydrogen as a rocket fuel is an example of a long-term commitment that began in the late 1940s. It was basic research. The development of this tricky fuel to the point of routine use over twenty years ago put the United States far ahead of the Soviet Union in the area of space propulsion. Only recently has the Soviet Union developed the expertise to use liquid hydrogen in its space shuttle.

NASA's contractual relationships with industry have supported short-term development, not advanced technology. America has been living off the technical capital of the 1950s and early 1960s, much of it the product of government in-house research. In 1988 the National Research Council criticized NASA's neglect of advanced technology research. For the preceding 15 years, less than 3 percent of NASA's total budget has gone to research. Of that 3 percent, virtually none went to applications more than five years in the future. Ironically, according to the National Research Council's study, the nation's "foremost technical need is for new propulsion systems, including nuclear space power systems and electric propulsion for flights to Mars and more distant planets"—the very programs Lewis Research Center was forced to give up in the 1970s.[33] Lewis Research Center in the 1990s is poised on the edge of a new era. One of its challenges is to see whether a balance between research and development can be restored.

NOTES

[1] See *Cleveland Plain Dealer*, 15 February 1973. See also internal Lewis Research Center document, "How Should NASA Conduct Research and Technology in Aeronautical Propulsion?" 27 January 1978. (Copy in author's files.) The Office of Aeronautics and Space Technology (OAST) managed the main programs of the three former NACA laboratories, Langley, Lewis, and Ames, and Dryden. OAST budget items on nuclear power and propulsion were reduced from $29.8 million in fiscal year 1972 to $17.1 million in 1973 to $4 million in 1974.

[2] "How Do You Measure a Person's Career?" *Lewis News*, 28 June 1974.

[3] These missions are detailed in a typescript by Walter T. Olson, "Some Highlights of Lewis Research Center Technical Achievements in the 1970s," January 1980.

[4] See shuttle accounts in Malcolm McConnell, *Challenger: A Major Malfunction* (New York: Doubleday, 1987); and Joseph J. Trento, *Prescription for Disaster* (New York: Crown Publishers, 1987).

[5] Lewis contributions to the shuttle are discussed in two documents: G. Mervin Ault to Director, "LeRC-Managed Technology Work for Space Shuttle," 9 June 1975, and an unsigned, undated typescript, "NASA Lewis Research Center's Role in Space Shuttle." (Copies in author's files.)

[6] See "Center's Future Looks Promising," *Lewis News*, 30 January 1970. *Aircraft Engine Noise Reduction*, Proceedings of a conference held May 16–17, 1972, at the NASA Lewis Research Center, NASA SP-311, 1972.

[7] "Refan Program Aimed at Quieting DC-9s, 727s," *Lewis News*, 13 July 1973.

[8] Bruce Murray, Michael C. Malin, and Ronald Greeley, *Earthlike Planets: Surfaces of Mercury, Venus, Earth, Moon, Mars* (San Francisco: W.H. Freeman, 1981), p. xi.

[9] Lewis Thomas, *The Lives of the Cell: Notes of a Biology Watcher* (New York: Viking Press, 1974), p. 43.

[10] "Pollution Course Taught at Lewis," *Lewis News*, 31 December 1970.

[11] "Center Helps Curb Air Pollution," *Lewis News*, 15 January 1971.

[12] "Big Benefits Come Right from Lewis," *Lewis News*, 17 December 1971.

[13] "NASA Aids Gas Turbine Car Study," *Lewis News*, 13 July 1973.

[14] Robert W. Graham to Director, 1 October 1970. Across the top of this document someone wrote, "Not received by Director." Graham sent a second more detailed memo, "Lewis Involvement in Electric Power Research and Development," 14 June 1971. File marked Ground Based Electric Power. Educational Services Office, NASA Lewis Research Center.

[15] Alvin M. Weinberg, *Reflections on Big Science* (Cambridge, Mass.: MIT Press, 1967), p. 156–160.

[16] Interview with Robert English by V. Dawson, 11 July 1986.

[17] The final report, *The Nation's Energy Future*, 1 December 1973 (WASH-1281) was submitted by Dr. Dixy Lee Ray, Chairman, U.S. Atomic Energy Commission. See also Eugene Ayres and Charles Scarlott, *Energy Sources: The Wealth of the World* (New York: McGraw-Hill, 1952).

[18] NASA TM X-71523, November 1973. See also *Wind Energy Conversion Systems*, Workshop Proceedings, NSF/RA/W-73-006, 1973. NSF's Research Applied to National Needs Directorate (RANN) had a solar power research program begun in 1971. See also "Solar Energy as a National Energy Resource," NSF/NASA Solar Energy Panel, December 1972. NTIS No. PB-221-659.

[19] "Solar Electric Replaces Kerosene and Diesel for Arizona Indian Village," *Lewis News*, 5 January 1979. The system was dedicated in January 1959.

[20] James Burnett to Director, 11 October 1974. File marked Ground Based Electric Power, Educational Services Office, NASA Lewis Research Center.

[21] Henry Kosmahl's invention, the Multistage Depressed Collector (NASA TN D6093, 1971) was patented in 1972. It is used in NASA's communications technology satellites like the ACTS. In 1987 NASA won an Emmy Award for outstanding achievement in television engineering because of the improvements in television broadcasting brought about by the development of communications satellites. See *Lewis News*, 2 October 1987.

[22] George Low, "Memorandum for the Record," 14 February 1975, Lewis file, NASA History Office, Washington, D.C. Funding for Lewis's ground-based energy work grew from about $3 million in fiscal year 1972 (NSF, ERDA, DOT, etc.) to $60–70 million in 1978 under DOE.

[23] This program is discussed in detail in Jeffrey L. Ethell, *Fuel Economy in Aviation*, NASA SP-462 (Washington, D.C.: U.S. Government Printing Office, 1983), p. 29–42.

[24] Ethell, *Fuel Economy in Aviation*, p. 43–57.

[25] John McCarthy, "Meet the Director," 8 November 1978.

[26] The National Research Council Turbine Engine Test Facilities Committee, *Advanced Gas Turbine Engine Development: The Potential Role of the NASA Lewis Research Center* (Washington, D.C.: National Academy of Sciences, 1977).

[27] Ibid.

[28] A lengthy discussion of Lewis's transition to computer analysis can be found in the transcript of Interview with William McNally by V. Dawson, 4 March 1985.

[29] "McCarthy Testimony Underscores Manpower Restraints at Lewis," *Lewis News*, 17 July 1981.

[30] Eugene J. McAllister, ed., *Agenda for Progress: Examining Federal Spending* (Washington, D.C.: The Heritage Foundation, 1981), p. 171–172. Some in Washington saw the Lewis closing as a *fait accompli;* for example, a headline for the *Defense Daily*, "Budget Cuts Forcing NASA to Close Lewis Research Center, FY '83 Aeronautics Budget Halved to $139 million." (vol. 119, no. 25, 9 December 1981).

[31] Transcript of Interview with William H. ("Red") Robbins by Michal McMahon and V. Dawson, 15 May 1986.

[32] See James R. Hawker and Richard S. Dali, "Anatomy of an Organizational Change Effort at the Lewis Research Center," NASA Contractor Report 4146, April 1988.

[33] Joseph F. Shea, "NASA Short on Research Budgeting," *The Cleveland Plain Dealer*, 1 August 1988. Shea chaired the Council's committee on space technologies to meet future U.S. needs.

ESSAY ON SOURCES

For a general overview of NACA history, I relied on Alex Roland's *Model Research: The National Advisory Committee for Aeronautics, 1915–1958* (NASA SP-4103, 1985), based on documents from the Washington Office, and James R. Hansen's *Engineer in Charge: A History of Langley Memorial Research Laboratory* (NASA SP-4305, 1987), which draws extensively on documents from Langley's archives. I found many of the views in Arthur L. Levine's dissertation, "United States Aeronautical Research Policy, 1915–1958" (Ph.D. Dissertation, Columbia University, 1963), provocative, if not solidly documented. Levine's views should be supplemented by Ira H. Abbott's "A Review and Commentary of a Thesis by Arthur L. Levine Entitled U.S. Aeronautical Policy 1915–1958" (April 1964, typescript, NASA History Office, Washington, D.C.). Jerome C. Hunsaker presents an uncritical review of NACA achievements in "Forty Years of Aeronautical Research, 1915–1955," *Smithsonian Report for 1955* (Washington, D.C.: Smithsonian Institution, 1956), p. 241–271. See also the portrait of Lewis drawn by James R. Hansen in *Aviation's Golden Age: Portraits from the 1920s and 1930s*, edited by William M. Leary (Iowa City: University of Iowa Press, 1989). Two histories of Ames Aeronautical Laboratory are also helpful: Elizabeth Muenger's *Searching the Horizon: A History of Ames Research Center, 1940–1976* (NASA SP-4304, 1985) and Edwin P. Hartman, *Adventures in Research: A History of Ames Research Center, 1940–1965* (NASA SP-4302, 1970). *Frontiers of Flight: The Story of NACA Research* (New York: Alfred A. Knopf, 1948) by George W. Gray is a concise descriptive history of the NACA to 1948; it contains some good detail on the early years of the Cleveland laboratory.

John Holmfeld's unpublished study, "The Site Selection for the NACA Engine Research Laboratory: A Meeting of Science and Politics" (Master's Essay, Case Institute of Technology, 1967), presents a well-documented story of the influence of personalities over objective criteria in the selection of the Cleveland location. I supplemented Holmfeld's work with the Greater Cleveland Growth Association Records, 1881–1971, Minutes of the Cleveland Chamber of Commerce, Ms. 3471. Also, Corporate Records of TRW, Inc. Ms 3942, Records 1900–1969, Series I: Corporate Records; Sub-series B: Loose Papers consisting of correspondence 1926–66 and Series II: Histories, Series V: outside activities. They provide a clearer picture of the role of Frederick Crawford, whom I also interviewed.

The only published source for Lewis history is *Liquid Hydrogen as a Propulsion Fuel, 1945–1959* (NASA SP-4404, 1978) by John L. Sloop. It contains many revealing historical details, particularly about the period of the 1950s. Although Sloop focuses on the historical development of the use of liquid hydrogen as a propulsion fuel, he relates the work at Lewis on high-energy rocket fuels to general developments in the field. Mr. Sloop also provided me with valuable documents from his personal files.

I located Lewis records after consulting a log containing Records Transmittal and Receipt forms. These included boxes 220, 221, 231, 257, 290, 295, 296, 297, 298, and 299 listed under Code 1300. These records, although historical, are no longer complete, but the product of considerable consolidation by records managers. I refer to documents from these boxes in my text as NASA Lewis Records, although I understand they will soon be shipped to the National Archives and Records Service. The photograph collection is stored at Plum Brook. A chronological log of photographs, with short descriptions, can be found in the Photography Laboratory. In addition, there is a Motion Picture Log and a separately prepared catalogue of NACA films, many of which are of considerable historical interest.

The Lewis Library has nearly all the back issues (1942-present) of the Lewis newspaper, called successively *Wing Tips, Orbit,* and *Lewis News*. In addition, the telephone directories from 1943 to the present have been bound. These are helpful for lists of personnel and, in the later years, organizational charts. The library has retained loose-leaf notebooks of NACA Inspections held every three years from 1947 to 1966. In addition, I used a loose-leaf notebook marked "History" which contains the texts of the "Smoker Talks" given by visiting dignitaries and staff talks given by the division heads in the early 1940s. The notebook also contains additional miscellaneous material, such as clippings and quotations from magazine and journal articles.

I found the references in NACA technical papers to be valuable historical sources. I used *NACA Annual Reports, Wartime Reports, Memoranda,* and *Notes*. In particular, the Langley file, an index of NACA reports by author, was useful as reference. The Lewis Technical Library has a good collection of aviation journals, most beginning in the 1940s; a few, such as the *Society of Automotive Engineering,* go back to the 1920s and 1930s. I also consulted Lewis records stored at the Federal Archives and Records Center, Chicago, Ill. The records consist of four boxes of NACA-Lewis Lectures, Speeches, Talks, and Broadcasts (January 1944 through December 1954). Similar records at the Federal Archives and Records Center in Dayton, Ohio, consist of 19 boxes of speeches, talks, and papers by Lewis authors, filed alphabetically by author's name. These cover the period 1951 to 1954 and 1955 through 1966. A collection of Centaur program records is stored in the vault of the Developmental Engineering Building at Lewis, for which Craig Waff and I prepared an inventory in September 1986.

Documents from the NASA History Office, Washington, D.C., also proved invaluable. Biographical files contain miscellaneous correspondence, transcripts of interviews, speeches, and photographs. An index to the Walter Bonney interviews was useful in locating these interviews. There are also interviews conducted by Eugene Emme of several key Lewis personnel.

To study the transition from the aircraft piston engine to jet propulsion, I began with *The Origins of the Turbojet Revolution* (Baltimore: The Johns Hopkins University Press, 1980) by Edward W. Constant II. Robert Schlaifer and S.D. Heron's *The Development of Aircraft Engines; The Development of Aviation Fuels: Two Studies of the Relations Between Government and Business* (Cambridge, Mass.: Harvard University Graduate School of Business Administration, 1950) was an invaluable source for factual information about aircraft piston engines and the early development of jet propulsion. For a glimpse of the role of George Mead on the Power Plants Committee, see Cary Hoge Mead, *Wings Over the World* (Wauwatosa, Wisc.: The Swanset Press, 1971). Especially helpful is Frank Whittle's "The Early History of the Whittle Jet Propulsion Gas Turbine," *Proceedings of the Institution of Mechanical Engineers,* 152 (1945), p. 419-435, and *Jet: The Story of a Pioneer*

(Frederick Mueller, 1953). See also Leslie E. Neville and Nathaniel F. Silsbee, *Jet Propulsion Progress: The Development of Aircraft Gas Turbines* (New York: McGraw-Hill, 1948) and "Historical Development of Jet Propulsion," in *Jet Propulsion Engines*, edited by O. E. Lancaster (Princeton: Princeton University Press, 1959), p. 3–53, which includes discussions of rocket propulsion. I was disappointed to find very little serious scholarly work on the transfer of German scientists and their technology to the United States after World War II. It was clear to me from studying the references in papers published by Lewis staff on various aspects of jet propulsion that German work on turbine cooling, inlets, and compressors was often the starting point for much creative work. Clarence G. Lasby's *Project Paperclip: German Scientists and the Cold War* (New York: Atheneum, 1971) is helpful but superficial. I also perused the ALSOS files in the National Archives, Record Group 165, Records of the War Department, General and Special Staffs, Box Intelligence Division, ALSOS Mission File, 1944–1945. At Wright-Patterson Air Force Base, I looked through sanitized ALSOS files in the History Office of the Logistics Command.

I found my best sources in the National Archives and Records Service, Suitland, Md. I consulted "Preliminary Inventory of the Textual Records of the National Advisory Committee for Aeronautics (Record Group 255)," compiled by Sarah Powell, June 1967, and "Special Study on the Records of the National Advisory Committee for Aeronautics," prepared by William H. Cunliffe and Herman G. Goldbeck, July 1973, to determine how to use this archive. An index of the "Correspondence Files (Decimal File)" and "Correspondence of NACA Committees and Subcommittees," prepared by Richard Wood, proved invaluable. Among other records, I consulted those of the Special Committee on Jet Propulsion, which contained correspondence, but not all the minutes of the meetings. I found the missing minutes in the NASA History Office. I also found relevant documents among the H. H. Arnold Papers in the Manuscript Division of the Library of Congress, Washington, D.C.

At Wright-Patterson Air Force Base I looked for documentation to illuminate the relationship between Lewis and Wright Field, but I was unable to locate the records of the Army (later Air Force) Liaison Office. I consulted records relating to jet propulsion in the History Offices of the Aeronautical Systems Division and the Logistics Command Division, and in the Aero Propulsion Laboratory. There are three catalogues of records: "Catalog of Histories and Source Materials in ASD Historical Division Files," AFSC Historical Publications Series 61-50-100, September 1961; "Guide to Research Studies Prepared by Office of History Headquarters Air Force Logistics Command," 1984; and "Archival Holdings," ASD-HO, 20 June 1986. See also James St. Peter, "History of the Gas Turbine Engine in the United States: Bibliography," WRDC-TR-2062.

The importance of British theoretical contributions to fluid dynamics and compressor design is discussed in Brian Nichelson's excellent Ph.D. Dissertation, "Early Jet Engines and the Transition from Centrifugal to Axial Compressors: A Case Study in Technological Change" (University of Minnesota, 1988). I was not able to find any solid historical studies specifically devoted to American postwar engineering education and the importance of German and British science and technology in reshaping engineering curricula in the 1950s. In my discussion of Lewis Laboratory's relationship with Case Institute of Technology, I relied on documents from the well-managed archives of Case Western Reserve University. Records consulted there were located under the headings Associations and Organizations: Government Groups, NASA, 19 DC and Case Institute of Technology Engineering Department Records, 19 FL. C. H. Cramer's *Case Western Reserve: A History of the University, 1926–1976* (Boston: Little, Brown and Company, 1976) provided valuable background. In this chapter I incorporated parts of my article "From Braunschweig to

Ohio: Ernst Eckert and Government Heat Transfer Research," published in *History of Heat Transfer*, edited by Edwin T. Layton, Jr., and John H. Lienhard (New York: American Society of Mechanical Engineers, 1988), p. 125–137. I am indebted to Edwin Layton, Ernst Eckert, and Simon Ostrach for their contributions to this chapter, including an unpublished paper by Simon Ostrach, "Memoir on Buoyancy-Driven Convection."

Serious history of the commercial development of post-World War II jet engines is limited. *History of the American Aircraft Industry: An Anthology*, edited by G. R. Simonson (Cambridge, Mass.: MIT Press, 1968) is a collection of superficial essays that barely mentions the relation of the NACA to industry. Charles D. Bright's *The Jet Makers: The Aerospace Industry from 1945 to 1972* (Lawrence, Kan.: Regents Press of Kansas, 1978), and *The Jet Age: Forty Years of Jet Aviation*, edited by Walter J. Boyne and Donald S. Lopez (Washington, D.C.: Smithsonian Institution Press, 1979) are helpful, as is Keith Hayward, *Government and British Civil Aerospace* (Manchester: Manchester University Press, 1983). Quite amusing biographies include Sir Stanley Hooker, *Not Much of an Engineer: An Autobiography* (Shrewsbury, England: Airlife, 1984) and Gerhard Neumann, *Herman the German* (New York: William Morrow, 1984). Company histories include *Seven Decades of Progress: A Heritage of Aircraft Turbine Technology* (Fallbrook, Calif.: Aero Publishers for General Electric Company, 1979); Michael Donne, *Leader of the Skies, Rolls-Royce: The First Seventy-five Years* (London: Frederick Muller Limited, 1981); and *The Pratt & Whitney Story* (Pratt & Whitney Aircraft Division of United Aircraft Corporation, 1950). Several articles published by the Howmet Turbine Components Corporation in the series "Classic Turbine Engines" edited by Robert B. Meyer, Jr., are useful. See, for example, Harvey H. Lippencott, "Pratt & Whitney Enters the Jet Age," *Casting About*, 1985, and Part II, *Casting About*, 1986. I obtained materials relating to the history of Pratt & Whitney and the Carrier Corporation from the United Technologies Archives, West Hartford, Conn.

NACA-NASA efforts in nuclear propulsion deserve a more detailed treatment than I was able to provide. *Atomic Shield, 1947/1952*, vol. 2 of *A History of the United States Atomic Energy Commission* (University Park: Pennsylvania State University, 1969) by Richard G. Hewlett and Francis Duncan is a valuable source. Unfortunately, I was unable to see a portion of the NACA collection in the National Archives (Record Group 255) that is yet to be declassified, despite a formal request. The best source for NASA's program in nuclear propulsion is James Arthur Dewar's "Project Rover: A Study of the Nuclear Rocket Development Program, 1953–1963" (Ph.D. Dissertation, Kansas State University, 1974). This is to be published in the near future by the Smithsonian Institution Press.

On the transition from the NACA to NASA, Robert L. Rosholt's *An Administrative History of NASA, 1958–1963* (NASA SP-4101, 1966) was dull but packed with information. I also gleaned important insights about the debates prior to the formation of NASA from Enid Curtis Bok Schoettle's chapter, "The Establishment of NASA," in *Knowledge and Power*, edited by Sanford A. Lakoff (New York: The Free Press, 1966). James R. Killian, Jr., *Sputnik, Scientists, and Eisenhower: A Memoir of the First Special Assistant to the President for Science and Technology* (Cambridge, Mass.: MIT Press, 1977) also provides interesting background. Nancy Jane Petrovic, "Design for Decline: Executive Management and the Eclipse of NASA," Ph.D. Dissertation, University of Maryland, 1982, has a provocative thesis useful for perspective in understanding Lewis's eclipse. T. Keith Glennan, "The First Years of the National Aeronautics and Space Administration," 1964, unpublished diary, Eisenhower Library, Abilene, Kan., provided me with important insights into his thinking about NASA's relationships with industry.

For the Apollo era, Arnold S. Levine touches on the problem of the autonomy of the research centers versus centralized management in *Managing NASA in the Apollo Era* (NASA SP-4102, 1982). Homer E. Newell, *Beyond the Atmosphere: Early Years of Space Science* (NASA SP-4211, 1980) provided me with a readable history of the early space program from the point of view of someone without a NACA background. If NASA reflected the triumph of technocracy as Walter A. McDougall argues in *. . . the Heavens and the Earth: A Political History of the Space Age* (New York: Basic Books, 1985), I found little evidence of the impact of this thinking on Lewis's management philosophy during the Apollo years. John Logsdon, *The Decision to Go to the Moon: Project Apollo and the National Interest* (Cambridge, Mass.: MIT Press, 1970) and Roger Bilstein, *Stages to Saturn: A Technological History of the Apollo/Saturn Launch Vehicles* (NASA SP-4206, 1980) helped me to understand the strategy of leap-frogging the Russians in the development of launch vehicles. Courtney G. Brooks, James M. Grimwood, and Lloyd S. Swenson, Jr., *Chariots for Apollo: A History of Manned Lunar Spacecraft* (NASA SP-4205, 1975) contains a useful discussion of the rendezvous decision, as does the recently published *Apollo: The Race to the Moon* by Charles Murray and Catherine Cox (New York: Simon and Schuster, 1989).

Interviews with present and former Lewis staff were often essential in helping me to understand complex technology. However, it was not always easy to weave events in individual careers into the larger story. These interviews can stand on their own as historical documents. They convey the enthusiasm of Lewis engineers for their work, and hopefully will provide insights for other historians. Most of my interviews were conducted at Lewis and taped. Those I transcribed are indicated by an asterisk.

Harrison Allen 3/20/85
G. Mervin Ault
Rudy Beheim 7/11/84
*Edmond Bisson 3/22/85
Don Buchele and Walton Howes 7/8/86
James Burnett 2/23/87
*Frederick C. Crawford 4/10/85 (TRW, Cleveland, Ohio)
*Robert English 7/15/86
*John Evvard 6/14/87 (Gilford, N.H.)
William Fleming 11/19/86 (Washington, D.C.)
*Stuart Fordyce 3/3/87
Robert Graham 2/27/85
*Jesse Hall 7/3/85
Melvin Hartmann 3/5/87
Seymour Lieblein 5/14/85
*Bruce Lundin 7/15/86
*William McNally 3/5/85 (North Royalton, Ohio)
*Herman Mark 3/12/85
Carl David Miller 9/12/84
*Wolfgang Moeckel 4/18/85
Charles Stanley Moore 8/9/84
James Modurelli 8/9/84
*Hans von Ohain 2/11/85 (Washington, D.C.)

*Walter T. Olson 7/17/84, 10/25/84

William Olsen

Paul Ordin 3/19/86 (Shaker Heights, Ohio)

*Simon Ostrach 9/29/87 (CWRU, Cleveland, Ohio)

*Ben Pinkel 8/4/85 (Santa Monica, Calif.)

*Irving Pinkel 1/30/85

Eli Reshotko (CWRU, Cleveland, Ohio)

*William H. Robbins 5/15/86, with Michal McMahon

*Larry Ross 2/3/87

*John Sanders 4/7/86

*Carl Schueller 10/12/84

Abe Silverstein 10/5/84, 10/2/85

*Harlan Simon 3/20/85

Ed Richley 2/24/87

John Stanitz (University Heights, Ohio)

*Peggy Yohner 3/21/85

LAND ACQUISITIONS AND NAME CHANGES

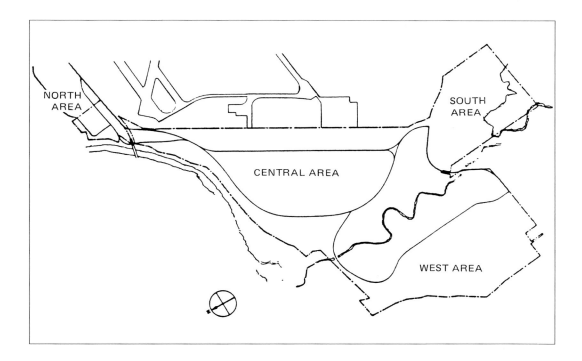

NORTH AREA

SOUTH AREA

CENTRAL AREA

WEST AREA

NASA Lewis Research Center is located on 351.32 acres of land in Cuyahoga County at the southwest boundary of the city of Cleveland, Ohio, adjacent to Cleveland Hopkins International Airport. Authorized by Act of Congress in June 1940, the National Advisory Committee for Aeronautics acquired the original parcel of land comprising 199.7 acres from the city in 1940 for $500. Ground was broken for the NACA Aircraft Engine Research Laboratory (AERL) on January 23, 1941. Research was initiated in May 1942. Formal Dedication Ceremonies were held on May 20, 1943. The laboratory was renamed the Flight Propulsion Research Laboratory on April 18, 1947, and the Lewis Flight Propulsion Laboratory (LFPL) on September 28, 1948 in honor of George W. Lewis. who had been the NACA director of aeronautical research from 1924 to 1947.

In 1952, to compensate for the loss of land no longer usable because of the expansion of the airport, the center acquired 9.8 acres known as the North Area in 1952 from the city of Cleveland. The Developmental Engineering Building (DEB) was constructed on this land in 1964.

In 1958, upon the formation of the National Aeronautics and Space Administration, the laboratory was renamed Lewis Research Center (LeRC). Between 1958 and 1962 the laboratory acquired an additional 139.7 acres, known as the West Area, located in the Rocky River Valley adjacent to the Rocky River Reservation, part of the Metro Parks System. Additional facilities were built in this area in the 1960s.

Between 1956 and 1977 Lewis managed the Plum Brook Station, near Sandusky, Ohio, about 50 miles from the center. Plum Brook Station was established to provide a more remote location for major facilities and test operations that were potentially hazardous, such as nuclear rocket testing. Originally known as the Plum Brook Army Ordnance Works, approximately 500 acres of land leased by the NACA from the U.S. Army in 1956 as the site for a nuclear reactor. By 1963 NASA had acquired ownership from the U. S. Army of the original parcel and additional land used for static tests of rocket systems. As of June 1968, NASA owned 5981 acres. Between 1969 and 1971 NASA purchased an additional 2100 acres to serve as a buffer zone. Because of the costs of the space shuttle, long-range development projects like nuclear and electric propulsion had to be curtailed. In 1973, NASA announced that Plum Brook, with its $200 million in facilities, would be closed. In 1977 Plum Brook was put on limited stand-by status, and the Space Power Complex was leased to the Garrett Corporation. In April 1983, about 1500 acres of land on the perimeter of the station were sold.

FACILITIES (1942–1987)

The first five buildings (Hangar, Engine Propeller Research Building, Fuels and Lubricants Building, Administration Building, and the Altitude Wind Tunnel) were included in the first appropriation by Congress in June 1940 (*Appendix to Congressional Record*, 11 June 1940, vol. 86, pt. 16, p. 3778). The entire appropriation was broken down as follows:

Item 1:	Power plant laboratory and shops	$3,950,000
Item 2:	Power plant wind tunnel	$3,100,000
Item 3:	Engine torque stands	$200,000
Item 4:	Fuels, lubricants, and instruments laboratory	$400,000
Item 5:	Hangar	$200,000
Item 6:	Administration Building	$250,000
Item 7:	Miscellaneous: heating, power, water supply, fences, fuel tanks	$300,000
		$8,400,000

The Icing Research Tunnel and the Jet Propulsion Static Laboratory were added during construction. The original seven buildings were completed by the end of World War II. Jet propulsion and rocket facilities were added during the NACA period, and it is clear that the designs of most of these facilities, many of which are currently in use, were developed from experience and expertise developed over time in smaller facilities.

The second large-scale building program at Lewis took place during the Apollo years and focused on nuclear rocket test facilities that were placed in operation at Plum Brook. In the 1970s expansion of facilities and new construction were at a virtual standstill. The closing of all the facilities at Plum Brook (with the exception of the operation of the large wind turbine) refocused attention on research facilities at Lewis in Cleveland. Further documentation of some of the smaller facilities can be found by consulting *Lewis Research Center: Master Facilities Plan 1985* (Whitley/Whitley, Inc.).

FLIGHT RESEARCH BUILDING (HANGAR–1942)

The hanger was built by the R. P. Carbone Construction Company to house various aircraft owned by or loaned to Lewis for flight research. The hangar is still in use.

ENGINE PROPELLER RESEARCH BUILDING (1942)

The contractor for the "Prop House" was also the R. P. Carbone Construction Company. Research on engine cowling and cooling, engine and propeller vibration, fuels and lubricants, carburetors, and engine installation problems was conducted in four 24-foot test cells, equipped to test engines of up to 4000 horsepower at sea level conditions. This was the first research facility to be completed. Research was formally initiated on May 8, 1942, in the "Prop House."

After jet engine research became the dominant concern of the laboratory, the building housed four test cells used for full-scale testing of jet engines. Under the supervision of the Materials and Thermodynamics Division, the effects of stress rupture, fatigue, and thermal shock were studied in alloys, cermets, and coatings under laboratory development. In 1958, it became the Electric Propulsion Research Building.

FUELS & LUBRICANTS BUILDING (1942)

Built by the James McHugh Company for research on aircraft engine fuels and lubricants, it originally consisted of 21 chemical laboratories, 16 physical laboratories and 13 small-scale test engines. Basic research in fuels and lubricants never stopped at Lewis. The building is still in use as the Chemistry Laboratory.

ALTITUDE WIND TUNNEL (1944)

This is historically the most important facility of the laboratory. Originally designed to test aircraft piston engines under simulated altitude operating conditions, the tunnel was adapted to test early turbojet and turboprop engines and ramjets. Tests provided data on the reliability and effectiveness of engine controls and afterburners and on the flow characteristics of inlet ducts and exhaust nozzles. Information could be obtained for the output, thrust, fuel consumption, and temperatures of both components under test and complete engine-propeller and propulsion-unit installations.

Contractor: Pittsburgh-Des Moines Steel Co.; Subcontractors: The Carrier Corp. (refrigeration system and heat exchanger); Collier Co. (electric systems and installations); General Electric Co. (drive motor and controls); York Ice Machine Co. (air dryer); Worthington Pump & Machinery Co. (exhausters); Toledo Scale Co. (balance equipment)

The Altitude Wind Tunnel was a closed circuit tunnel with a test section 20 feet in diameter. The tunnel drive consisted of a fan 31 feet in diameter, with a drive motor of 18,000 horsepower. It was capable of producing an air velocity as high as 425 miles per hour at simulated altitudes of 30,000 feet, down to a low of 250 miles per hour at 1000 feet. The Refrigeration Plant housed in a building next to the tunnel was designed and built by the Carrier Corporation. It contained 14 Carrier centrifugal compressors. A unique heat exchanger allowed the tunnel to be cooled to a minimum temperature of –48°F using freon-12 as the refrigerant. To prevent exhaust gases from entering the tunnel air stream, the tunnel was designed with a special air scoop. The contaminated air was treated in a special exhauster building adjacent to the tunnel.

At the time of construction, it was the only known wind tunnel specifically designed to test aircraft engines at simulated altitude conditions. With a test section large enough for both propeller and engine mount, tests in the tunnel assisted in solving cooling problems on the engine for the B-29; the first wind tunnel tests on American jet engine prototypes were conducted here.

Engines Tested

Bell YP-59A (I-16 engine), February–May 1944

Boeing B-29 (R-3350 engine), May–September 1944

Westinghouse 19B and 19XB Turbojet, September–November 1944

Douglas XTB2D-1 (4360 Engine) November–December 1944

GE TG-180 Engine and Afterburner Performance, January–February 1945; March–August 1946; September–December 1947

Lockheed YP-80A (I-40 Engine), March–May 1945

NACA Ram Jet (20''), May–June 1945; January–March 1946; August–November 1946

Lockheed TP80S (I-40 engine), July 1945

Republic YP-47M (Propeller Tests), August–October 1945

Lockheed XR-60 (4360 engine), November–December 1945

GE TG-100A Turboprop, November–December 1945; January 1946

Westinghouse X24C-4B engine, January–September 1947

Johns Hopkins Ram Jet (18''), January–February 1948

GE TG-180 (Engine and Afterburner Performance), February–April 1948

GE TG-180G Engine and Afterburners, June–December 1948; January 1949

NACA Ram Jet 16'' Free Jet, January–May 1949

GE TG-190 High Altitude Starting Test, June–September 1949

Armstrong-Siddeley Python Turboprop, September–December 1949

GE TG-190D, B-7, RX Engines Integrated Electronic Control Tests (347), January–June 1950

Westinghouse 24C-7 and C-8 Engine and Afterburner Performance and Cooling Tests, September–December 1950

Westinghouse 24 C-7 and C-8 Engine and Afterburner Performance and Cooling Tests, January–May 1951

Westinghouse J-40-WE6, September–December 1951; January–September 1952

Allison J-71, August–December 1952; January–February 1953

Allison T-38, March–November 1953

Pratt & Whitney J-57, November 1953–February 1955

Wright J-65, March–June 1955

Allison J-71, August–November 1955

Avon, January–November 1955

J-57 Noise Program, January–May 1957

Ace Piloted Ram Jet, May 1957–January 1958

Solid Rocket Test, February 1958; May 1958–February 1959

Liquid Hydrogen-Oxygen Rocket Test, September 1958–June 1959

One Axis Table, November 1958–June 1959

Storable Propellant, 1959 (entire year)

Space Capsule Mockup, 1959 (entire year)
Operation Dizzy in gimbal, Project Mercury, March–December 1959

[Source: Ronald J. Blaha, "Completed Schedules of NASA-Lewis Wind Tunnels, Facilities and Aircraft; 1944-1986" (February 1987)]

After the formation of NASA, the Altitude Wind Tunnel was converted to a vacuum facility to test rockets in 1958 and was used for spacecraft separation tests and the development of the Mercury retro-rockets. A "Gimbal rig" was installed for astronaut training in 1959. In the early 1960s the "space power chamber" was used to test the Centaur rocket. In the early 1980s, an effort to rehabilitate the tunnel for research on icing, and propeller-powered and vertical/stationary takeoff and landing (V/STOL) vehicles failed. At present, the grand old lady stands empty.

ICING RESEARCH TUNNEL (1944)

The Icing Tunnel owes its existence to the much larger and no longer used Altitude Wind Tunnel. Designed to share the refrigeration system of the Altitude Wind Tunnel, its purpose was and is to test various aircraft components under simulated icing conditions. The tunnel was designed as an atmospheric tunnel, with an 4160-horsepower electric motor to simulate speeds of 300 miles per hour in a 6-foot wide by 9-foot long test section. Air temperature can be varied from 30° to −45°F. It has its own heat exchanger, similar to the one that was designed by the Carrier Corporation for the Altitude Wind Tunnel. Its spray system, designed to simulate natural icing conditions, was inadequate until a unique vaporizing spray system was designed in about 1950 by H. Whitaker, H. Christensen, and G. Hennings. With reliable testing possible in the early 1950s, the tunnel contributed to the development of the hot-air anti-icing systems now in general use on jet aircraft.

After NASA came into being, the tunnel narrowly missed being closed down. However, in 1978, with increased emphasis on helicopters and general aviation aircraft and concern over fuel conservation, interest in icing problems reawakened and the icing program was reactivated. The tunnel underwent a major renovation in 1986.

It was designated an International Historic Mechanical Engineering Landmark by the American Society of Mechanical Engineers in 1987 for its unique heat exchanger and spray system. [Sources: "Icing Research Tunnel" brochure produced for the American Society of Mechanical Engineers landmark designation ceremony, 20 May 1987; George Gray, *Frontiers of Flight* (New York: Knopf, 1948), p. 316.]

ENGINE RESEARCH BUILDING (1942–1947)

Throughout the NACA period, the Engine Research Building (ERB) was the research heart of Lewis. The building consists of multipurpose flexible space covering 4.25 acres which can be adapted to changing research priorities. It is still in use for basic research on engine systems, components, fuels, lubricants, and seals.

At an initial cost of $9,033,000, the original equipment consisted of 30 single-cylinder test engines, 4 multicylinder test engines, 6 supercharger test stands, 4 gas turbine test stands, an altitude chamber for testing engine accessories, laboratories for the study of carburetors, ignition systems, automatic engine controls, piston rings, cylinder barrels, fuel injection systems, mixture ratio indicators, vibration and stress of engine parts, heat transfer, and waste heat recovery.

The Southwest Wing was added in 1944 for research on compressors and turbines for jet engines. The four altitude chambers in the "four burner area," completed in 1947, were designed by Ben Pinkel. They were the prototypes for the test chambers later constructed at Lewis and by industry. They were 10 feet wide by 60 feet long, with an air supply of 80 pounds per second. The first engine tested in this area was the Rolls Royce Nene to a simulated altitude of 64,000 feet in 1947-1948. No data on succeeding tests until 1953 were available.

The Sam W. Emerson Co. of Cleveland was responsible for the construction of the Engine Research Building in addition to the Administration Building, the Altitude Wind Tunnel Office Buildings, and the Gatehouse. Subcontractors included: Feldman Bros., plumbing process piping; Martien Electric Co., electrical systems; Roots Connersville Co., exhaust evacuators; York Ice Machinery Co., exhaust gas coolers; Buffalo Forge Co., cooling air fans; A.E. Magher Co., refrigerated air systems; Westinghouse, G.E., and Midwest Dynamometer & Engineering Corp., dynamometers; Dravo Corp., air compressors; Hagan Corp. and Republic Flow Meter Co., automatic controls. Charles Stanley Moore was the engineer in charge of its design.

Research Programs in Southwest Wing 23 Four Burner Area

J-65-B3 Inlet Airflow Distortion, December 1953–February 1954

J-65-B3 Performance, March–May 1954

J-65-B3 Inlet Airflow Distortion, May–August 1954

J-65-B3 High Ram Investigation, August 1954 with engine changes

J-47 Investigation with X-25 Fuel, September 1954 J-47-23; October 1954 J-47-17

J-47 Turbine Blade Temperature, October–December 1954

J-47 and A. B. Investigation with X-25 Fuel, January–March 1955

RA-14 Avon Investigation, March–October 1955

J-65-W4 Turbine Blade Investigation, November 1955–February 1956

J-65-W4 Flight Performance and Surge Investigation, February–March 1956

J-65-W5 X-35 Project Bee, April–November 1956

J-65-B3 Turbine Temperature Program, November 1956–February 1957

J-65-W16A Short Combustor Test with X-35 and Propane, February–May 1957

RE-3 Engine Combustor Tests, June 1957–March 1958

5000 lb. JP-4-GOX Rocket Cooling Test, June 1958–July 1959

Research Programs in Southwest Wing 24 Four Burner Area

J-47 F9F Ejector Investigation, November 1953–January 1954

J-47 Special Fuel Investigation, January–April 1954

J-71-A2 Engine and Afterburner Investigation, April 1954–April 1955

J-47 High Velocity Afterburner, April–September 1955

J-47 Air Cooled Turbine and X-35 Fuel, September–December 1955

J-47 Air Cooled Plug Nozzle, December 1955–February 1956

J-47-17 with x-35 Afterburner, March–September 1956

J-65 Zip Program, July–September 1956

J-65 W5 Bee Project Spare Heat Exchanger and Control, December 1956–February 1957

J-65-W4 Mach 3 with Water Injection, May 1957–March 1958

J-47 Hot Rod Engine, January 1957–March 1958

Ejector Test, May–August 1958

1000 lb. Rocket Engine Test, August 1958–March 1959

At present 200 test installations support Lewis's work on both terrestrial and space propulsion systems. The building houses laboratories for testing related to compressors, combustors, fuels, turbines, turboprops, bearings, seals, and lubricants.

8 × 6 SUPERSONIC WIND TUNNEL (1949)

The 8 × 6 Supersonic Wind Tunnel is used to study propulsion systems, including external studies of inlets and exit nozzles, combustion fuel injectors, flame holders, exit nozzles, and controls on ramjet and turbojet engines. It was originally designed as an open or non-return wind tunnel. Because the exhaust gases, air, and noise were vented to the outside, it was described as "an 87,000-horsepower bugle aimed at the heart of Cleveland!" [Donald D. Baals and William R. Corliss, *Wind Tunnels of NASA* (NASA SP-440, 1981), p. 53.] The noise from tunnel testing broke the windows of the Guerin House in the Rocky River Valley next to the laboratory site.

The name 8 × 6 refers to the size of the test section, which is 8 feet high, 6 feet wide, and 25 feet long. Speeds between Mach .55 and 2.1 (360 to 1387 miles per hour) with an altitude range from sea level to up to 40,000 feet are attainable. Flexible side walls alter the nozzle contour to control the Mach number at which the tunnel is operated. A seven-stage axial compressor is driven by three electric motors that yield a total of 87,000 horsepower. This compressor is located upstream from the test section.

Because the 150,000 pounds of air per minute taken from the atmosphere contained large amounts of moisture, large beds of activated alumina are necessary to dry the air prior to testing. At the conclusion of each run, heating to reactivate the alumina is necessary.

In 1950, because of excessive noise, resonator chambers were added to damp out sound frequencies from 5 to 11 cycles per second. A reinforced concrete muffler structure attenuates sounds of higher frequencies.

In 1956 a $2 million renovation made the tunnel capable of testing at transonic in addition to supersonic speeds. The test section was modified by boring 4700 holes to allow the air to "bleed" through the walls, thus eliminating the shocks and pressure disturbances at transonic speeds that caused "choking." (The concept of the slotted wall was pioneered at Langley.)

A return leg was later added so that the tunnel could be operated as either an open system during propulsion system tests, with large doors venting directly to the atmosphere, or as a closed loop during aerodynamic tests. In the late 1960s, a second 9 x 15 subsonic test section was added for use in testing scale models or propulsion systems for vertical and short takeoff and landing aircraft. For a list of tests conducted see Ronald J. Blaha, "Completed Schedules of NASA-Lewis Wind Tunnels, Facilities and Aircraft, 1944–1986" (February 1987).

MATERIALS AND STRUCTURES COMPLEX (1949)

This facility for basic research and development of materials has evolved with changing research priorities. Initially it was used to investigate alloys and "cermets" (composites of ceramics and metals) to be used in turbines of jet engines, where temperatures are the hottest. In conjunction with developing interest in nuclear propulsion, a cyclotron was acquired from General Electric in 1949 to investigate the problems of embrittlement of materials after radiation. Research tools currently include a metallographic electron microscope, tensile and fatigue laboratories, electron beam welders, a 100-ton extrusion press, and a 30,000° arc plasma heat source for applying coatings and evaluating materials. A 69-inch cyclotron can accelerate all light ions to variable energies to a maximum of 90 MeV. It is currently being used for cancer research and patient therapy through the Cleveland Clinic.

PROPULSION SYSTEMS LABORATORY (1952, 1969)

The purpose of the Propulsion Systems Laboratory is to test full-scale turbojet, ramjet, and rocket engines under simulated altitude conditions. The prototypes for the test chambers of the Propulsion Systems Laboratory were designed by Ben Pinkel and placed in operation in 1947 in the Southwest Wing of the Engine Research Building, known as the four burner area. In 1952, in response to the need to test larger engines, the Propulsion Systems Laboratory (PSL) 1 and 2, each 24 feet long and 14 feet in diameter, were built on Walcott Road and were used between 1952 and 1979. In 1969 PSL 3 and 4, 40 feet long and 25 feet in diameter, were added at the present site of the Propulsion Systems Laboratory. The present laboratory can accommodate engines with as much as 100,000 pounds of thrust. Unlike wind tunnel tests, only the engines, not the engine cowlings or mounts, can be tested in these chambers.

PSL 3 and 4 had their own computer processing system between 1972 and 1983. It was built around the SEL 8600 computer system, which could monitor 1600 voltage and pressure scanner inputs and 35 words of discrete inputs. The facility also supported five alphanumeric displays. Data were then carried to the IBM 360/370 for final processing.

10 × 10 SUPERSONIC TUNNEL (1955)

At a cost of $32,856,000, this tunnel was built under the National Unitary Wind Tunnels Plan, by Act of Congress, October 27, 1949. It was designed by Eugene Wasielewski as a continuous-flow tunnel to operate at speeds between Mach 2.0 and 3.5 (1320 to 2311 miles per hour) at altitudes ranging from 50,000 to 150,000 feet. It can be used either as a closed-circuit tunnel for aerodynamic tests or an open-end cycle for combustion propulsion research. The main compressor is driven by four 37,500-horsepower electric motors. A secondary compressor requires three 33,334-horsepower motors. The flexible wall of the test section, composed of highly polished stainless steel plates, 10 feet wide, 76 feet long, 1 3/8 inch thick, is controlled by a series of hydraulic jacks.

The 10 × 10 tunnel was intended to supplement the work of the 8 × 6 Supersonic Wind Tunnel at speeds between Mach 2 and 3.5. Altitude pressure simulation can be varied from 50,000 to 150,000 feet. It is particularly useful for testing full-size and scale models of supersonic ramjets, turbojets, and components for aircraft and missile applications.

One of the problems that had to be overcome in the design of a supersonic tunnel to be used for engine testing was that, as the air expanded in the nozzle during acceleration to supersonic speeds, it cooled rapidly, causing condensation of the water vapor in the air. In addition to passing the intake air over activated alumina to a dewpoint of –40°F in the air dryer, an air heater had to be added upstream. Nevertheless, not all the problems unique to engine testing have been solved: "The tunnel nozzle expands the air a bit too far at the higher Mach numbers, and it is impossible to simulate altitudes below 55,000 feet where the air is more dense." [Donald D. Baals and William R. Corliss, *Wind Tunnels of NASA* (NASA SP-440, 1981), p. 70]

The first test of the General Electric J-79 engine for the first U.S. supersonic bomber, the Convair B-58 Hustler, proved extremely useful. R. H. Widmer, Assistant Chief Engineer of the Convair Division of the General Dynamics Corporation, wrote, "Almost needless to say, we consider this test a major milestone in the B-58 program. It has given us reasonable assurance that there is no significant coupling of the engine and inlet automatic control systems. It has given us dependable data on buzz limits of our inlet. And it has shown that the results should not be severe, if the B-58 is inadvertently operated in the buzz region. Based on results of this test, we have made some significant changes in the inlet control system. The net result of the above is that we can proceed into supersonic flight testing of the B-58 with a great deal more confidence, and with the knowledge that some very costly and time-consuming flight testing has been avoided." (Letter quoted in *Wing Tips*, 16 January 1957)

The CADDE I (Central Automatic digital data encoder) was located in this tunnel. This system translated the data from the test section to binary-coded decimal numbers, which were recorded on magnetic tape, reduced by an electronic computer, and transmitted to the control room of the tunnel.

In the late 1960s the Quiet Fan Test Facility, an outdoor test stand capable of supporting an aircraft engine fan that operates at speeds of up to 47,000 revolutions per minute, was added.

For a complete list of tests, see Roland J. Blaha, "Completed Schedules of NASA-Lewis Wind tunnels, Facilities and Aircraft, 1944-1986" (February 1986).

ROCKET ENGINE TEST FACILITY (1957)

Because of the possible danger involved in the storage and handling of cryogenic liquid propellants, the Rocket Engine Test Facility Complex was built on 10 acres in the South Area, where it is separated by a buffer of empty land from what is called the "Central Area" of the center. The purpose of the Rocket Engine Test Facility is to test full-scale hydrogen-fluorine and hydrogen-oxygen rocket thrust chambers at chamber pressures to 2100 psia and thrust levels to 20,000 pounds. Work on the design of the facility began in 1954 under the auspices of the Rocket Branch of the Fuels and Combustion Research Division.

As early as 1944, rocket testing had been carried on in four cinder block test cells. These were supplemented by four larger test cells built in the early 1950s. In 1952 the laboratory bought a hydrogen liquefier, and a smaller prototype for the present facility was built in this area.

The new Rocket Engine Test Facility, built at a cost of $2.5 million and completed in 1957, includes two major buildings and several support service buildings. Test Stand A was designed for sea-level testing of vertically mounted rocket engines that exhaust into an exhaust gas scrubber and muffler. The A stand has a capability of testing engines with chamber pressures up to 4300 psia and thrust levels up to 50,000 pounds.

Test Stand B, designed by Anthony Fortini and Vearl N. Huff in 1959 but not built at Lewis until after 1980, can test horizontally mounted rocket engines exhausting into an exhaust diffuser, cooler, and a nitrogen-driven two-stage ejector system. The B stand, for altitude testing in a space environment, has the capability of testing engines with chamber pressures up to 1000 psia and thrust levels up to 1500 pounds.

The support systems include storage dewars for cryogenic fuels and a large water reservoir. Smaller buildings include a block house for observation, a pump house, a helium compressor shelter, and a liquid hydrogen pump vaporizer shelter. In 1984 the facility was modified to provide the capability for testing extremely large area ratio nozzles (to 1000:1).

The facility has been designated a National Historic Landmark because of its significant role in the development of liquid hydrogen as a rocket fuel. It was used in the development of the Pratt & Whitney RL 10 engine for the Centaur rocket and the J-2 engine, with its 200,000-pound thrust, for the second stage of the Saturn V rocket. The hydrogen-oxygen engines currently used by the Space Shuttle were also tested in this facility.

For additional source information, see John L. Sloop, *Liquid Hydrogen as a Propulsion Fuel, 1945-1959* (NASA SP-4404, 1978); Wayne Thomas, "Description of the Rocket Engine Test Facility" (unpublished Report, Lewis Research Center, 1984); and James F. Connors and Robert G. Hoffman, "The Aerospace Technology Laboratory (A Perspective, Then and Now)," NASA Technical Memorandum 82754. For information on the design of Test Stand B, see Anthony Fortini, TNB-257-1959, TM 5-14-59E, May 1959, TMX-100, September 1959.

DEVELOPMENTAL ENGINEERING BUILDING (1964)

The Developmental Engineering Building was conceived and built during the Apollo era. According to laboratory lore, its K-shaped design honors John F. Kennedy. Completed in May 1964, it provided office space for 800 engineers. An L-shaped annex completed in October 1964 could accommodate an additional 300 engineers.

ELECTRIC PROPULSION LABORATORY (1961)

The Electric Propulsion Laboratory, now in use, supplemented the early work on electric propulsion carried out in the old Engine Propeller Research Building. Its purpose is to test electric thrusters, spacecraft, and related equipment at an altitude range of several hundred miles with simulated near vacuum space environmental conditions.

It consists of two large vacuum chambers. The smaller is 63 feet long and 15 feet in diameter. This chamber can simulate environmental conditions encountered by a space vehicle as it travels from lift-off to altitudes of over 100 miles. The larger chamber is 70 feet long and 25 feet in diameter and can simulate altitudes up to 300 miles. It is lined with cryogenic condensers that operate at –300°F.

ENERGY CONVERSION LABORATORY (1962)

During the Apollo years, the Energy Conversion Laboratory was used for advanced study of energy conversion and photovoltaic applications for space vehicles. In the 1970s, when the energy crisis turned dominant research concerns away from space toward limited earth resources, research was directed toward ground-based energy systems, including improved solar cells for electric vehicles, environmental monitoring systems for air and water pollution, and thermionic and heat pipe applications.

ZERO GRAVITY RESEARCH FACILITY (1966)

Designed for the study of components, combustion, and the behavior of liquids and gases under low acceleration or near zero gravity conditions, the present Zero Gravity Research Facility was preceded by a series of experimental facilities, beginning with the elevator shafts of the Terminal Tower Building. The first so-called "drop tower" was constructed in 1956. At an initial cost of $3,370,000, the present facility consists of a concrete-lined shaft that extends 506 feet into the ground, within which a steel vacuum test chamber 20 feet in diameter and 460 feet high has been placed. The pressure before a test is reduced to 13.3 newtons per square meter. Two modes of operation are possible. One is to let the test object free fall, resulting in about 5.15 seconds of near weightlessness. The second is to propel the object under experiment upward from the bottom of the chamber, then let it fall back into the styrofoam bed at the bottom. This nearly doubles the time of weightlessness to 10 seconds.

In a study of significant landmarks in the development of manned space flight, Harry Butowsky stated in "Man in Space National Historic Landmark Theme Study," May 1984:

> The Zero Gravity Facility is significant because it is the only such facility in NASA's inventory that can study the behavior of liquids in a low gravity environment . . . Information concerning liquid sloshing which can change the center of mass of a space vehicle and thus effect vehicle stability and control is absolutely essential to the successful performance of liquid high-energy space vehicles such as the Centaur and Saturn upper-stages. The study of the effects of liquid sloshing on the performance of upper stage liquid rockets was therefore essential to the successful completion of the objectives of the American Space Program . . . Research and data developed here involving the physics of liquids in a zero-gravity environment was indispensable to the successful development of these high-energy liquid fueled rockets.

RESEARCH AND ANALYSIS CENTER (1979–1980)

During the retrenchment period of the 1970s the Research and Analysis Center (RAC) was the only major new facility to be built at Lewis. This centralized computer facility housed the Univac 1100/42, purchased in 1975. Lewis acquired the IBM 370/3033 in 1980, the largest general purpose computer then available. This system, which replaced the IBM 360/67 in use since 1966, made possible interactive calculations, graphics, and large analytical studies. Although interactive computing started in 1955, when the CADDE I system was placed in the 8 × 6 Supersonic Wind Tunnel, the RAC Building has facilitated the shift to the current emphasis on this "interactive" or "open" computer philosophy, as opposed to the classical "batch" type or "closed shop" of previous computer operations.

The first computing equipment was a "differential analyzer" used to reduce icing data, probably acquired in 1949. Electronic, as opposed to mechanical, computing began in the mid-1950s with the purchase of the IBM 604. Prior to the purchase of the CADDE system, test data were processed from large manometer boards, which contained tubes of mercury to record pressures. Photographs were taken of the manometer boards, then the film was developed and the information transferred to IBM cards. The time lag between completion of testing and reduction of data was usually three weeks.

List of Batch-Type Computer systems (not inclusive)

Differential Analyzer, 1949

IBM 601, in use 1954-1956. A "mechanical" type system with mechanical storage, the IBM 601 was programmed through a wire board with output to cards. It processed at a speed of 10 instructions per second. It was used in business data processing and later to process test data.

IBM 604, in use 1955-1957. The first "electronic" type calculator at Lewis, the IBM 604 was programmed through a wiring panel. Input was entered on punched cards, which were read into a card reader. It was used in the 8 x 6 supersonic wind tunnel.

Card Program Calculator (CPC), 1954-1956. Used to process scientific data, the CPC was programmed by cards, which eliminated the need for the wire board.

OODAC (Our Own Doggone Automatic Calculator), 1956-1957. Designed at Lewis by the instruments division to meet specific needs, it was a modification of an IBM 604 and was used to process paper tape data.

3 IBM 650 Magnetic Drum Data Processing Machines, acquired between 1955 and 1957, used until the early 1960s. They were used to handle analytical calculations and in a few cases data reduction. The computer speed was 150 instructions per second.

Sperry Rand Univac 1103, in use 1955-1966. A vacuum tube computer, input was by means of paper tape, with output printed on flexiwriters. Because all experimental data processing was handled by the Univac 1103, it was the most important system for the laboratory during this period. Several languages for this system were developed at Lewis to adapt it to specific requirements.

During the Apollo era, the laboratory acquired additional computing capability through the addition of the IBM 704, IBM 7090, and IBM 1401 and the addition of direct couple systems for use in analytical processing.

Cray 1S/2200, 1982-1985

Cray X/MP-24, acquired 1985

Interactive Systems (not inclusive)

CADDE I (Central Automatic Digital Data Encoder). In use from 1955 to 1968, CADDE was the first centralized computer system at Lewis and the first to record data on magnetic tape (quarter inch). It replaced the old system of processing data using banks of manometers, which were then photographed and data reduced by female "computers." After the film was developed, the information had to be transferred to IBM cards for processing. Although it had four tape drives, it could only record data from one facility at a time. It served the 10 × 10 Supersonic Wind Tunnel and four additional facilities. The system could provide feedback of data during a test, making it possible to modify a test in progress. Computations were available in the control room 30 seconds after the data were taken in the test section. Data were recorded from Automatic Voltage Digitizers (AVDs) and from a Lewis-built Digital Automatic Multiple Pressure Recorder (DAMPR) system.

CADDE II, in use from 1968 to 1980, could record at rates up to 100 samples per second and could record data from three facilities concurrently. It served 63 facilities.

IBM 360/67, in use from 1966 to 1980

IBM 370/3033, acquired 1980

POWER SYSTEMS FACILITY (1989)

Ground was broken for the Power Systems Facility in February 1986. The first new building at Lewis since the RAC building was completed in 1980, the $6.1 million facility is intended for research and development of the power system for the space station. This will include the development and integrated testing of both photovoltaic and solar dynamic power systems.

PLUM BROOK STATION, SANDUSKY, OHIO

Located about 50 miles from Lewis, the facilities at Lewis's Plum Brook Station consisted of an Engineering Office Building and large facilities for full-scale testing of rockets (mainly nuclear) and their components. Various storage and pumping facilities for handling cryogenic fuels were also located here.

The station included about twelve to fourteen smaller research facilities, for example, the Cryogenic Propellant Research Facility, the High Energy Rocket Engine Research Facility, the Nuclear Rocket Dynamics and Control Facility (1959; see description in *Orbit*, 31 July 1959), the E Site Dynamics Research Facility (1960), and the Altitude Rocket Test Facility (B-1) (1961). Plum Brook had a staff of approximately 500 people.

Nuclear Research Reactor Facility (1956–1961)

The original purpose of the reactor facility, designed by Ben Pinkel, was for research associated with aircraft nuclear propulsion. However, when the facility was completed in 1959, the interest in aircraft nuclear propulsion had waned. Instead, research was directed to support the development of a nuclear rocket, in particular, the effect of radiation on materials. As *Orbit*, the laboratory newspaper, stated in its 14 August 1959 issue:

> The primary objective of the Nuclear Research Reactor Facility is to provide the means for making the various types of investigations needed to assist the development of the space vehicle reactor. These include pumped loop studies of the performance and behavior of fuel elements and other reactor components; effects of radiation on reactor materials and the interaction between reactor materials; the effect of radiation on vehicle structure, fluids, and equipment; shield studies; and nuclear physics and solid state physics experiments pertinent to the development of the space vehicle reactor.

The 60-megawatt reactor was a modification of the Atomic Energy Commission's Materials Testing Reactor at the National Reactor Testing Station in Idaho. It is composed of a graphite-uranium core. The core is approximately a 30-inch cube, which holds 27 fuel elements of an enriched uranium-aluminum alloy. The core is contained in a pressure tank shielded by special heavy-density concrete. Additional shielding is provided by a pool of water divided into four quadrants. Movable bridges permit access to the concrete platform near the top of the pressure tank. Further containment is provided by a cylindrical steel tank. A system of water canals 25 feet deep were used to move radioactive test materials from the reactor to storage areas and to the seven hot cells in the associated hot laboratory.

Planning began in 1954. Authorized by Congress May 23, 1955 (P.L. 44, 84th Congress), the selection of the site was announced on September 20, 1955, after a survey of 19 locations by Nuclear Development Associates. Ground was broken on September 26, 1956. Construction was completed in 1961. An Atomic Energy Commission provisional operating license was granted on March 14, 1961, and on June 14 the reactor became operational. Full capacity was reached on April 21, 1963. A ten-year operating license was granted by the Atomic Energy Commission on April 12, 1965. The initial cost was $14,536,000.

In 1973 the reactor was shut down. The facility is currently leased to the Garrett Corporation.

(For specific accomplishments, see J. B. Barkley, Jr., "Significant Experiences of the NASA Plum Brook Reactor Facility," NASA TM X-52491, 1968.)

Hot Hydrogen Heat Transfer Facility (1966)

Authorized in 1962 for research on nuclear rocket nozzles and their components, the facility consisted of a heat exchanger to supply hot hydrogen gas to simulate the temperatures of a nuclear rocket reactor. It consisted of an induction-heated, graphite pebble bed heater capable of temperatures of 3500°F. In 1971 the facility was converted to a hypersonic tunnel by the addition of a heat ejector and three 42-inch water-cooled nozzles for Mach 5, 6, and 7 operation. [Source: Donald D. Baals and William R. Corless, *Wind Tunnels of NASA* (NASA SP-440, 1981), p. 98–99]

Spacecraft Propulsion Research Facility (1968)

Intended for hot firings of full-scale launch vehicles under space vacuum and thermal conditions, the Spacecraft Propulsion Research (B-2) Facility simulated orbital altitudes of 100 miles for periods of up to two weeks. The test building is approximately 70 feet high and extends below ground about 176 feet. It could accommodate launch vehicles 22 feet in diameter and 50 feet high. The first test in the facility was hot firing of two RL-10 engines to modernize the Centaur vehicle. Testing of the NERVA (Nuclear Engine for Rocket Vehicle Application) propellant feed system was also carried on here. In June 1974 it was placed on standby status.

It was nominated for the National Register of Historic Places in May 1984. See Harry Butowsky, "Man in Space National Historic Landmark Theme Study."

Space Power Facility (1969)

The facility is essentially a very large vacuum tank to provide a space environment for the study of nuclear propulsion. At the time it was built, it was the largest in the world. The test chamber itself is 100 feet in diameter and 122 feet high, making a high-vacuum volume of 800,000 cubic feet available. It was designed to include the capability for the ground test of advanced nuclear-electric space power systems. For this reason it is surrounded by a concrete shell 6 to 7 feet in thickness. Nuclear reactors at power levels up to 15 MW (thermal) can be safely operated in the test chamber. Major programs: Skylab Shroud Separation Tests, Isoe Brayton Conversion Technology, Centaur/Viking Shroud Qualification, Reactor Brayton Conversion Technology, High Voltage Solar Array and Spacecraft Technology. Placed on stand-by in 1975, the Space Power Facility is currently undergoing rehabilitation for use in the space station program.

MANAGEMENT STRUCTURE

THE NACA PERIOD: 1942–1958

George Lewis did not believe in organization charts, which he regarded as excessively bureaucratic. Lewis Laboratory during the NACA period had no formal organizational charts, although complete lists of personnel and their assigned jobs exist for January 1942 and December 1949.

In January 1942 the organizational structure was divided into two parts: administrative, under Edward R. Sharp, Construction Administrator, and construction under Ernest G. Whitney, Senior Mechanical Engineer. Sharp was named Manager in December 1942 and Director in 1947, a position that he held through the transition to NASA. He retired in December 1960 and died in July 1961.

January 1943, four research divisions organized:
Fuels and Lubricants Division, Addison Rothrock
Thermodynamics Division, Ben Pinkel
Engine Installation Division, E. G. Whitney
Engine Research Division, C. S. Moore

March 1943, Engine Research Division divided into:
Engine Components Research Division, C. S. Moore
Engine Research Division, John H. Collins

April 1943, Engineering Services Division, Charles A. Herrmann
Flight Research Division, Joseph Vensel

July 1943, Supercharger Division, Oscar Schey

October 1943, Engine Installation Division, Abe Silverstein

First Major Reorganization, October 1945

Manager: Edward Sharp
Chief of Research: Addision Rothrock
Executive Engineer: Carlton Kemper

Fuels and Thermodynamics Division, Ben Pinkel
    Fuels, Louis Gibbons
    Combustion, Ted Olson
    Thermodynamics, Eugene Manganiello

Compressor and Turbine Division, Oscar Schey
    Basic, Frank Marble
    Applied, Robert O. Bullock

Engine Performance and Materials, John Collins
    Operation and controls, Arnold E. Biermann
    Engine Performance Branch, John C. Sanders
    Materials, Milton C. Shaw

Wind Tunnels and Flight Division, Abe Silverstein
    Icing, Willson Hunter
    Flight, Joseph Vensel
    Altitude Wind Tunnel, Alfred W. Young
    Supersonic Wind Tunnels, Louis Monroe

    Assistants to Division Chief
        John C. Evvard
        William Perl
        Irv Pinkel
        Newell D. Sanders

In August 1949 Abe Silverstein became Chief of Research to fill the vacancy created by the transfer of Addison M. Rothrock to the NACA Headquarters office. Eugene J. Manganiello was appointed Assistant to Silverstein, and Jesse H. Hall was designated "Staff Assistant to the Chief of Research." Carlton Kemper, Executive Engineer, was reassigned to the Office of the Chief of Research to report to Silverstein. All research divisions were placed under the immediate supervision of Silverstein. In a memo dated December 21, 1949, Silverstein stated, "To clarify the line organization of the research divisions, the line of command for laboratory research operation is authorized to pass through and only through the Chief of Research, Abe Silverstein, Assistant Chief of Research, Eugene J. Manganiello, and from there through the Division, Branch, Section and any group leadership."

John Collins was appointed Assistant Chief of Research for Coordination, Intelligence, and Liaison. Ben Pinkel and Oscar Schey were also designated Assistant Chiefs of Research.

Second Major Reorganization, October 1949

Compressor and Turbine Division, Oscar Schey, Chief

Engine Research Division, Eugene Wasielewski, Chief
    Bruce Lundin, Assistant Chief

Fuels and Combustion Division, Walter T. Olson, Chief
    Louis C. Gibbons, Associate Chief
    Henry Barnett, Assistant Chief

Materials and Thermodynamics Division, Ben Pinkel, Chief

Physics Division, Newell D. Sanders, Chief
   I. Irving Pinkel, Associate Chief

Supersonic Propulsion Division, J. C. Evvard, Chief
   D. D. Wyatt, Assistant Chief

Minor Reorganizations During the NACA Period

The office of Chief of Research was abolished and Silverstein became Associate Director in 1952; Eugene Manganiello became Assistant Director.

In December 1954, the Supersonic Propulsion Division was expanded to include the Special Projects Branch, 8 x 6 Supersonic Tunnel Branch, the Operations Branch, and the 10 x 10 Supersonic Tunnel Branch.

On December 22, 1955, the Flight Problems Research Division was created under I. Irving Pinkel. I. A. Johnsen and E. E. Bisson were appointed Assistant Division Chiefs.

After Ben Pinkel, Chief of the Materials and Thermodynamics Research Division, left to join the Rand Corporation in August 1956, his division was divided into the Materials and Structures Research Division and the Nuclear Reactor Research Division.

Organization Under NASA: 1958-1977

The first chart under the new NASA structure was prepared under Sharp as director in March 1959. Although the laboratory was renamed Lewis Research Center, there was considerable continuity between the NACA and NASA management structure until December 1961. A new organizational chart prepared by Abe Silverstein after his return from Headquarters clearly shows the new division between research and development. The 1963 chart shows the projects added to the development side.

Bruce Lundin became Director in 1969, but the real organization changes do not show up until 1973, when nuclear research was terminated. Charts for 1959, 1961, 1963, 1968, and 1973 are included to show changes in organization under the NASA structure.

NASA–LEWIS ORGANIZATION CHART 1947

EXECUTIVE ENGINEER
C. Kemper — Adm.

MANAGER
E. R. Sharp — Adm.

SERVICE DEPT.
C. A. Herrmann — Adm.

MECHANICAL SERVICES DIVISION
W. E. Dewey

ENGINEERING SERVICES DIVISION
C. S. Moore — ERB

BUILDINGS AND GROUNDS DIVISION
B. G. Gulick — Util.

FABRICATION DIVISION

INSTRUMENT DIVISION
R. E. Tozier — TSB

ADMINISTRATIVE DEPT.
E. C. Braig, Jr. — Adm.

BUDGET OFFICE
W. J. McCann — Adm.

FISCAL DIVISION
C. H. Dawson — Adm.

PROCUREMENT DIVISION
J. R. Braig — Adm.

PERSONNEL DIVISION
J. D. Tousignant — Adm.

CHIEF OF RESEARCH (DEPT.)
A. M. Rothrock — Adm.

COMPRESSOR AND TURBINE RES. DIVISION
O. W. Schey — Adm.

ENGINE PERFORMANCE AND MATERIALS DIVISION
J. H. Collins, Jr. — Adm.

FUELS AND THERMODYNAMICS RES. DIVISION
B. Pinkel — Adm.

WIND TUNNEL AND FLIGHT DIVISION
A. Silverstein — Adm.

NASA–LEWIS ORGANIZATION CHART 1952 (HYPOTHETICAL)

EXECUTIVE ENGINEER
C. Kemper

DIRECTOR
E. R. Sharp

SECURITY OFFICER
H. B. Bracey

CHIEF OF RESEARCH
A. Silverstein

ASST. CHEIF OF RESEARCH
E. J. Manganiello

ASST. FOR PLANNING & LIAISON
J. H. Collins, Jr.

COMPRESSOR & TURBINE RESEARCH DIVISION
O. W. Schey

ENGINE RESEARCH DIVISION
E. W. Wasielewski

FUELS & COMBUSTION RESEARCH DIVISION
W. T. Olson

MATERIALS & THERMODYNAMICS RES. DIVISION
B. Pinkel

PHYSICS DIVISION
N. D. Sanders, I. I. Pinkel

SUPERSONIC PROPULSION DIVISION
J. C. Evvard

ADMINISTRATIVE DIVISION
J. D. Tousignant

BUDGET OFFICE
V. Gordon

FISCAL DIVISION
E. J. Baxter

CONTRACTOR & CONSTRUCTION ADMINISTRATOR
J. R. Braig

CONTRACT ADMINISTRATION DIVISION
M. V. Organ

PROCUREMENT DIVISION
W. Dey Jr.

PERSONNEL DIVISION
J. S. Brown

RESEARCH REPORTS DIVISION
B. Mulcahey

ENGINEERING DIVISION
W. J. McCann

ENGINEERING DRAFTING
L. J. Stitt

ELECTRICAL ENGINEERING DIVISION
K. D. Brumbagh

MECHANICAL ENGINEERING DIVISION
H. Kottas

FACILITIES ENGINEERING DIVISION
B. G. Gulick

TECHNICAL SERVICES DIVISION
C. A. Herrmann

ASST. FOR PLANNING
C. S. Moore

MECHANICAL SERVICES DIVISION
S. V. Kramer

ELECTRICAL OPERATIONS DIVISION
W. Maxim

FABRICATION DIVISION
W. E. Dewey

MECHANICAL OPERATIONS DIVISION
T. M. McComb

PLANT OPERATIONS DIVISION
J. E. Everett

NASA–LEWIS ORGANIZATION CHART 1959

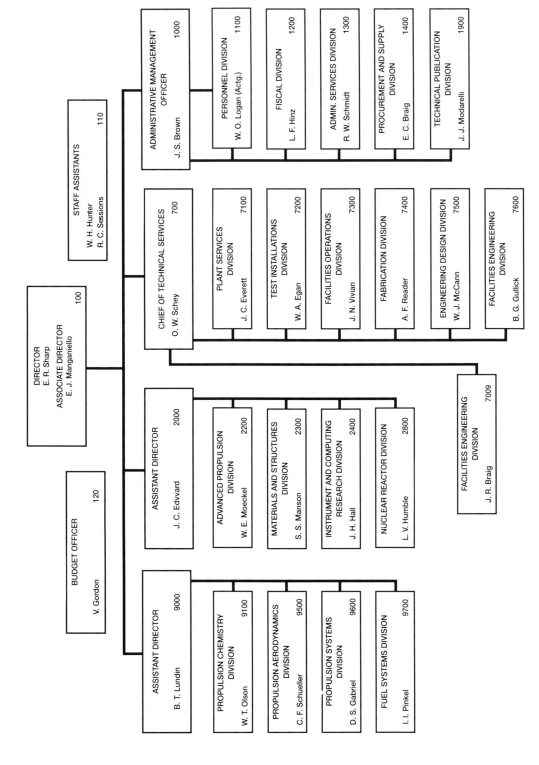

DIRECTOR
E. R. Sharp
ASSOCIATE DIRECTOR
E. J. Manganiello
100

BUDGET OFFICER
V. Gordon
120

STAFF ASSISTANTS
W. H. Hunter
R. C. Sessions
110

ADMINISTRATIVE MANAGEMENT OFFICER
J. S. Brown
1000

PERSONNEL DIVISION
W. O. Logan (Actg.)
1100

FISCAL DIVISION
L. F. Hinz
1200

ADMIN. SERVICES DIVISION
R. W. Schmidt
1300

PROCUREMENT AND SUPPLY DIVISION
E. C. Braig
1400

TECHNICAL PUBLICATION DIVISION
J. J. Modarelli
1900

CHIEF OF TECHNICAL SERVICES
O. W. Schey
700

PLANT SERVICES DIVISION
J. C. Everett
7100

TEST INSTALLATIONS DIVISION
W. A. Egan
7200

FACILITIES OPERATIONS DIVISION
J. N. Vivian
7300

FABRICATION DIVISION
A. F. Reader
7400

ENGINEERING DESIGN DIVISION
W. J. McCann
7500

FACILITIES ENGINEERING DIVISION
B. G. Gullick
7600

FACILITIES ENGINEERING DIVISION
J. R. Braig
7009

ASSISTANT DIRECTOR
J. C. Edvvard
2000

ADVANCED PROPULSION DIVISION
W. E. Moeckel
2200

MATERIALS AND STRUCTURES DIVISION
S. S. Manson
2300

INSTRUMENT AND COMPUTING RESEARCH DIVISION
J. H. Hall
2400

NUCLEAR REACTOR DIVISION
L. V. Humble
2800

ASSISTANT DIRECTOR
B. T. Lundin
9000

PROPULSION CHEMISTRY DIVISION
W. T. Olson
9100

PROPULSION AERODYNAMICS DIVISION
C. F. Schueller
9500

PROPULSION SYSTEMS DIVISION
D. S. Gabriel
9600

FUEL SYSTEMS DIVISION
I. I. Pinkel
9700

NASA–LEWIS ORGANIZATION CHART 1961

DIRECTOR
Abe Silverstein
DEPUTY DIRECTOR
E.J. Manganiello
ASST TO THE DIRECTOR
J.E. Connors

BUDGET OFFICER
V. Gordon

PLUM BROOK STATION DIRECTOR
A.D. Johnson

DEVELOPMENT ASSOCIATE DIRECTOR
B.T. Lundin

RELIABILITY AND QUALITY ASSURANCE
R.R. Godman, Chief
E.F. Baehr, Asst. Chief

ADVANCED DEVELOPMENT AND EVALUATION
D.S. Gabriel, Chief
B. Lubarsky, Asst. Chief

PROJECT MANAGEMENT
I.A. Johnsen, Chief
J.H. Childs, Asst. Chief

DEVELOPMENT PLANS AND PROGRAMS
C.F. Schueller, Chief

NUCLEAR REACTOR
L.V. Humble, Chief

SYSTEMS ENGINEERING AND REQUIREMENTS
H.M. Henneberry, Chief

MATERIALS AND STRUCTURES
S.S. Manson, Chief
G.M. Ault, Asst. Chief

RESEARCH ASSOCIATE DIRECTOR
E.J. Manganiello
DEPUTY ASSOCIATE DIRECTOR
J.C. Evvard

RESEARCH PLAN AND PROGRAMS
S.C. Himmel, Chief

INSTRUMENT AND COMPUTING
J.H. Hall, Chief
R.E. Tozier, Asst. Chief

FLUID SYSTEM COMPONENTS
I.I. Pinkel, Chief
E.E. Bisson, Asst. Chief

TECHNICAL SERVICES
O.W. Schey, Chief
C.A. Herrmann, Assoc. Chief

ADMINISTRATION ASSISTANT DIRECTOR
H.C. Barnett

ELECTROMAGNETIC PROPULSION
W.E. Moeckel, Chief

CHEMISTRY AND ENERGY CONVERSION
W.T. Olson, Chief

NASA–LEWIS ORGANIZATION CHART 1963

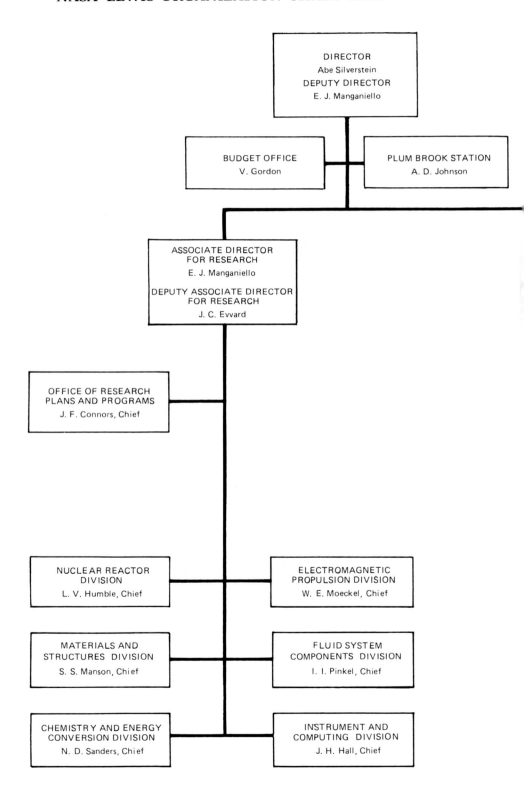

DIRECTOR
Abe Silverstein
DEPUTY DIRECTOR
E. J. Manganiello

BUDGET OFFICE
V. Gordon

PLUM BROOK STATION
A. D. Johnson

ASSOCIATE DIRECTOR
FOR RESEARCH
E. J. Manganiello

DEPUTY ASSOCIATE DIRECTOR
FOR RESEARCH
J. C. Evvard

OFFICE OF RESEARCH
PLANS AND PROGRAMS
J. F. Connors, Chief

NUCLEAR REACTOR
DIVISION
L. V. Humble, Chief

ELECTROMAGNETIC
PROPULSION DIVISION
W. E. Moeckel, Chief

MATERIALS AND
STRUCTURES DIVISION
S. S. Manson, Chief

FLUID SYSTEM
COMPONENTS DIVISION
I. I. Pinkel, Chief

CHEMISTRY AND ENERGY
CONVERSION DIVISION
N. D. Sanders, Chief

INSTRUMENT AND
COMPUTING DIVISION
J. H. Hall, Chief

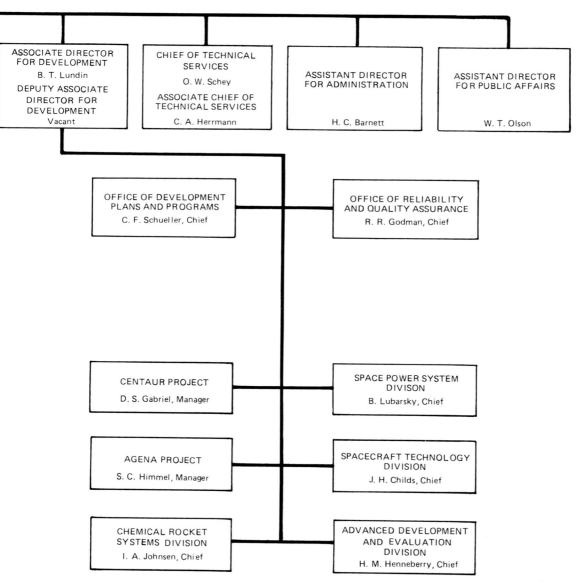

ASSOCIATE DIRECTOR FOR DEVELOPMENT
B. T. Lundin
DEPUTY ASSOCIATE DIRECTOR FOR DEVELOPMENT
Vacant

CHIEF OF TECHNICAL SERVICES
O. W. Schey
ASSOCIATE CHIEF OF TECHNICAL SERVICES
C. A. Herrmann

ASSISTANT DIRECTOR FOR ADMINISTRATION
H. C. Barnett

ASSISTANT DIRECTOR FOR PUBLIC AFFAIRS
W. T. Olson

OFFICE OF DEVELOPMENT PLANS AND PROGRAMS
C. F. Schueller, Chief

OFFICE OF RELIABILITY AND QUALITY ASSURANCE
R. R. Godman, Chief

CENTAUR PROJECT
D. S. Gabriel, Manager

SPACE POWER SYSTEM DIVISON
B. Lubarsky, Chief

AGENA PROJECT
S. C. Himmel, Manager

SPACECRAFT TECHNOLOGY DIVISION
J. H. Childs, Chief

CHEMICAL ROCKET SYSTEMS DIVISION
I. A. Johnsen, Chief

ADVANCED DEVELOPMENT AND EVALUATION DIVISION
H. M. Henneberry, Chief

NASA–LEWIS ORGANIZATION CHART 1968

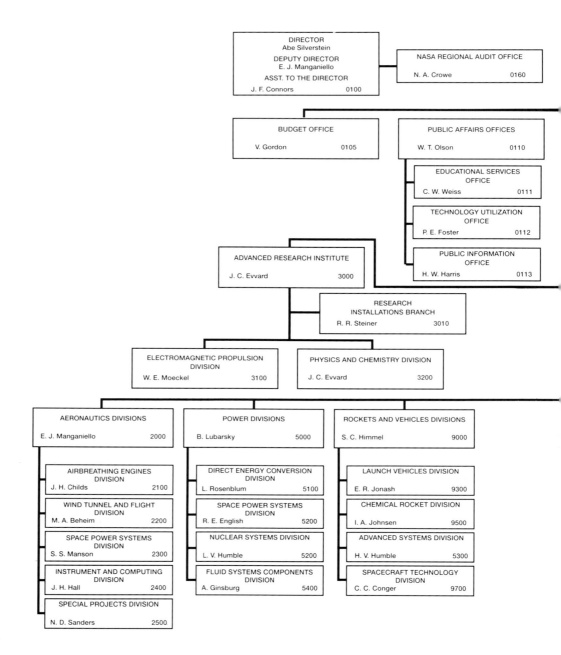

DIRECTOR
Abe Silverstein
DEPUTY DIRECTOR
E. J. Manganiello
ASST. TO THE DIRECTOR
J. F. Connors 0100

NASA REGIONAL AUDIT OFFICE
N. A. Crowe 0160

BUDGET OFFICE
V. Gordon 0105

PUBLIC AFFAIRS OFFICES
W. T. Olson 0110

EDUCATIONAL SERVICES OFFICE
C. W. Weiss 0111

TECHNOLOGY UTILIZATION OFFICE
P. E. Foster 0112

ADVANCED RESEARCH INSTITUTE
J. C. Evvard 3000

PUBLIC INFORMATION OFFICE
H. W. Harris 0113

RESEARCH INSTALLATIONS BRANCH
R. R. Steiner 3010

ELECTROMAGNETIC PROPULSION DIVISION
W. E. Moeckel 3100

PHYSICS AND CHEMISTRY DIVISION
J. C. Evvard 3200

AERONAUTICS DIVISIONS
E. J. Manganiello 2000

POWER DIVISIONS
B. Lubarsky 5000

ROCKETS AND VEHICLES DIVISIONS
S. C. Himmel 9000

AIRBREATHING ENGINES DIVISION
J. H. Childs 2100

DIRECT ENERGY CONVERSION DIVISION
L. Rosenblum 5100

LAUNCH VEHICLES DIVISION
E. R. Jonash 9300

WIND TUNNEL AND FLIGHT DIVISION
M. A. Beheim 2200

SPACE POWER SYSTEMS DIVISION
R. E. English 5200

CHEMICAL ROCKET DIVISION
I. A. Johnsen 9500

SPACE POWER SYSTEMS DIVISION
S. S. Manson 2300

NUCLEAR SYSTEMS DIVISION
L. V. Humble 5200

ADVANCED SYSTEMS DIVISION
H. V. Humble 5300

INSTRUMENT AND COMPUTING DIVISION
J. H. Hall 2400

FLUID SYSTEMS COMPONENTS DIVISION
A. Ginsburg 5400

SPACECRAFT TECHNOLOGY DIVISION
C. C. Conger 9700

SPECIAL PROJECTS DIVISION
N. D. Sanders 2500

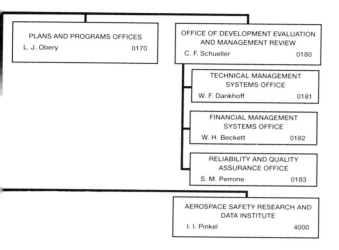

PLANS AND PROGRAMS OFFICES
L. J. Obery 0170

OFFICE OF DEVELOPMENT EVALUATION
AND MANAGEMENT REVIEW
C. F. Schueller 0180

TECHNICAL MANAGEMENT
SYSTEMS OFFICE
W. F. Dankhoff 0181

FINANCIAL MANAGEMENT
SYSTEMS OFFICE
W. H. Beckett 0182

RELIABILITY AND QUALITY
ASSURANCE OFFICE
S. M. Perrone 0183

AEROSPACE SAFETY RESEARCH AND
DATA INSTITUTE
I. I. Pinkel 4000

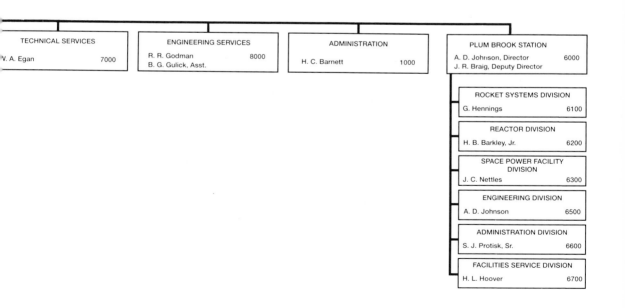

TECHNICAL SERVICES
V. A. Egan 7000

ENGINEERING SERVICES
R. R. Godman 8000
B. G. Gulick, Asst.

ADMINISTRATION
H. C. Barnett 1000

PLUM BROOK STATION
A. D. Johnson, Director 6000
J. R. Braig, Deputy Director

ROCKET SYSTEMS DIVISION
G. Hennings 6100

REACTOR DIVISION
H. B. Barkley, Jr. 6200

SPACE POWER FACILITY
DIVISION
J. C. Nettles 6300

ENGINEERING DIVISION
A. D. Johnson 6500

ADMINISTRATION DIVISION
S. J. Protisk, Sr. 6600

FACILITIES SERVICE DIVISION
H. L. Hoover 6700

NASA–LEWIS ORGANIZATION CHART 1973

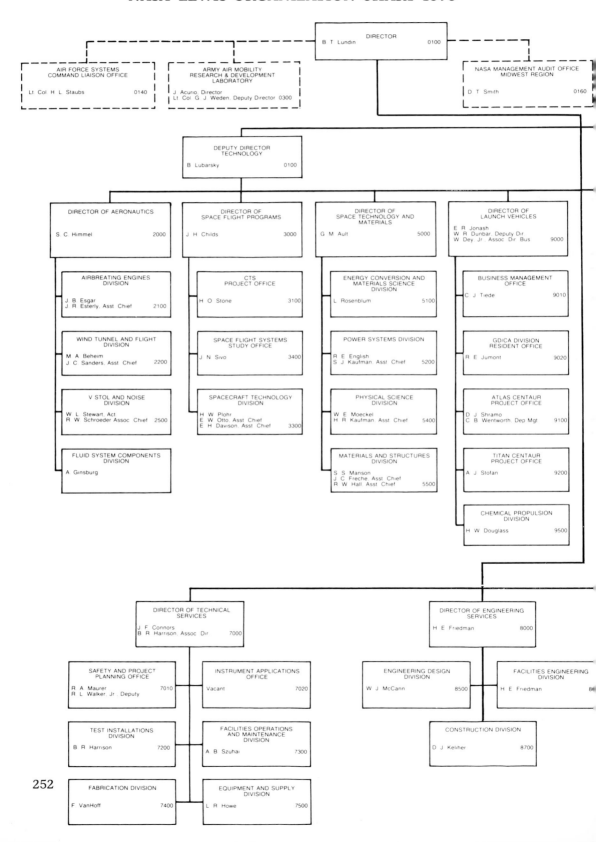

DIRECTOR
B T Lundin   0100

AIR FORCE SYSTEMS
COMMAND LIAISON OFFICE
Lt Col H L Staubs   0140

ARMY AIR MOBILITY
RESEARCH & DEVELOPMENT
LABORATORY
J Acurio, Director
Lt Col G J Weden, Deputy Director   0300

NASA MANAGEMENT AUDIT OFFICE
MIDWEST REGION
D T Smith   0160

DEPUTY DIRECTOR
TECHNOLOGY
B Lubarsky   0100

DIRECTOR OF AERONAUTICS
S. C. Himmel   2000

DIRECTOR OF
SPACE FLIGHT PROGRAMS
J H Childs   3000

DIRECTOR OF
SPACE TECHNOLOGY AND
MATERIALS
G M Ault   5000

DIRECTOR OF
LAUNCH VEHICLES
E R Jonash
W R Dunbar, Deputy Dir
W Dey, Jr, Assoc Dir Bus   9000

AIRBREATING ENGINES
DIVISION
J B Esgar
J R Esterly, Asst Chief   2100

CTS
PROJECT OFFICE
H O Stone   3100

ENERGY CONVERSION AND
MATERIALS SCIENCE
DIVISION
L Rosenblum   5100

BUSINESS MANAGEMENT
OFFICE
C J Tiede   9010

WIND TUNNEL AND FLIGHT
DIVISION
M A Beheim
J C Sanders, Asst Chief   2200

SPACE FLIGHT SYSTEMS
STUDY OFFICE
J N Sivo   3400

POWER SYSTEMS DIVISION
R E English
S J Kaufman, Asst Chief   5200

GD/CA DIVISION
RESIDENT OFFICE
R E Jumont   9020

V STOL AND NOISE
DIVISION
W L Stewart, Act
R W Schroeder Assoc Chief   2500

SPACECRAFT TECHNOLOGY
DIVISION
H W Plohr
E W Otto, Asst Chief
E H Davison, Asst Chief   3300

PHYSICAL SCIENCE
DIVISION
W E Moeckel
H R Kaufman, Asst Chief   5400

ATLAS CENTAUR
PROJECT OFFICE
D J Shramo
C B Wentworth, Dep Mgt   9100

FLUID SYSTEM COMPONENTS
DIVISION
A Ginsburg

MATERIALS AND STRUCTURES
DIVISION
S S Manson
J C Freche, Asst Chief
R W Hall, Asst Chief   5500

TITAN CENTAUR
PROJECT OFFICE
A J Stofan   9200

CHEMICAL PROPULSION
DIVISION
H W Douglass   9500

DIRECTOR OF TECHNICAL
SERVICES
J F Connors
B R Harrison, Assoc Dir   7000

DIRECTOR OF ENGINEERING
SERVICES
H E Friedman   8000

SAFETY AND PROJECT
PLANNING OFFICE
R A Maurer
R L Walker, Jr, Deputy   7010

INSTRUMENT APPLICATIONS
OFFICE
Vacant   7020

ENGINEERING DESIGN
DIVISION
W J McCann   8500

FACILITIES ENGINEERING
DIVISION
H E Friedman   8

TEST INSTALLATIONS
DIVISION
B R Harrison   7200

FACILITIES OPERATIONS
AND MAINTENANCE
DIVISION
A B Szuhai   7300

CONSTRUCTION DIVISION
D J Keliher   8700

FABRICATION DIVISION
F VanHoff   7400

EQUIPMENT AND SUPPLY
DIVISION
L R Howe   7500

252

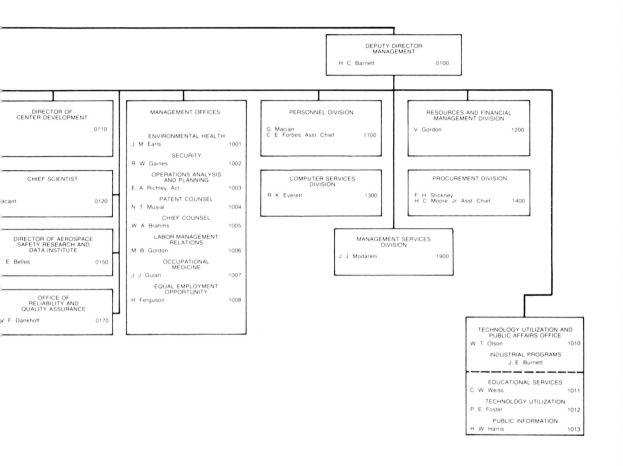

DEPUTY DIRECTOR
MANAGEMENT
H C Barnett   0100

DIRECTOR OF
CENTER DEVELOPMENT
0110

CHIEF SCIENTIST
acant   0120

DIRECTOR OF AEROSPACE
SAFETY RESEARCH AND
DATA INSTITUTE
E Belles   0150

OFFICE OF
RELIABILITY AND
QUALITY ASSURANCE
W F Dankhoff   0170

MANAGEMENT OFFICES

ENVIRONMENTAL HEALTH
J M Earls   1001

SECURITY
R W Gaines   1002

OPERATIONS ANALYSIS
AND PLANNING
E A Richley Act   1003

PATENT COUNSEL
N T Musial   1004

CHIEF COUNSEL
W A Brahms   1005

LABOR-MANAGEMENT
RELATIONS
M B Gordon   1006

OCCUPATIONAL
MEDICINE
J J Gulan   1007

EQUAL EMPLOYMENT
OPPORTUNITY
H Ferguson   1008

PERSONNEL DIVISION
G Macian
C E Forbes Asst Chief   1100

COMPUTER SERVICES
DIVISION
R K Everett   1300

MANAGEMENT SERVICES
DIVISION
J J Modarelli   1900

RESOURCES AND FINANCIAL
MANAGEMENT DIVISION
V Gordon   1200

PROCUREMENT DIVISION
F H Stickney
H C Moore Jr Asst Chief   1400

TECHNOLOGY UTILIZATION AND
PUBLIC AFFAIRS OFFICE
W T Olson   1010

INDUSTRIAL PROGRAMS
J E Burnett

EDUCATIONAL SERVICES
C W Weiss   1011

TECHNOLOGY UTILIZATION
P E Foster   1012

PUBLIC INFORMATION
H W Harris   1013

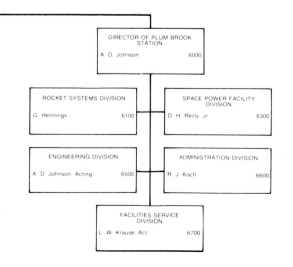

DIRECTOR OF PLUM BROOK
STATION
A D Johnson   6000

ROCKET SYSTEMS DIVISION
G Hennings   6100

SPACE POWER FACILITY
DIVISION
D H Reilly Jr   6300

ENGINEERING DIVISION
A D Johnson Acting   6500

ADMINISTRATION DIVISION
R J Koch   6600

FACILITIES SERVICE
DIVISION
L W Krause Act   6700

253

NASA–LEWIS ORGANIZATION CHART 1978

DIRECTOR J F McCarthy, Jr
DEPUTY DIRECTOR B Lubarsky
ASSOCIATE DIRECTOR S C Himmel — 0100

NASA OFFICE OF AUDIT N.E. REGION, LeRC BRANCH — R D Rhodes — 0160

AIR FORCE SYSTEMS COMMAND LIAISON OFFICE — Maj. A J Willoughby — 0140

PROPULSION LABORATORY U.S. ARMY R&T LABORATORIES — J Acurio, Director — 0300

SHUTTLE ASSESSMENT OFFICE — H W Douglass — 0150

OFFICE OF EQUAL EMPLOYMENT OPPORTUNITY — H Ferguson — 0180

CHIEF SCIENTIST — W E Moeckel — 0120

OFFICE OF RELIABILITY AND QUALITY ASSURANCE — W F Dankhoff — 0170

OFFICE OF TECHNOLOGY UTILIZATION AND PUBLIC AFFAIRS — W T Olson — 0110

DIRECTOR OF ADMINISTRATION — W Dey, Jr — DIRECTOR RESOURCES AND FINANCIAL MANAGEMENT — V Gordon — 1000

DIRECTOR OF TECHNICAL SERVICES — J F Conners — 7000

DIRECTOR OF ENGINEERING SERVICES — J B Esgar — 8000

DIRECTOR OF LAUNCH VEHICLES — L J Ross — 9000

DIRECTOR OF SPACE SYSTEMS AND TECHNOLOGY — D J Shramo — 6000

DIRECTOR OF AERONAUTICS — W L Stewart — 2000

DIRECTOR OF ENERGY PROGRAMS — G M Ault — DEPUTY DIRECTOR TECHNOLOGY — R E English — DEPUTY DIRECTOR PROJECT MANAGEMENT — H O Slone — 4800

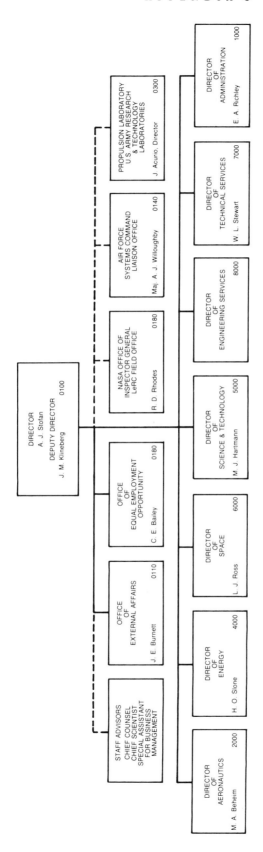

NASA–LEWIS ORGANIZATION CHART 1982

DIRECTOR
A. J. Stofan
DEPUTY DIRECTOR
J. M. Klineberg   0100

STAFF ADVISORS
CHIEF COUNSEL
CHIEF SCIENTIST
SPECIAL ASSISTANT
FOR BUSINESS
MANAGEMENT

OFFICE
OF
EXTERNAL AFFAIRS
J. E. Burnett   0110

OFFICE
OF
EQUAL EMPLOYMENT
OPPORTUNITY
C. E. Bailey   0180

NASA OFFICE OF
INSPECTOR GENERAL
LeRC FIELD OFFICE
R. D. Rhodes   0180

AIR FORCE
SYSTEMS COMMAND
LIAISON OFFICE
Maj. A. J. Willoughby   0140

PROPULSION LABORATORY
U.S. ARMY RESEARCH
& TECHNOLOGY
LABORATORIES
J. Acurio, Director   0300

DIRECTOR
OF
AERONAUTICS
M. A. Beheim   2000

DIRECTOR
OF
ENERGY
H. O. Slone   4000

DIRECTOR
OF
SPACE
L. J. Ross   6000

DIRECTOR
OF
SCIENCE & TECHNOLOGY
M. J. Hartmann   5000

DIRECTOR
OF
ENGINEERING SERVICES   8000

DIRECTOR
OF
TECHNICAL SERVICES
W. L. Stewart   7000

DIRECTOR
OF
ADMINISTRATION
E. A. Richley   1000

A P P E N D I X D

BUDGET
(1942–1977)

A comparison of the budgets of the three NACA laboratories shows that throughout the NACA period, Lewis had an only slightly lower total budget than Langley. In contrast, Ames received sometimes less than half that of the other two laboratories. This is because, even in the NACA era, Lewis depended on large facilities for engine testing. They are expensive to build and to run.

During the NASA period, between 1959 and 1968, the Lewis budget was substantially larger than that of Langley or Ames, a fact that reflects the greater number of development projects supervised by Lewis. Construction of the large rocket test facilities at Plum Brook was begun at this time. In 1963 funding for the construction of NASA facilities reached its height, with Lewis receiving $44.8 million. This figure can be compared to funds for the construction of facilities at Langley at $9.8 million, Ames at $14.4 million, and Kennedy Space Center at $334 million. In terms of the total NASA budget, Lewis had become a small fish in a very large pond. Nevertheless, between 1959 and 1965, the year that Lewis received its largest appropriation, its budget had increased from $39.19 million to $393.30 million. By 1968 it had declined to an all time low of $199.64.

NATIONAL ADVISORY COMMITTEE FOR AERONAUTICS
(in dollars)

	HEADQUARTERS	LANGLEY	AMES	LEWIS	WALLOPS	DRYDEN
1940	157,946	1,641,150	104,020			
1941	196,935	2,091,889	229,307			
1942	328,979	4,215,736	828,921	421,789		
1943	371,353	6,002,447	1,604,651	4,559,693		
1944	416,586	7,667,537	2,535,386	7,972,423		
1945	407,806	10,832,226	3,050,071	10,455,750		
1946	764,200	13,616,625	4,921,660	13,930,715		
1947	623,612	11,826,315	3,962,356	12,354,438		
1948	1,392,862	13,694,187	5,134,140	12,708,420		
1949	788,356	15,327,202	6,126,230	14,315,302	643,376	326,922
1950	895,124	16,705,748	6,990,932	16,043,756	466,407	685,072
1951	1,081,842	17,631,974	7,535,318	16,416,186	803,904	919,281
1952	1,200,616	19,692,928	8,277,495	18,381,205	777,545	1,208,163
1953	1,137,088	19,261,787	7,794,571	17,292,736	594,371	1,368,065
1954	1,340,524	19,503,862	7,980,951	17,598,976	756,093	1,437,368
1955	1,338,752	20,117,456	8,498,011	18,207,519	687,925	1,705,182
1956	1,541,237	22,083,125	11,269,561	21,996,415	910,217	1,913,134
1957	1,623,981	27,976,270	13,267,350	25,662,580	1,001,005	2,117,607
1958	1,958,201	32,774,912	20,312,089	30,461,848	2,323,465	2,565,353

(Not including Western Coordinating Office, Wright-Patterson Coordinating Office, Paris Office)

Sources: *The Budget*, 1940-1955; *NACA Annual Reports*, 1956-1958; Alex Roland, *Model Research*

NATIONAL AERONAUTICS AND SPACE ADMINISTRATION (1958–1977)
(in millions of dollars)

	TOTAL	LEWIS
1959	330.9	39.19
1960	523.6	44.85
1961	964.0	58.14
1962	1,825.3	108.28
1963	3,674.1	345.70
1964	5,100.0	381.81
1965	5,250.0	393.30
1966	5,175.0	317.16
1967	4,968.0	244.88
1968	4,588.9	199.64
1969	3,995.3	183.7
1970	3,749.2	207.5
1971	3,312.6	245.3
1972	3,310.1	257.4
1973	3,407.6	331.
1974	3,039.7	303.
1975	3,321.2	283.9
1976	3,551.8	303.6
1977	3,819.1	340.1

Totals include Research & Development, Construction of Facilities, and Research and Project Management monies.

NASA Historical Data Book, 1958-1968, vol. 1, *NASA Resources* (NASA SP-4012, 1988), p. 384. Lewis Research Center Financial Office.

LEWIS RESEARCH CENTER PERSONNEL (1941–1983)

In 1941, a nucleus of 150 staff was transferred from Langley Memorial Aeronautical Laboratory to the new Aircraft Engine Research Laboratory. During the NACA period, the staff remained at a relatively constant level. In 1962 the staff began to expand rapidly, reaching its highest level in 1965, with 4,815 employees. After 1966 the staff totals began to decline. The most dramatic reduction in staff occurred between 1972 and 1974, reaching its lowest level in 1982.

Source: *Lewis Research Center: Master Facilities Plan* (Whitley/Whitley, 1985)

STAFF PERSONNEL (1941–1966)

	1941	1946	1951	1956	1961	1962	1963	1964	1965	1966
Permanent Employees	150	1,084	2,613	2,723	2,718	3,815	4,577	4,805	4,815	4,819
Temporary Employees	N/A	N/A	24	29	30	32	32	32	32	32
Temporary Summer Employees	0	0	0	20	65	90	100	100	170	211
Service Contractor Personnel	0	N/A	N/A	N/A	30	50	145	115(C) 115(PB)	178(C) 118(PB)	191(C) 127(PB)

C = Cleveland
PB = Plum Brook

STAFF PERSONNEL (1967–1976)

	1967	1968	1969	1970	1971	1972	1973	1974	1975	1976
Permanent Employees	4,676	4,452	4,269	4,200	4,036	3,796	3,343	3,089	3,042	3,025
Temporary Employees	59	28	44	45	36	27	25	49	63	70
Temporary Summer Employees	193	103	82	98	140	129	71	132	177	175
Service Contractor Personnel	233(C) 144(PB)	221(C) 137(PB)	247(C) 142(PB)	275(C) 107(PB)	371(C) 122(PB)	399(C) 122(PB)	392(C) 129(PB)	342(C) 113(PB)	101(C)[b]	142(C)[b]

C = Cleveland
PB = Plum Brook

STAFF PERSONNEL (1977–1983)

	1977	1978	1979	1980	1981	1982	1983
Permanent Employees	3,013	2,914	2,848	2,822[a]	2,690[a]	2,485[a]	2,629[a]
Temporary Employees	78	88	99	105[a]	88[a]	181[a]	117[a]
Temporary Summer Employees	176	103	67	183[a]	180[a]	170[a]	159[a]
Service Contractor Personnel	136(C)[b]	245(C)[b]	278(C)[b]	518 (C)[a]	307(C)	323(C)	770(C)[a]

Data as of June 30, 1984, in each case except as follows:
[a]May 15, 1984
[b]March 31, 1984
C = Cleveland
PB = Plum Brook

INDEX

Advanced Research Projects Agency (ARPA) (U.S.), 168, 188

Aeronautics textbooks, 94

Aircraft engines, 1-15
—air-cooled (radial) vs. liquid-cooled, 6, 7, 8, 23-24 (photo: 100)
—effects of Korean War, 142-143
—fuel conservation, 208
—industry vs. government R&D, 8-9, 127
—innovations, 14
—Quiet Engine Program, 203, 204
—superchargers, 24-25

Aircraft Industries Association, 119

Aircraft safety, 109-123
—crash fire research, 117-123
—icing research, 109-117 (photos: 111, 113)
—lightning hazards, 120
—seats and seating, 120

Airfoil shapes, 4, 139-140

Air pollution, 204, 205

Air Transport Association, 119

Albers, Lynn U., 102

Alexander, Charles, 161

Algranti, Joseph S., 122

Allen, A.G., 50, 51

Allen, Harvey, 73, 162

Allen, Julian, (photo: 74)

Allis-Chalmers firm, 47, 50, 51, 52, 53, 66

Allison engine, see General Motors

American Airlines, 117

American Federation of Government Employees (AFGE), 208

American Legion, 151

American Rocket Society, 154

American Society of Mechanical Engineers (ASME), 102, 104, 137

Ames Aeronautical Research Laboratory (Sunnyvale CA), 6, 53, 110, 111, 112, 114, 162, 164, 179, 181, 196
—transfers icing research to Lewis, 113

Anderson, U.S. Sen. Clinton B. (NM), 185

Anderson, William J., 93

Apollo fire (1967), 123

Apollo, Project, 163, 164, 169, 170, 177, 180, 182, 183, 186, 189, 193 (photo: 194)

Appleby, Margaret, 32

Applications research, 109, 161, 180

Arab oil embargo (1973-74), 206, 208

Armstrong, Neil A., 197

Armstrong Siddeley firm, 66

Army Ballistic Missile Agency, see Marshall Space Flight Center

Arnold, U.S. Army Gen. Henry Harold, 6, 9, 19, 25, 29, 41, 48-49, 51, 57
—(photo: 111)
—1942 directive, 19

Astronaut training, 121-122, 213

Atomic Energy Commission (AEC) (U.S.), 77-78, 156, 163, 196, 207

AT&T Bell Laboratories (Murray Hill NJ), 181

Ault, Mervin, 193, 213

Automobile engines, 42-43

Aviation Writers Association, 65

Axial-flow compressor, 52, 57, 66, 91, 139-140 (photos: 50, 69, 140, 141, 142)

Ayer, Bruce, 73

Ayres, Eugene, 206-207

B-17 "Flying Fortress" (U.S.), 25

B-29 "Superfortress" (U.S.), 29, 65

Baehr, E.F., 193

Baeumker, Adolf, 5

Baldwin, L.V., 158

Banks, F. Rodwell, 71

Barna, Gerald, 207

Barnett, Henry C., 118

Battelle Institute (Columbus OH), 72

Beam, Walter I., 11

Becker, John, 79

Bee, Project, 155, 166

Bell Aircraft (Buffalo NY), 41
—Airacomet (P-59A), 55, 56
Bell, Lawrence, 11, 19
Benser, William A., 140
Bernardo, Everett, 82 (photo: 83)
Bernatowitz, Daniel T., 207
Berry, Major John, 13
Betz, Albert, 74
B.F. Goodrich Co. (Akron OH), 110
Big Joe, 121, 177
Bisson, Edmond, 72, 92-93
Black, Dugald O., 119
Blackshear, Perry, 103
Blunt body theory, 162
Bolton, Rep. Frances P. (Ohio), 65
Botta, U.S. Navy Cdr. Rico, 7
Boeing firm, 204
Boelter, L.M.K., 98, 114
Bogert, U.S. Army Col. H.Z., 132
Boksenbom, A.S., 158
Bolz, Ray, 95
Bossart, Karl, 189
Bowden, Dean, 114
Bristol firm, 66
British aviation, 5, 6, 7, 41, 49, 66, 71, 74, 81; 89, 118,
    131, 136-138, 139-142, 196
—superiority of engines, 136-138
Brooklyn Bridge, 168
Brown University, 102
Brun, Rinaldo J., 116
Brush Development Co., 90
Buller, Elmer, 121
Bullock, Robert O., 140
Burton, Harold H., 13
Busch, Arthur M., 119, 121
Busemann, Adolf, 43, 67, 74
Bush, Vannevar, 6, 9, 11, 14, 29, 46, 48, 50-51, 53, 77, 82,
    114 (photo: 127)
—on competition, 82
—on fundamental research, 71, 84, 89, 180
Business Week, 162
Bussard, Robert W., 184

Caldwell, Frank W., 8
California Institute of Technology, 46, 48
Calvert, Clyde S., 82
Campini, Secondo, 48
Canright, Richard, 155
Cape Canaveral (FL), 121, 169, 190, 192
Carrier Corp., 27, 28, 29
Carrier, George F., 102
Case School of Applied Science (later Case Institute of
    Technology), 91, 93-97, 150, 156, 163, 177, 195-196
Centaur, see rockets
Childs, Howard, 160, 185
Christie, A.G., 47
City College of New York, 35
Civil Aeronautics Administration, 111, 112, 118-119
Clarke Thomson (Philadelphia), 3

Cleveland (OH), 1-2, 10-11, 177, 204, 205, 212
—advantages as lab site, 10-13, 195-196
—Cuyahoga River, 205
—Hopkins International Airport, 197
Cleveland Electric Illuminating Company, 13
Cleveland Plain Dealer, 21, 182 (cartoon: 80)
Cleveland Press, 36
Cleveland Pneumatic firm, 11, 33
Cohen, Clarence B., 92, 153
Cold War, 97, 136, 144, 159, 161, 162, 213
Collins, John, 71, 136
Columbia University, 152
Communications satellites, 207
Compound engines, 70, 82-85
Compressor research, 139-141
Concorde (British-French), 196
Conger, C.C., 193
Conrad, E.W., 183
Constant, Edward W., 44
Constant, Hayne, 49, 140
Contracts, 192, 202-203
Corn blight, 205
Cornell University, 101
Cortright, Edgar M., 160, 164, 183, 188, 190
Crash photography, 119
Crawford, Frederick C., 10, 13, 177
Crop diseases, 205

Davidson, E.H., 193
DeBus, Kurt H., 190
DeFrance, Smith, 8
De Havilland firm, 66, 138, 143
Deissler, Robert, 101
Dennis, W.R., 121
Department of Energy (U.S.), 207, 210
Department of Transportation (U.S.), 203, 206
Deutsche Versuchsanstalt (DVL), 5, 25, 66-67, 97
Diesel engines, 23-24
Dietrich, Joseph, 76
Differential analyzer, 114-115 (photo: 115)
Disher, John, 75, 164
Dobson, Wilbur, 188
Doolittle, James, 160 (photo: 121)
Douglas Aircraft firm, 155, 204
Douglas, Donald, 11
Draft, 32-33, 91
Drake, Robert, 101
Dryden, Hugh L., 46, 47, 89-90, 132-134, 136, 149, 151,
    153, 154, 155, 160, 161, 162, 163, 170, 180, 181, 185,
    195 (photos: 90, 166)
"Dryden Plan," 160, 163
Ducted fan engine design, 48, 55
Dunbar, Russel, 190
Durand, William Frederick, 46-47, 48, 50, 51, 52, 54-55
    (photo: 47)
—visits Langley (1942), 54
Dupont Co., 90

"Earth Satellites and Interplanetary Travel" (1956 lecture), 153-154

Eaton Industries, 11, 33, 196

Ebert, William, 66

Echo project, 193

Eckert, Ernst, 67, 97-98, 101, 103, 104, 153
—heat transfer frontier, 97-99

Ehricke, Krafft, 154, 168

Eisenhower, U.S. Pres. Dwight D., 153, 161, 162, 163, 188 (photo: 166)

Electric propulsion, 154, 156, 161, 162, 177, 179, 185-186, 188, 203, 215 (photo: 188)

Emmy Award (1977), 210

Enders, John H., 112

Energy crisis, 206-210

Energy research, 206-210, 214

Energy Research and Development Administration (U.S. ERDA), 207

Energy Sources: The Wealth of the World, 207

Engineer in Charge, 162

Engineers and Scientists Association, 208

Engines, history of, 43

Englert, Gerald W., 82

English, Robert E., 156, 158, 160, 206, 207

Environmental movement, 204

Environmental Protection Agency (EPA) (U.S.), 204, 206

Environmental research, 204-206

Ethyl Corp. (Detroit), 7

European aviation, 1, 4, 7, 72

Everett, John, 119

Evvard, John, 72, 74-75, 77, 92, 95, 96, 102, 153, 154, 157, 182, 205 (photo: 93)

Fedden, Roy, 42

Federal Aviation Administration (FAA), 203

Federal Bureau of Investigation (FBI), 152

Finger, Harold B., 140, 156, 164, 185

Finnegan, Patrick, 207

Fleming, William A., 182

Flight Magazine, 131

Ford Foundation, Ford, Helen G., 19-20, (photo: 21)

Ford Motor Co., 90

Fordyce, J. Stuart, 204

Fleming, William A., 79

Franz, Anselm, 45, 66, 95, 98

Friction, 92-93

Fuel economy, 205

Fusion research, 77, 207

Gabriel, Dabniel J., 190

Gagg, Rudolf, 13

Gas turbines, 3
—Swampscott (MA) conference (1945), 79

Gas Turbine Collaboration Committee (U.K.), 66

Gelder, Thomas, 114

General Accounting Office (U.S. GAO), 152

General Dynamics, 168, 189, 190, 192, 203

General Electric Co., 19, 30, 49, 50, 51, 52, 53, 54, 55, 57, 58, 79, 81, 109, 130, 131, 132, 133, 143, 144, 184, 204, 208
—fan design contract, 203-204
—Supercharger Division (West Lynn MA), 41
—Steam Turbine Division (Schenectady NY), 47
—selected to copy Whittle engine, 51

General Motors (Allison Division), 7, 8, 46, 81, 90, 130, 132, 133
—Allison engine, 7, 26-27, 81 (photo: 26)

General Motors (Fisher Body Division), 33

German aviation, 1, 4, 5, 6, 19, 25, 41, 43, 46, 57, 66-68, 74, 89, 92
—"buzz bomb" (V-1 "pulse-jet"), 67-68, (photo: 68)
—education, 94, 95, 97

Gerstein, Melvin, 153

Gibbon, Louis C., 118

Gildersleeve, Clifford, 10

Gilruth, Robert, 121, 164

Glendinning, W.G., 118

Glenn, U.S. Marines Col./U.S. Sen. John H., 170, 213

Glennan, T. Keith, 94-95, 163, 165, 177, 179, 184-185, 195, 196, 214 (photo: 166)

Goddard, Robert H., 6, 48, 151, 154, 168

Goddard Space Flight Center (Greenbelt MD), 164, 169, 179, 180, 193

Goett, Harry, 164

Gold, Harold, 121

Gordon, S., 158

Gosney, Mary Lou, 35

Graham, Robert W., 156, 158, 168, 206

Gray, Robert, 190

Gray, Vernon, 114 (photo: 115)

Griffith, A.A., 49, 140

Grimwood, James, 161

Grissom, Virgil I. (Gus), 122

Groves, Leslie, 78

Gutstein, Martin U., 207

Gwinn, W.P., 133

Hall, Eldon, 156, 164, 167

Hamilton-Standard Propellers Company, 8

Hansberry, Harvey L., 118

Hansen, Arthur, 195

Hansen, James, 162

Harding Junior High School (Lakewood OH), 94, 150

Hardy, J.K., 111, 114

Harrison, William, 32

Hartmann, Melvin J., 140

Harvard University, 91, 103

Hawaii, 207

Hayes, Wallace D., 102

Hazon, Ronald, 7

Hawkins, James, 32

Heat transfer, 97-99, 101-103, 114, 168

Heat Transmission, 98

Hemke, Paul E., 91

Heritage Foundation, 213
Hero of Alexandria, 44
Heron, Sam D., 7-8
Herrmann, Charles, 19-20
Hibbard, Robert, 205
Hicks, Bruce, 76
High Speed Panel, 72-73
High-speed photography, 24, 72
Himmel, Seymour C., 193
Hindenberg explosion (1937), 168
Hitler, Adolf, 5, 6, 57
Hobbs, Leonard S., 71, 135
Hoffer, Eric, 201
Holliday, William T., 36
Holmes, D. Brainerd, 170, 183
Honeywell (Minneapolis), 121
Hosenball, Neil, 190, 192
Howell, A.R., 140
Hornet engines, 6
Hrones, John, 195
Huff, Vearl, 76
Humble, Leroy V., 82
Hunsaker, Jerome, 76, 81
Hunter, Wilson H., 110 (photo: 111)
Hyatt, Abe, 167
Hyland, Robert E., 158
Hypersonic flight, 153

Ide, John Jay, 5
International Federation of Professional and Technical
    Engineers, 208
International Geophysical Year (1957-58), 149, 153, 157
Introduction to the Transfer of Heat and Mass, 101

Jackass Flats (NV), 184
Jackson, Thomas W., 101
Jacobs, Eastman N., 34, 42, 44, 48, 49, 54, 55, 57, 72, 77,
    89, 139
Jet propulsion, 1, 23, 41-58, 65, 71, 131, 161
    —educational challenge, 91, 95
    —no commercial applications seen, 83
Jet Propulsion Laboratory (JPL) (CalTech, Pasadena CA),
    70-71, 76, 91, 155, 180, 189, 193
    —rocket experiments, 75
    —transfers from U.S. Army to NASA (1958), 165, 179
Jet Propulsion Laboratory (Case), 95
Johash, Edmund R., 160
Johns Hopkins University/Applied Physics Laboratory,
    89, 90, 91, 150
Johnsen, Irving A., 140
Johnson, Robert L., 93
Jonash, Ed, 190
Junkers and Heinkel-Hirth Cos., 66
Jupiter exploration, 202

Kalitinsky, Andrew, 47, 78
Kantrowitz, Arthur, 77, 140
Kaplan, George, 207
Kaufman, Harold R., 188

Keirn, U.S. Col. Donald, 41, 51, 55, 57, 71, 76, 184
Kemper, Carlton, 7, 23, 130, 132 (photos: 24, 74)
Kennedy, U.S. Pres. John F., 169, 182, 195, 197
Kindelberger, Dutch, 11
Kiwanis Clubs, 151
Klapproth, John F., 140
Kline, D.B., 113
Klinghorn, George F., 82 (photo: 83)
Knocking research, 24
Knolls Atomic Power Laboratory, 103
Korean War (1950-1953), see aircraft engines
Kosmahl, Henry, 208
Krasnican, M.J., 121
Kroon, R.P., 53
Kurzweg, Hermann, 74

Lake Erie, 112, 155, 196, 204, 205
Laminar flow airfoils, 48
Langley Memorial Aeronautical Laboratory (Hampton
    VA), 3, 7, 8, 52-53, 74, 92, 110, 121, 140, 160, 162,
    164, 177, 179, 181, 196
    —fusion research, 77
    —Lunar Orbit Rendezvous (LOR) plan, 183
    —personnel switch to Lewis, 33-35, 72, 91, 92, 152
Lausche, Mayor Frank J., 22, 36
Lewis, George William (1882-1948), 1, 3, 14, 20, 22, 32,
    49, 52, 54, 55, 57, 67, 72-73, 75, 136 (photos: 2, 3, 12,
    111)
    —Cleveland lab named after, 84-85
    —testifies on budget (1940), 9
    —visits Germany (1936), 4-5, 25
    —visited by Tizard, 45
Lewis Research Center (Cleveland) (see also NACA)
    — aeronautics research renewed, 196
    —Aerospace Safety Research and Data Institute, 123
    —Aircraft Engine Research Laboratory dedication
        (1943), 36, (photo: 36)
    —Air Mobility Research and Development
        Laboratory (U.S. Army), 204
    —Altitude Chamber, 132
    —Apollo 1 fire (1967), 123
    —"Apprenticeship School," 32
    —basic research vs. applications, 99, 162, 178-179,
        181, 193, 195, 215
    —budgets, 196-197, 202-203, 212, 213
    —Case Institute of Technology, 93-97, 195-196
    —Centaur/Agena project moved from Marshall
        (1962), 190, 193
    —Editorial Office, 32
    —energy research, 206-210, 214 (photo: 211)
    —environmental research, 204-206
    —first look by journalists (1945), 65-66
    —industry relations, 127, 208
    —groundbreaking (1941), 1, 20, 22 (photo: 2)
    —Heritage Foundation backs closure, 213
    —IBM computers, 114, 212
    —Jet Propulsion Static Test Laboratory (1943), 42, 57,
        (photo: 58)

—Neil A. Armstrong ties, 197
—Plum Brook facility, 155, 156, 184-185, 201, 206, 207 (photos: 187, 192)
—possible transfer to ERDA, 208, 210
—Project Mercury, 119, 180 (photo: 122)
—propeller research ceremony, 21-22
—reorganization (1945), 72
—research agenda memo (1945), 69-70
—rocket/space research, 151, 153, 154, 157, 159-161, 168-169, 177, 183, 196-197 (photo: 151)
—staff, 65, 89-91, 164, 177, 182, 196, 202-203, 206, 212, 213, 214
—social life, 35
—supersonic wind tunnel (1949), 73
—technical library, 67
—visit by Rolls Royce group (1955), 143
Lewis, James P., 114
Lewis, William, 111, 112, 114
Ley, Willy, 151
Liberty engine (World War I), 11
Lieblein, Seymour, 140
Lindbergh, Charles, 6
—meets Arnold, 6
Lippisch, Alexander, 98
Liquid Hydrogen as a Propulsion Fuel, 168
Littell, 73
Littlewood, William, 83, 117
Lockheed firm, 203
Lockheed P-80 Shooting Star, 65, 71, (photo: 66)
Lorin, Rene, 68
Los Alamos (NM), 77, 90, 184
Low, George, 101, 153, 164, 208
Lubarsky, Bernard, 158, 160
Luftfahrtforschungsanstalt (LFA), 67, 97
Luidens, Roger, 153
Lunar Excursion Module (LEM), 183
Lundin, Bruce T., 82, 127, 157, 158-159, 161, 181-183, 190, 201-203, 206, 207- 208, 210, 212 (photos: 83, 202)
—space research memo (1957), 159-160
Lunney, Glynn S., 121
Lyon, Alfred J., 51

Malina, Frank, 46, 76
Mach-Zehnder interferometer, 98, 101
Malina, Frank, 151
Mandel, George, 67
Manganiello, Eugene, 68, 82, 94, 95-96, 157, 160, 179-180, 184 (photos: 83, 180)
Manhattan Project, 77, 78
Manned Spacecraft Center (later renamed Johnson Space Center) (Houston TX), 169, 205
Marble, Frank, 140
Mariner project, 193, 204
Marks, Lionel S., 91
Martin, Glenn L., 11
Martinuzzi, P.F., 137
Mars exploration, 154, 156, 157, 177, 183, 185, 193, 202, 215 (photo: 188)

Marshall, U.S. Army Gen. George, 29
Marshall Space Flight Center, 161, 166, 169, 179, 180, 182, 183, 186, 188, 189, 190, 193
Maslen, Steven H., 103, 153, 158, 181
Massachusetts Institute of Technology (MIT)/Radiation Laboratory, 6, 90, 101, 09, 114, 184
—Lexington Report, 184
MASTIF, 121-122
Matos, Cruz, 207
McAdams, Prof. William H., 29, 98
McCarthy Jr., John F., 210, 212, 213
McDougall, Walter, 162
Mead, George, 6, 7, 8, 9, 31, 129
Medieros, Arthur A., 140
Melzer, Henry, 57
Mendelssohn, Alexander, 102
Mercury (planet) exploration, 202
Mercury, Project, 120, 121-122, 162, 163-164, 165, 170, 177, 180 (photo: 122)
Mergler, Harry, 114, 195
Metropolitan-Vickers, 66
Metzenbaum, U.S. Sen. Howard (Ohio), 213
Meyer, Andre J., 121
Meyer, Richard, 140
Meyer, W.R., 121
Mickelson, William, 160, 185
Miller, Cearcy D., 24, 72
Miller, Philip N., 160
Miller, Riley, 76
Miller, Robert R., 121
Mirels, Harold, 92, 103, 153, 181
Moeckel, Wolfgang C., 72, 92, 153-154, 156, 157, 158, 185-186, 188
Mount Washington Research Station (NH), 114
Moon (Earth's) exploration, 157, 158, 162, 164, 166, 169, 182-183, 188, 189, 204
Moore, Charles Stanley, 20
Moore, Franklin K., 92, 103
Moore-Brabazon, British Lt. Col. J.T.C., 49
Morris, Dorothy, 67
Moss, Sanford, 42
Mroz, Thaddeus S., 207
Munk, Max, 91
Muroc Dry Lake (CA), 19, 54, 55

NACA Aircraft Engine Research Laboratory (Cleveland), 1, 8, 9
—first budget, 9-10
—site selection, 10, 11, 12, 13
—renamed Flight Propulsion Research Laboratory (1947), 84
—renamed Lewis Flight Propulsion Laboratory (1948), 84
NACA Graduate Study Leave Act (1950), 96
NACA Special Committee on Jet Propulsion (Durand Committee), 46-51, 53, 55, 89
—special Washington meeting (1942), 55
—drops Jacobs' Jeep project (1943), 56
NACA Subcommittee on Rocket Engines, 151

Nahigyan, Kervork K., 42, 55, 57
National Academy of Engineering, 103
National Academy of Sciences, 153
National Advisory Committee on Aeronautics (NACA), 1-15, 56-57
—agreement on nuclear propulsion with AEC (1948), 78, 156
—Alsos mission (1945), 66-67, 71, 76
—budget problems, 151-152, 162
—creation (1915), 2
—between the two world wars, 3, 79
—McCarthism's impact on, 151-152
—place in aviation, 34, 74, 79, 135
—reports process, 32, 67, 74
—space research, 149, 155, 157, 161
—staff, 161
—transition into NASA (1958), 163-166, 168, 170, 179
—"Young Turks Dinner" (1957), 160
National Aeronautical Research Policy (1946), 70, 84
National Air Races, 11, 13, 14 (photo: 14)
National Bureau of Standards (U.S.), 2, 23, 89
—Buckingham report (1923), 43
National Defense Research Committee (NDRC), 46, 89
National Aeronautics and Space Administration (NASA), 84, 121-123, 161, 162
—budget, 169, 196-197, 201
—relationship with military, 204
—transition from NACA (1958), 163-166, 168, 170, 179 (photo: 167)
National Aeronautics and Space Act (1958), 163, 179
National Research Council of Canada, 114
National Research Council (U.S.), 212, 215
National Science Foundation (NSF) (U.S.), 163, 207
Naval Aircraft Factory (Philadelphia), 8, 9
Naval Research Laboratory (Washington DC), 70-71, 153, 164
"Needle engine," 133
Newell, Homer D., 188
Nettles, Cary, 190
Newton, Gaylord W., 7
Newton's Third Law of Motion, 43-44
New York Times, 178
Nicks, Oran, 164
Nixon, U.S. Pres Richard M., 207
North American Aviation, 123
North Atlantic Treaty Organization (NATO), 144
North, Warren, 164
Nuclear propulsion, 70, 77-78, 84, 154, 156, 158, 161, 162, 179, 185 (photos: 78; cartoon: 80)
—at Lewis (1945-1972), 77-78, 156, 177, 182-185, 203, 215
—Nuclear Energy Propulsion for Aircraft (NEPA), 78, 184-185
—Nuclear Engine for Rocket Vehicle Applications (NERVA) (Rover), 185
Nutt, Arthur, 7

Oakar, U.S. Rep. Mary Rose (Ohio), 213
Oberth, Hermann, 154, 168

Office of Scientific Research and Development (OSRD) (U.S.), 29, 77
Oak Ridge National Laboratory (TN), 78, 90, 184, 206
Ohio State University, 98, 168
Ohio State Law School, 190
Olson, Walter T., 72, 75-76, 91, 97, 157, 158, 160 (photo: 98)
—advocates rocket/space research, 154, 158-159
—visits England (1947), 138
Operation Paperclip, 74, 98
Ordin, Paul, 76, 158
Origins of the Turbojet Revolution, 44
Ostrach, Simon, 102-103, 181, 195
Oswatitsch, Klemens, 74
Oswatitsch, Herman, 92

Packard Co., 81
Page, U.S. Col. Edwin R., 7, 42 (photo: 43)
Palasics, John, 82
Pan Am, 117
Pease, Donald. J., 213
Perkins, Porter, 116
Perl, William, 92, 102
—arrested in Rosenbergs case, 151-152
Perry, Len, 190, 192
Pesman, Gerald J., 118, 119, 121
Petroleum industry, 7
Photos, 204
Pinkel, Benjamin (Ben), 25, 26-27, 31, 41, 42, 55, 71, 78, 79, 82, 83, 84, 102-103, 113, 123, 129, 132, 141, 184 (photo: 83)
Pinkel, Irving, 72, 112, 113, 117, 119, 121, 157 (photo: 121)
Piston engines, 69, 81, 82, 102
Pittsburgh-Des Moines Steel Co., 27
Plohr, H. Warren, 121, 193
Plum Brook facility, see Lewis Research Center
Prandtl, Ludwig, 5, 97-98
Pratt & Whitney company (CT), 1, 8, 19, 23, 46, 66, 71, 81, 84, 119, 130, 131, 132, 133, 135, 136, 143-144, 168-169, 184, 189, 204, 208 (photos: 143, 191)
Preston, G. Merritt, 119, 121
Proprietary rights, 129-136
Prutton, Carl, 97
Puckett, Allen, 92
Puerto Rico, 207
Purdue University, 101
Putnam, Palmer, 207

Quitter, John, 190

Rabb, Leonard, 121
Rail accelerator, 157
Ramjets ("flying stovepipes"), 65, 68, 70, 76, 92, 157
Ranger project, 193
Ravenna Arsenal (Ohio) crash tests, 119-120 (photo: 120)
Ray, Dixy Lee, 207
Rayle, Warren, 207
Raytheon Corp., 103

RCA firm, 170
Reagan, U.S. Pres. Ronald W., 213
Reciprocating engines, 70
Redding, Arnold, 140
Reflections on Big Science, 206
Reid, Henry, 51, 55, 66, 160
Reiss, Sam, 67
Rensselaer Polytechnic Institute, 91, 164
Rentschler, Frederick B., 6
Reshotko, Eli, 91, 153, 195
Ribner, Herbert, 92
Rickover, U.S. Adm. Hyman, 103
Ritter, William K., 140
Robbins, William (Red), 213
Robinson, Russell, 66-67, 73, (photo: 74)
Rockets, 6, 8, 48, 65, 69-70, 72, 75-76, 121-122, 149-151,
    154, 155, 158, 161, 164, 166-169 (photos: 151, 152,
    158)
    —Agena, 193, 197
    —Atlas, 121, 168, 169, 177, 189, 197, 201 (photo: 192)
    —Centaur, 84, 166-169, 179, 188-190, 193, 201 (photo:
    192)
    —fuels, 76, 84, 150, 151, 155, 162, 166-168, 193
    (photo: 156)
    —Nova, 182, 183
    —Rover/NERVA, 184
    —Saturn, 166-169, 179, 182-183, 185, 189, 193, 197,
    201
    —Soviet, 151
    —Space Shuttle main engines, 202
    —Thor, 193
    —Titan, 197
    —V-2s, 6, 72, 75, 77, 99, 154
Rodert, Lewis A., 110, 111, 118, 120 (photo: 112)
Rohsenow, Warren, 101
Rolls Royce Co., 66, 81, 132, 136, 142, 143-144
    —Avon engine, 138, 144
    —Nene engine, 131, 132-135, 138 (photo: 133)
    —Tay engine, 143
Rom, Frank E., 158, 184
Rosenbergs, Ethel and Julius, 152
Rosenblum, Louis, 204, 207
Rothrock, Addison, 23, 31-32, 71-72, 76, 90, 157 (photos:
    73, 74)
Rover firm, 66
R.P. Carbone Construction Co., 20
Rutgers University, 98
Ryschkewitsch, Eugen, 98

Sam W. Emerson Co., 21
Sams, Eldon W., 158
Sanders, John C., 82, 102 (photo: 83)
Sanders, Newell D., 82, 157, 164 (photo: 83)
Saturn (planet) exploration, 202
Saturn (rocket), see rockets
Savino, Joseph M., 207
Scarlott, Charles, 207
Schey, Oscar, 24-25, 71-72, 79, 127, 136
Schlichting, Herman, 67

Schmidt, Ernst, 67, 97, 102-103
Schwenk, Francis C., 164
Schwartz, Harvey, 207
Science (AAAS), 6
Science, the Endless Frontier, 181
Schelp, Helmut, 98
Schueller, Carl F., 183
Seamans, Robert, 169, 189
Sears, William, 92
Selden, R.F., 118
Serafini, John, 116
Sharp, Edward Raymond (Ray), 20-21, 27, 32, 35, 36, 41,
    71, 73, 90, 141, 153, 166, 170, 212 (photos: 22, 121)
Shepherd, Alan B., 122, 170
Shoults, D. Roy, 49, 51, 184
Shure, Lloyd, 207
Siegel, Robert, 101
Siekel, George, 207
Silverstein, Abe, 27, 30, 58, 71, 73-74, 79, 81, 91-92, 94,
    97, 99, 102, 112, 118, 137, 150, 153, 155-157, 159,
    160, 162, 163, 164, 166, 167, 168, 169-170, 177-183,
    184-186, 188-190, 192-193, 197, 202, 203, 212 (photos:
    74, 165, 194, 197)
    —retirement (1969), 197
    —landing landing "O.K." memo (1960), 164
Simkinson, Scott, 121
Simon, Harlan, 190, 192
Simon, Sidney, 77
Sloop, John, 76, 150-151, 158, 168
Smithsonian Institution, 2
S. Morgan Smith Co., 207
Society of Automotive Engineers, 151
Soderberg, C. Richard, 47
Solar energy on Earth, 207-208
Solar propulsion, 154, 186, 205
    —Sunflower, 186
Soviet aviation research, 82, 132, 135
Space age, 158
Space debate (post-Sputnik), 158-162
"Space cadets," 157
Space Task Force, 121
Space Shuttle, 201, 202, 214
Space Nuclear Propulsion Office (NASA-AEC), 185
Space Station, 214
Sparrow, Ephraim M., 103
Spitfire (British), 25
Sputnik, 149, 157-158, 162
Squires, Arthur, 193
Stack, John, 73, 160, (photo: 74)
Standard Oil of New Jersey, 90
Standard Oil of Ohio, 90
Stanford University, 91
Stanitz, John, 139
Stein, Samuel, 202
Stevenson, Jr., A.R., 50, 53
Stever, H. Guyford, 163 (photo: 165)
Stever Committee, (photo: 165)
Stofan, Andrew J., 213
Stokes, Louis, 213

Stradivari, Antonio, 32
Strip mining, 205
Stuhlinger, Ernst, 154, 188
Summerfield, Martin, 76
Surveyor program, 169, 189, 192, 204
Supersonic flight, 70, 72-75, 92, 157, 196
Swenson, Loyd, 161

Taylor, Edward, 71, 135
Thermal Radiation and Heat Transfer, 101
Thomas, Lewis, 204
Thomas, Ronald L., 207
Thomas, U.S. Rep. Albert, 152-153
Thompson, Floyd, 160
Thompson Products (later TRW), 10, 30, 33, 90, 186, 196
Tischler, A.O., 158, 167
Tizard, Sir Henry
    —visits U.S. (1940), 45-46, 47
Towers, U.S. Rear Adm. John H., 9, 46
Tozier, Robert, 32
Trans World (TWA), 117
Traupel, Walter, 140
Traveling wave tube, 208 (photo: 210)
Treatise on Space Travel (1903), 168
Tribology, 92-93
Truman, U.S. Pres. Harry S, 81 (photo: 112)
    —orders crash fire program, 119
Tsiolkovsky, Konstantin, 168
Turbofan technology, 203
Turbojet engines, 19, 30, 41, 65, 66, 70, 71, 79, 155, 157, 177 (photos: 56, 143)
    —first flight (1939), 45
    —in commercial use, 116-117, 143
Turboprops, advanced, 208 (photo: 211)
Turner, Leroy, 92

United Aircraft, 83
United Technologies (Hamilton-Standard), 208
U.S. Air Force, 84, 98, 112, 119, 134, 136, 137, 149, 155, 162, 168, 184, 193, 196, 204, 212
U.S. Army, 2, 55, 57, 81, 84, 119, 149, 151, 165-166, 204
U.S. Army Air Corps./Army Air Forces, 73, 75, 78, 79, 84, 118, 130, 131, 132 U.S. Army Power Plants Laboratory (Dayton OH), 6, 8, 9
U.S. Navy, 2, 53, 55, 81, 84, 131, 132, 149, 161, 162, 164
    —Terrier and Talos missiles, 84
U.S. Weather Bureau, 2, 111
University of Akron, 190
University of California at Berkeley, 98
University of California at Los Angeles, 98, 114
University of Minnesota, 101, 103, 206
University of Pennsylvania, 113
University of Rhode Island, 102
Uranus exploration, 202
Useller, James W., 122

Vanguard satellite program, 153, 157, 161, 164
Venus exploration, 193, 202, 204
Vermont, 207

Verne, Jules, 182
Victory, John, 4, 10-11, 13, 90, 129, 157
Vietnam War, 196-197
Viking, Project, 204
Von Braun, Wernher (1912-1977), 6, 153, 161, 165, 166-170, 182, 183, 188-189, 193 (photo: 194)
Von Glahn, Uwe, 114
Von Karman, Theodore, 46, 76, 89, 92, 102, 129, 152
Von Ohain, Hans, 43-45, 66, 95, 97-98, 137
V-2 rocket, see rockets

Walker, Ernest, 119
Warfare, 1, 15
Warner, Edward P., 135
War on Poverty, 196-197
Warshawsky, Isidore, 32, 160
Wasielewski, Eugene, 49, 139
Wasp engines, 6
Water pollution, 204
Way, Stuart, 53
Weatherhead Co., 90
Weather satellites, 164
Webb, James E., 123, 169, 177, 195 (photo: 178)
Wege zur Raumschiffahrt (1929), 154
Weinberg, Alvin, 206
Weiss, Sol, 119
Weske, John R., 91
Westinghouse firm, 47, 52, 53, 54, 58, 81, 131, 132, 133, 137, 139, 142 (photo: 142)
Weston, M., 193
Westover, U.S. Gen. Oscar, 5
Whitaker, Halbert, 114
Whitney, Ernest G., 8, 20
Whittle, Frank, 136, 139
Whittle, British Air Commodore Frank, 41, 43-45
    —Power Jets Ltd., 47, 50, 65
Whittle engine, 49-51, 55, 56, 58
Wind energy (turbines), 207 (photo: 209)
Wind tunnels, 3, 4, 8, 12, 14-15, 53, 73-75, 90-91, 110, 113, 143, 163, 164, 202, 204
    —Altitude Wind Tunnel (Lewis) (opened 1944), 27-31, 58, 73, 81-82, 110, 121-122, 127, 132, 144, 177, 213 (photos: 28, 66, 142, 143)
    —"duct tunnels" (Lewis), 74, 102 (photo: 75)
    —German, 66-67, 73
    —Icing Research Tunnel (Lewis) (1944-1957, reopened 1978), 27, 110 (photos: 116, 117)
    —"stack tunnels" (Lewis), 74
    —supersonic, 66-67, 72-75
    —Unitary Wind Tunnels Plan (1949), 73, 136
Wing Tips (Lewis newspaper, later Orbit and Lewis News), 25, 33-35, 201
Wolfenstein, Lincoln, 140
Women workers, 33-34, 114-115 (photo: 115)
Wright Aeronautical company (OH), 1, 6, 7, 8, 19, 23, 46, 50, 66, 81, 130 (photo: 30)
Wright Brothers (Wilbur and Orville), 1, 13, 34, 36 (photo: 36)
Wright Cyclone engine, 22, 29, 30

Wright, Lyle, 208
Wu, Chung-Hua, 140
Wyatt, Demarquis D., 73, 74, 75, 160, 163-164, 169
Wynne, William, 119

X-1, 157
X-15, 162

Yale University, 94, 110
''Yankee'' turbojet, 53-54, 137

Yeager, Chuck, 157
Young, Anthony, 110
Young, Pearl, 32, 34

Zelanko, Charles, 110
Zobel, Theodor, 67, 98
Zucrow, Maurice, 151

About the Author

Virginia P. Dawson received her doctorate in the History of Science and Technology from Case Western Reserve University in 1983. She has published numerous articles and reviews, as well as a book on eighteenth century biology, *Nature's Enigma* (1987). In 1988 Dr. Dawson was awarded the Robert H. Goddard Essay Award for her article on Lewis Laboratory's role in shaping the early years of NASA. She has taught the history of science and technology at Case Western Reserve University, Oberlin College, and Cleveland State University. She is currently an adjunct professor at Cleveland State University.

THE NASA
HISTORY SERIES

HISTORIES

Anderson, Frank W., Jr., *Orders of Magnitude: A History of NACA and NASA, 1915–1980* (NASA SP-4403, 2d ed., 1981).

Benson, Charles D., and William Barnaby Faherty, *Moonport: A History of Apollo Launch Facilities and Operations* (NASA SP-4204, 1978).

Bilstein, Roger E., *Orders of Magnitude: A History of the NACA and NASA, 1915–1990* (NASA SP-4406, 1989).

Bilstein, Roger E., *Stages to Saturn: A Technological History of Apollo/Saturn Launch Vehicles* (NASA SP-4206, 1980).

Boone, W. Fred, NASA *Office of Defense Affairs: The First Five Years* (NASA HHR-32, 1970, multilith).

Brooks, Courtney G., James M. Grimwood, and Lloyd S. Swenson, Jr., *Chariots for Apollo: A History of Manned Lunar Spacecraft* (NASA SP-4205, 1979).

Byers, Bruce K., *Destination Moon: A History of the Lunar Orbiter Program* (NASA TM X-3487, 1977, multilith).

Compton, W. David, *Where No Man Has Gone Before* (NASA SP-4214, 1989).

Compton, W. David, and Charles D. Benson, *Living and Working in Space: A History of Skylab* (NASA SP-4208, 1983).

Corliss, William R., NASA *Sounding Rockets, 1958–1968: A Historical Summary* (NASA SP-4401, 1971).

Ezell, Edward Clinton, and Linda Neumann Ezell, *On Mars: Exploration of the Red Planet, 1958–1978* (NASA SP-4212, 1984).

Ezell, Edward Clinton, and Linda Neuman Ezell, *The Partnerships: A History of the Apollo-Soyuz Test Project* (NASA SP-4029, 1978).

Green, Constance McL., and Milton Lomask, *Vanguard: A History* (NASA SP-4202, 1970; also Washington: Smithsonian Institution Press, 1971).

Hacker, Barton C., and James W. Grimwood, *On the Shoulders of Titans: A History of Project Gemini* (NASA SP-4203, 1977).

Hansen, James R., *Engineer In Charge: A History of the Langley Aeronautical Laboratory, 1917–1958* (NASA SP-4305, 1987).

Hall, R. Cargill, *Lunar Impact: A History of Project Ranger* (NASA SP-4210, 1977).

Hallion, Richard P., *On the Frontier: Flight Research at Dryden, 1946–1981* (NASA SP-4303, 1984).

Hartman, Edwin P., *Adventures in Research: A History of Ames Research Center, 1940–1965* (NASA SP-4302, 1970).

Levine, Arnold, *Managing NASA in the Apollo Era* (NASA SP-4102, 1982).

Muenger, Elizabeth A., *Searching the Horizon: A History of Ames Research Center, 1940–1976* (NASA SP-4304, 1985).

Newell, Homer E., *Beyond the Atmosphere: Early Years of Space Science* (NASA SP-4211, 1980).

Pitt, John A., *The Human Factor: Biomedicine in the Manned Space Program, 1980* (NASA SP-4213, 1985).

Roland, Alex, *Model Research: The National Advisory Committee for Aeronautics, 1915–1958* (NASA SP-4103, 1985).

Roland, Alex, *A Spacefaring People: Perspective on Early Spaceflight* (NASA SP-4405, 1985).

Rosenthal, Alfred, *Venture into Space: Early Years of Goddard Space Flight Center* (NASA SP-4103, 1985).

Rosholt, Robert L., *An Administrative History of NASA, 1958–1963* (NASA SP-4101, 1966).

Sloop, John L., *Liquid Hydrogen as a Propulsion Fuel, 1945–1959* (NASA SP-4404, 1978).

Swenson, Llyod S., Jr., James M. Grimwood and Charles C. Alexander, *This New Ocean: A History of Project Mercury* (NASA SP-4201, 1966).

REFERENCE WORK

Aeronautics and Space Report of the President, annual volumes for 1975–1986.

The Apollo Spacecraft: A Chronology (NASA SP-4009, vol. 1, 1969; vol. 2, 1973; vol. 3, 1976; vol. 4, 1978).

Astronautics and Aeronautics: A Chronology of Science, Technology, and Policy, annual volumes with an earlier summary volume, *Aeronautics and Astronautics, 1915–1960.*

Dickson, Katherine M., ed., *History of Aeronautics and Astronautics: A Preliminary Bibliography* (NASA HHR-29, 1968, multilith).

Ezell, Linda Neuman, *NASA Historical Data Book,* vol. II *Programs and Projects 1958–1968* and vol. III *Programs and Projects 1969–1978* (NASA SP-4012, 1988).

Hall, R. Cargill, *Project Ranger: A Chronology* (JPL/HR-2, 1971, multilith).

Hall, R. Cargill, ed. *Essays on the History of Rocketry and Astronautics: Proceedings of the Third through the Sixth History Symposia of the International Academy of Astronautics* (NASA CP-2014, 2 vols., 1977).

Looney, John J., ed., *Bibliography of Space Books and Articles from Non-Aerospace Journals, 1957–1977* (NASA HHR-51, 1979, multilith).

Roland, Alex F., *A Guide to Research in NASA History* (NASA HHR-50, 6th ed., 1982, available from NASA History Office).

Skylab: A Chronology (NASA SP-4011, 1977).

Van Nimmen, Jane, and Leonard C. Bruno, with Robert L. Rosholt, *NASA Historical Data Book, 1958–1968,* vol. 1, *NASA Resources* (NASA SP-4012, 1976).

Wells, Helen T., Susan H. Whiteley, and Carrie E. Karegeannes, *Origins of NASA Names* (NASA SP-4402, 1976).

☆ U.S. GOVERNMENT PRINTING OFFICE: 1991—292-107